NOBODY WAVED GOOD-BYE and other plays

A Revision of *On Stage*

Edited by
HERMAN VOADEN, M.A., C.D.A.
Formerly Director of English
Central High School of Commerce, Toronto

The Macmillan Company of Canada Limited Toronto

The Cover Picture: A scene from *Nobody Waved Good-bye.* Peter sings to Julie at a table in the outdoor restaurant (p. 59): "And thus did my false love, my false love to me."

(Photo – The National Film Board of Canada)

Printed in Canada by the T. H. Best Printing Company Limited

We stumble after a truth and a beauty we have only dimly conceived – or never conceived.

If we have guessed at it at all, if we have held it however fleetingly, it is only as a vision – a symbol half caught in some ill-explored region of the mind.

We live and act in the mysterious influence radiated by these symbols of an ideal future. As we dream to-day, men will live to-morrow, though we do not recognize our dreams and can give no account of them. To-morrow sleeps in each man's brain. If he can be roused to interest in it, so much the better for him and it.

In this lies the supreme value and power of the drama. It can create interest in the unachieved grandeur, the undeveloped powers of man. With a sharper touch than any other art it can quicken into life the realities that wait beyond and above the confusion of the day. It can set before men's eyes a conception of life which is better and nobler than its present attainment. It can make move before him the dreams that lie hidden in his thought – the dreams that, though he know it not, make possible and worthy the daily futilities of existence.

STORM JAMESON

Modern Drama in Europe

FOREWORD

During the twenty and more years of its life, *On Stage* was a best-seller among Canadian one-act play collections, and increased in popularity from year to year. This was not only because of the quality, interest, and range of its material, but also because it embodied (particularly when it first appeared) a new and vigorous idea – the idea of the "on stage" approach. It was an idea that challenged classroom boredom, that called for activity, participation, and a mood of hearty but intelligent enjoyment. The present collection, a revision of *On Stage*, maintains this emphasis.

In a documentary film entitled *No Reason to Stay*, shown on the CBC television series "N.F.B. Presents", the eighteen-year-old high-school drop-out who plays the lead is critical of our educational system, charging that teachers are "boring to death thousands of innocent students. . . . To educate is to encourage. You do not encourage, you discourage. To educate is to interest. You do not interest, you bore." This is an extreme statement, of course, but to the extent that it is true, or has been true, *Nobody Waved Good-bye and Other Plays*, like its predecessor, *On Stage*, meets this criticism in a positive way.

The introductory material outlining the "on stage" approach should not be regarded as of value only in the event that the play is read and acted aloud; it should be of great value to the silent reader as well. It should help him to read the plays as they should be read – with a feeling for the appearance, voice, manner, and emotion of the actors.

Thus several of the theatre plays are analysed in terms of their structure. It is true that this is done from the point of view of the actor – to help him interpret his role. But this should be valuable to the silent reader as well – to help make him aware of the shape and movement of the play as he reads. The same applies to the suggestions for casting and interpreting each of the roles. These will help the silent reader to identify himself with the various characters.

An innovation that should be particularly helpful is the inclusion in footnote form of questions and essential explanatory material. This should make the reading of the plays easier for both teacher and student and contribute to a clearer understanding and a more intelligent study of the texts. Designed to increase discrimination and clarify judgment, the footnotes balance the "on stage" emphasis through an emphasis on literary values and ideas. The combination of the two approaches should stimulate teachers and students alike to a new and vital approach to the theatre. And this material, along with the plays, is presented in an attractive format, with many illustrations.

We are fortunate to be able to include *Nobody Waved Good-bye* in our volume, and to offer it for the first time to schools and to the Canadian reading public. When the film was first shown, a friend expressed the opinion that it should be shown to every teacher and student in Canada. The editor believes that after it has been seen, or the script studied closely, most teachers will agree that this play has great meaning for young people. Its publication in this collection means that it will reach a continually growing audience.

We are equally fortunate in having obtained a successful CBC television documentary drama which explores the whole subject of the Western and provides us with an interesting example of this twentieth-century dramatic form.

A second example of radio drama has been included in this volume – *The Land of Ephranor* by Joseph Schull. This is one of the finest plays produced during the first exciting years of the Canadian *Stage* series under Andrew Allan's direction.

Six of the best and most popular of the plays from *On Stage* have been retained. These are *The Odyssey of Runyon Jones*, *Brothers in Arms*, *Campbell of Kilmohr*, *The Grand Cham's Diamond*, *A Night at an Inn*, and *A Marriage Proposal*. The Clark-Baukage translation of *A Marriage Proposal*, which was so successful in *On Stage*, has been retained.

Three notable one-acters have been added: Shaw's witty *The Dark Lady of the Sonnets*, Peter Shaffer's London and

New York success, *The Private Ear* (part of a double bill with *The Public Eye*), and one of the best examples of Theatre of the Absurd, *A Resounding Tinkle* by N. F. Simpson.

The editor and publishers are proud that one third of the plays in this book are Canadian. Not only does it contain *Nobody Waved Good-bye*, the most successful Canadian feature-length film produced to date, but also *The Western Hero*, written for the CBC by an expatriate Canadian, Gerald Weales, *The Land of Ephranor* by Joseph Schull, and *Brothers in Arms*, the classic Canadian one-acter by Merrill Denison.

The plays vary in depth, so that teachers may choose material best suited to the needs of individual classes. The easiest ones are, perhaps, *A Marriage Proposal*, *The Grand Cham's Diamond*, and *Brothers in Arms*. The most difficult are *A Night at an Inn*, *The Dark Lady of the Sonnets*, *The Private Ear*, *A Resounding Tinkle*, and *Campbell of Kilmohr*.

There is a growing conviction among many educators that the understanding and appreciation of good movies, television, and radio is as important as the understanding and appreciation of good literature, and that both might be part of a broadened English course. The argument is a strong one, since students will be spending a considerable part of their future leisure time watching movies and television, and listening to radio. They should know the difference between the good and the bad in these media, as well as in other art forms. It can be argued that too much of our education today is irrelevant to the student's experience – that education is often out of touch with reality. For the past seventy years the screen has made a tremendous impact on society. We live in a world increasingly dominated by the image and its associated sound, rather than the printed word. Education, if it is to prepare the student and develop his critical faculties, must take this aspect of our culture into account.

The film, television, and radio scripts in this volume will provide an opportunity for teachers to begin to redress this balance, and to bring the teaching of drama, at least, into line with the reality of the student's world and experience.

The editor and publishers are grateful to members of the Manitoba English Curriculum Committee for their interest in the preparation of this volume and for their advice on the plays to be included in it.

They also wish to acknowledge their indebtedness to Mr. Tom Daly and Mr. Don Owen of the National Film Board for their kind and understanding co-operation in making *Nobody Waved Good-bye* available to us, to Mr. Owen for his introductory note, and to Miss Linda Delton for preparing the script. They are grateful also to Mr. Gerald Weales and Mr. Vincent Tovell, who provided comments on *The Western Hero*, and to Mr. Joseph Schull and Mr. Herbert Whittaker, who wrote notes for *The Land of Ephranor* and *A Resounding Tinkle*.

The editor is indebted to many individuals who helped, directly and indirectly, in preparing the volume. He particularly wishes to thank the teachers who were associated with him at the Central High School of Commerce – among them Mr. G. K. D. Alderson, Mr. J. Adams, Miss Irene Allan, and Miss Grace Docter – and also Mr. and Mrs. Fred Langford, Mr. and Mrs. D. E. Smith, and Mr. Charles Rittenhouse, who made valuable assessments of *On Stage* or suggested plays that might be considered for the revised text.

He is grateful to the editorial staff of the Macmillan Company of Canada for their interest and constructive suggestions, and especially to Miss Gladys Neale, Manager of the School Book Department of Macmillans, and to his wife, Violet – both of whom have given him valuable criticism, help, and encouragement.

CONTENTS

PUBLISHER'S NOTE

Herman Voaden, the editor of this volume, is well known as teacher, leader in the arts, theatre director, and playwright. At the Central High School of Commerce, Toronto, where he was Director of the English Department for many years, he pioneered in progressive educational methods, including the "play approach" to drama. He recently resigned from this post to devote all his time to writing.

Mr. Voaden has long been in the forefront of the movement to create a more favourable climate for the arts, and to bring them closer to the people of Canada. He was the first president of the Canadian Arts Council (now the Canadian Conference of the Arts), and has been active in this organization throughout the twenty years of its existence.

For the Toronto Play Workshop, a centre he founded for the writing and production of Canadian plays and for experimentation with new stage techniques, Mr. Voaden wrote and produced five "symphonic" plays, *Rocks*, *Earth-Song*, *Hill-Land*, *Murder Pattern*, and *Ascend as the Sun*; two dance dramas, *Romeo and Juliet* and *The Masque of the Red Death*; and also a dramatization of *Maria Chapdelaine*. He presented the first Canadian productions of T. S. Eliot's *Murder in the Cathedral* at Queen's University, Kingston, and at Massey Hall, Toronto, and was given the Canadian Drama Award for outstanding contributions to the Canadian theatre.

In recent years Mr. Voaden has had a wide range of interests, but has continued his activities as a dramatist in writing the libretti for Frederick Jacobi's opera *The Prodigal Son* and Godfrey Ridout's oratorio based on the Book of Esther. He has also written a play about Emily Carr, the noted British Columbia painter and writer, which was given its first production at Queen's University, Kingston, and presented again in the autumn of 1966 by the Bastion Theatre of Victoria, B.C., as part of the centennial celebrations of that province.

INTRODUCTION

FOUR PLAYS FOR MODERN MEDIA

For three thousand years the theatre has maintained its essential character, with players enacting a story, tragic or comic, before an audience. The resulting interplay between player and spectator is the basic dramatic experience. Eight of our plays belong to this continuing tradition.

The turn of the century brought remarkable scientific developments. One of the most miraculous was the motion picture. Perhaps you have seen some of the old "silents". They had some sub-titles, and background music was provided by a piano or organ, but the story was told essentially in terms of visual action – pantomime and movement. Then came the "talkies", bringing the film closer to the tradition of the theatre. The introduction of colour, the wide screen, and stereophonic sound has provided the director with additional resources.

Theatre in this new form is no longer the theatre in which actors in a hall play directly to an audience. The personal contact – the interplay of thought and emotion between actor and spectator – is lost. The two-dimensional images of the players, enlarged on a screen, play in shadow-like fashion to audiences in a thousand halls for short or long runs over the years, careless of how the viewers respond to their playing. They play, these images, to audiences numbering in the hundreds of thousands – sometimes millions.

The film has the strength and dramatic appeal of the traditional theatre – the complications and tensions of plot, and the revelation of character. But its new and powerful appeal lies in its continual visual interest. In *Nobody Waved Good-bye* it is difficult to define what constitutes a "scene", so swiftly do they change. But there are at least fifty separate visual sequences, and within each of these sequences there is constant fluidity and change in the camera work. The result is that as we watch the film we have a vivid sense of our physical world as we know it; we see a police station, a shopping centre, restaurants, a barber shop, elevators, homes, and highways by day and at night. At times this visual interest achieves, particularly in the hands of a creative director and cameraman, a compelling lyricism. This is especially the case in *Nobody Waved Good-bye* in the scenes showing the rapture of the young lovers – in the graveyard, on the bridge, on the motor-bike, and in the canoe on a quiet lagoon.

Nobody Waved Good-bye is deeply moving; it has the ring of truth. It is a bitter, sharp, and relentless study of the disintegration of a young life – of the collapse of moral values. There is final hope, however, that love and a sense of responsibility will check this disintegration before it is too late.

Nobody Waved Good-bye will open up a new world to students – the world of film technique and art.

Television theatre, like the motion picture, is produced for the great audience – the audience of hundreds of thousands and millions. It was a later development than the film. It was later even than radio. Although the small television screen cannot give us the spectacular visual effects that the motion picture screen can, the two media have more and more in common each year. As the producer of *The Western Hero* points out, some television drama is now produced with movie cameras; the remainder is done with electronic cameras, permitting the shooting of scenes out of sequence, with subsequent editing. However, even as late as 1960, when *The Western Hero* was produced, this was not possible, and the production of a television play had to be a continuous performance, as with a stage play.

One of the advantages of television is that its impact can be direct and *immediate* on a vast audience. It was estimated that as many as ten million viewers watched a Sunday evening production of *Death of a Salesman*, the great play by Arthur Miller. The potential television audience runs to thirty or forty million – as great as in the heyday of radio.

Television also has an advantage over the film in its greater intimacy. The viewers are in their homes. The close-up is important in this respect, and the voice provides the direct person-to-person communication that makes radio effective.

Television brings the movie into the home, not only the television dramas and serials specially produced for the medium, but the tremendous number of commercial films – many of them of a high calibre – which are presented daily.

The basis of the film industry is the full-length film drama. This is not the case with television. Drama is only a small part of the total range of the medium. The documentary is of great importance, and it is interesting and fitting that *The Western Hero*, the example of television theatre, like the film, *Nobody Waved Good-bye*, combines both dramatic and documentary elements. Both borrow something of their strength and interest from their documentary style and character.

Our next two plays are splendid examples of another important kind of twentieth-century theatre – radio drama. Radio drama flourished particularly during the late thirties and forties, before the appearance of television. The audience was as great as the present audience for television.

It is true that television drama has to a large extent supplanted radio drama. But radio drama is still important – particularly in Canada, where there are weekly broadcasts of the classics and of exciting contemporary and Canadian plays.

There have been no significant changes in the form developed by Corwin and other writers – English, American, and Canadian – of that period. The proof is in the fact that *The Land of Ephranor*, rebroadcast in a new production in March 1966, was not in any sense "dated" in its technique.

Radio was the marvel of its time and it is still an important dramatic medium. Although its audience is not as large as the television audience, it is a devoted and intelligent one. The radio play has won acceptance as a significant art form, comparable to the stage play, the film, and television drama.

The central theme of *The Odyssey of Runyon Jones* – the loyalty of a little boy to his dog – is touching, both in its comic and in its tragic aspects; it has a well-nigh universal appeal. There is no better example of radio's ability to create vividly a fantastic world of the imagination. *The Land of Ephranor* is an admirable companion piece to Corwin's play. It has a special charm and magic of its own. Together, the two dramas exhibit the full range of the art of the radio play.

EIGHT THEATRE PLAYS

Our first two plays are fairly representative of the great traditions of comedy and tragedy in the theatre. It is true that *A Marriage Proposal* has some value as a social documentary, revealing the life of the Russian landed upper-classes before the revolution. It gives us a picture of their "hunting and shooting" society. Doubtless Chekhov had heard them in their family quarrels, arguing about their land and dogs – talking about their peasants and their hunting experiences. (Some of them ride only "to flatter the Count".) But essentially the play is what Harold Clurman calls a "romp-like" or theatrical comedy, in the great tradition that stretches back through the *commedia dell'arte* to the Greek comedies. It is a play for comedians.

Campbell of Kilmohr is an impressive example of tragedy in the theatre. Like *A Marriage Proposal*, it has elements which mirror life in a certain period – Scotland after the '45 uprising. But it is in the mood and spirit of the great Greek tragedies – especially at its close, when the mother of Dugald Stewart triumphs over defeat and death, asserting the dignity and greatness of the human spirit.

The next two plays are in what Clurman calls the "upstart realistic theatre" tradition of the nineteenth and twentieth centuries. *The Grand Cham's Diamond* gives us a picture of life in suburban London; *Brothers in Arms* of the conflict between backwoodsmen and city visitors in Ontario's northland. Each play has elements of broad comedy or farce, and *The Grand Cham's Diamond* has a lively melodramatic element as well. Both hold a mirror up to nature, reflecting life essentially in its comic values.

The Grand Cham's Diamond starts out as an amusing picture of suburban English family life; it changes swiftly to farcical melodrama. It is a delightful and durable example of farce comedy – a wonderfully hilarious piece, centred around the redoubtable Ma Perkins, who has her "bit of fun for onct".

Brothers in Arms is one of the best-known and most frequently performed Canadian one-act plays. Although many years have passed since it was written, its satire of the little man in big business, of the romantic heroine, and of military life, all seen through the eyes of two backwoodsmen, is still valid.

The plays of Lord Dunsany break from this realistic theatre tradition. *A Night at an Inn* is a thriller, full of mystery and horror, written by a consummate master in the art of telling the strange and fantastic tale.

George Bernard Shaw was an angry young man, a rebel, a non-conformist, even before the turn of the century. Reformer, poet, wit – all are brilliantly heard in *The Dark Lady of the Sonnets.*

Our last two plays suggest new directions in which the theatre is moving. *The Private Ear* has much in common with the plays of such young English dramatists as Harold Pinter, Arnold Wesker, and John Osborne. It is critical of the "establishment" – of accepted traditions and attitudes.

A Resounding Tinkle is in the tradition of Eugene Ionesco. It is a notable example of Theatre of the Absurd.

THE PLAY: A CO-OPERATIVE PROJECT

The art of the theatre is twofold. Plays are *written* by the dramatist working alone, just as the composer, painter, sculptor, poet, and novelist work alone. But they are *produced* by a co-operative effort involving many people. The task of the painter, sculptor, poet, or writer is largely completed with his solitary effort. Only the framing of the picture, the casting of the clay, the printing of the words remains. A co-operative effort is necessary to interpret the work of composer and dramatist. The music of the composer requires special talent to bring it to life. But the play which the dramatist has written in the solitude of his study can be given straight to the people. It is true that specialists in directing, acting, and production can contribute to the effectiveness of the presentation. But any group of individuals, young or old, can band themselves together to read or act a play, deriving at least social benefits from the experience, and usually some artistic profit as well.

These social benefits are apparent to anyone who reviews the history of the theatre, which had its origins in primitive folk festivals, in communal worship, in processions and celebrations. Down the centuries the theatre has been the people's art. But only in the last fifty years have these social values been rationalized and used deliberately with a full sense of the contribution they can make toward enriching school and community experience.

On Stage was sub-titled *Plays for School and Community*. It is hoped that this book, like its predecessor, will be used to stimulate co-operative play projects in the community as well as in the school. In the school this co-operative activity will take the form of class productions and school performances. From the school should radiate many of the community's most worthwhile interests and activities. From the the school the plays should be made known to the community and used by community groups. Perhaps in a prairie town the teacher will help to organize a reading club, studio play workshop, or little theatre organization. These clubs can carry on their activities along the lines outlined later, and the seeds of social, recreational, and cultural activity planted in the school will be nurtured and will grow to full fruition in the community.

THEATRE IN THE SCHOOL

Dramatic training can make a special contribution to the education of our young people. The actor learns how to use his voice properly, to project his words clearly, and to speak pleasantly and with expression. School dramatics offer a functional kind of voice training, less self-conscious than public speaking, the old-fashioned elocution, or the modern speech and diction course.

Then there are values in the shaping of personality and character. In acting, a student gains courage. He acquires self-confidence and poise. His range of experience is widened through reliving the experiences of other people. It is not necessary or wise to cast to type at all times. Much can be done to develop a better character and a better attitude toward life by non-type casting – by giving a gentle part to a rough boy, and a violent, emphatic part to a shy, retiring student, for example. The psychological values of this type of casting are only now beginning to be understood.

As suggested in the previous section, the stage provides valuable training in democracy. The presentation of a play is an enterprise, a co-operative project in which each must play his part. In this project leaders are developed, and the student learns how to follow and work with others in a common task. Moreover, it is easy for a teacher to know and to influence his students when they are engaged with him in such a project. He becomes a friend and companion, as well as an instructor.

The best English teacher is not content with an intellectual approach to his subject. Although it is difficult to do, he must stimulate a more delicate and imaginative reaction to experience. He must be concerned with the inculcating of ideals, with the refining and disciplining of emotions. In achieving these aims, the theatre, which is above all a world of ideals and emotions, has much to offer. It can help us to give a well-rounded training to our boys and girls.

COMMUNITY DRAMA

It is hardly necessary to urge the importance of the theatre in the community. It is one of the great humanizing and civilizing arts. Its special importance is that it provides a common meeting-ground where poetry and prose may be combined with the arts of music and decoration (painting, architecture, and sculpture). Joined to these other arts is the theatre's own art: that of the actor who, with voice and pantomime, enacts a sequence of life in the costumes and against the setting devised by the artist, and sometimes to a background of music supplied by the composer.

In the community this book will be available to the individual reader. It is hoped that students will keep it in their own personal libraries and continue to use it when they are adults. One of life's finest pleasures is in having your own library and watching it grow, year after year.

How can this book be used by groups of people in the community? First, it can be used by reading and study clubs. There is no better way to combine pleasure and self-improvement than to form such a club with your friends. If you have several copies of the play, each part can be read by a different person, or if you have one good reader he can read the entire play. Then you can discuss the play and problems in connection with its plot, character, ideas, setting, and style. It is a good plan to have one or two panel leaders to direct this discussion. These leaders can prepare reports on the play and perhaps on other plays of a similar nature or by the same author. They can quote from the latter for comparative purposes.

A second type of activity is provided by a studio, laboratory, or workshop drama group. Such a group will pay more attention to production than will a reading group. The plays can be read or memorized. They should be rehearsed and presented in at least a workable stage setting, and with some stage movement and "business". Costumes and make-up will also help. These performances can be given in homes which have fairly large rooms, or in a special hall. The presentation can be followed by a discussion in which the play, the production, and the acting are reviewed.

If a full-length play is to be read, and you wish to leave time for discussion, you need read or act only a portion of the work, picking out the most interesting scenes and connecting them with narrative. When only a limited number of books is available, scenes requiring a small number of players can be chosen.

The editor was once connected with a studio group which followed an interesting plan. The group met once a week. Early in the evening they rehearsed the play which was to be given the following week. Then at eight-thirty the main body of the members arrived, and saw the performance of the play for that week, given in costume and make-up. Sometimes the players memorized their parts. Then followed a discussion of the play and the production. The evening closed with the casting of the play which was to be rehearsed the following week.

If you want to simplify your production problems, place the readers at tables, preferably at a higher level than the spectators. One reader can connect the scenes and help the audience to visualize the movement by reading the stage directions. It is a good plan to separate this person from the others by having him stand at a desk, or sit at a table apart from the actors.

An improvement on this plan which will give added interest and concentrate attention on those who are speaking is to have desk lights at each table, with the rest of the hall in relative darkness. When an actor is not in the scene he turns his light off. With this help the audience more readily follows those who are speaking.

The final step is to have a public performance of the play before an audience.

CLASS READINGS AND PRODUCTIONS

In the simplest class reading students stand at their desks, or go to the corners or the front of the room. Parts are assigned, and read without preparation. They are changed frequently, to maintain interest. The teacher may read one part. The reading should be as spirited and vital as possible.

An improvement on this is the class reading in which there is preparation but no memorization. The parts are assigned ahead of time. Still another plan is to have the readers at raised tables, desks, or lecterns, as suggested previously.

It is hoped that you will not be satisfied with a mere reading, but will have sufficient space at the front of the classroom to arrange some kind of simple stage setting. Three chairs together will make a settee. A fireplace can be imagined, or some object placed in the required spot to represent it. Two chairs back to back and two or three feet apart will represent a door opening, if you cannot use a real door. Properties like glasses and plates can be imagined.

If you have a larger room or hall to use as your theatre, and can separate your actors from the audience by a certain space – at least a few feet – the performance will gain in reality. Some boxes raising the stage eight inches or a foot above the floor level will add to the actor's confidence, and make him feel that he is in a world apart from the audience. It is extremely difficult to play an emotional part when someone is sitting close to you.

Another scheme for staging the play is the so-called arena method. The play is acted in the centre of the classroom or any hall, gymnasium, or large corridor that is available. If it is acted in a classroom and the desks can be cleared, so much the better. Good performances can be staged with the actors restricted in their movements by desks, but with chairs that are not required cleared to leave passageway. The members of the class who are not taking part sit in the seats, or on the desk tops, at the circumference of the room. If necessary they can stand. The actors may rotate so that their backs are never turned for a long period on any one section of the audience. It is usually possible to have them face one another so that each is looking toward one group of spectators.

Before you start to do the play you must choose your

actors. The best way to make the choice, once you know what the person is like, is to select a characteristic line for him. Begin with the most important role. If you have a boy's part, have each of the boys in turn read a line from it. In a few minutes every boy in the class can say the words. Then the teacher, perhaps with the help of the class, will choose the three or four students who read the part well. After further trial, using this or other lines, the best player for the part can be chosen.

Reading performances, with the players holding their books, are valuable, but much more valuable are performances in which the parts are memorized. If you plan to have such performances, five or six plays might be chosen for class production – enough to give each student one good stage part.

If effort in memorization and rehearsal are taken into consideration when determining the student's literature mark, the results will be encouraging. It is only natural that students will memorize their parts and rehearse the plays with greater enthusiasm when they have this incentive.

The one disadvantage of this method is that there is inequality in the number of lines that have to be memorized. Nevertheless, since the best and brightest students will probably be awarded the longest parts in the try-outs, there is not likely to be any difficulty in this respect. The longest parts are likely to be the best parts; they give the actor something to get his teeth into; he is able to impress the audience in a way that the player with the short part is usually unable to do. Therefore he is likely to receive a higher mark to reward his efforts.

There are other schemes for dividing up the lines of the play. If the teacher and class wish to concentrate on only one, two, or three plays, two or more casts can be chosen. The advantage of this method is that less rehearsal is required, since movements and gestures can be rehearsed with the other players watching. It is possible to have several casts performing one play. Another advantage of this method is that by the time the play has been given several times the standard of performance improves greatly. Each cast tries to excel the work of the preceding one.

Still another scheme is to divide the play into scenes and change the players at the end of each of these. In *A Marriage Proposal*, for example, two students would begin as Tschubukov and Lomov, two more would play the scene between Natalia and Lomov, three would enact the scene following the father's entrance, two the scene between father and daughter, and three the final sequence.

A plan that will allow for an even more equitable distribution of lines is to allot the parts on the basis of a division of pages – attempting to avoid breaking up speeches midway (unless they are very long) and keeping the natural scene division mentioned above in mind if this is possible. In this way two pages of a scene for two players might be assigned to two actors – or three pages of a scene for three characters to three actors.

THE WRITING OF ONE-ACT PLAYS

Having read the plays in this volume, students and readers interested in play-writing might attempt to write their own plays. They should know, if they have followed the discussions of the plays fairly carefully, what constitutes a good one-act play; the various kinds of plays that can be written; and the relative importance of setting, plot, characters, dialogue, and theme or ideas.

It is best to begin by dramatizing a poem or a short story. Remember that you should keep your action in one place and select but a single incident. This incident should be the one which holds out the greatest opportunities for interesting action. In writing the play, your first problem is to tell the audience about the characters and what has happened before the curtain opens. You must do this in as brief and interesting a fashion as possible. Then your next concern is to build the plot through a series of dialogues and incidents to a climax. Two principles should be followed in developing the plot.

The audience must be expecting something to happen, and you must frequently surprise them with what happens. These are the two dramatic principles of suspense and surprise. The best way to create interest is to establish a conflict between your characters. The climax should come fairly close to the end of the play.

It is important to ask yourself what impression or mood you want to create in the mind of the audience; then you must strive with all your skill to create this impression or mood. There must be a unity in the play and in its effect on the audience.

When you have written a successful adaptation of a poem or a short story, you should proceed to an original one-act play. Determine whether you are going to write farce, melodrama, domestic comedy, drama of ideas, or tragedy. Once you have selected your theme, begin to plan your play. Write out all you know about your characters; work out carefully the sequence of scenes within the play, building to the climax. Then when you are ready, sit down to write the play. It is best to write it at "white heat". The important thing is to get the first draft of the play on paper in as few sittings as possible. Then when the first draft is completed you are ready to go over it a second time more carefully. Make whatever changes and additions are necessary.

When your play is being produced, you should attend every rehearsal. If certain speeches or scenes are weak, re-write them until they are satisfactory to yourself and to the director and actors. Remember, only when your play has had a successful performance can you call it a play.

PRODUCING THE PLAYS

For exterior scenes and for the sky which is seen through windows and open doors, use the back wall of the stage, plastered and painted a uniform neutral grey or bluish-grey tint. This plaster wall or cyclorama can be lighted any colour required.

Schools often make the mistake of purchasing expensive front curtains. It is wiser to economize on these curtains and leave money for curtaining the stage proper.

Three types of stage scenery may be used in mounting the plays in this volume. The first type is the curtain set. Curtains should be of heavy velour; if a lighter material, such as flannelette, must be used, they should be lined. They should be in strips, from six to eight feet wide, so that doors and windows and other units can be inserted between them. They can be hung on wires tightly stretched, or on pipe or wood battens. If a sufficient number of wires or battens are provided, these strips can be moved forward or hung in any desired arrangement on the stage. At either side of the stage they will form wing entrances through which actors can enter or leave the stage.

The curtains should ordinarily hang in folds. They should be either a very dark colour – preferably blue – or a neutral grey or buff, which will make them responsive to colours that are thrown on them. If the curtains must be lined it is possible to combine the two colours, so that by reversing the curtains the lighter and happier or the darker and more richly poetic feeling can be created.

The second type of stage scenery is called the poetic "unit" set. It consists of a number of elements – tall pillars, arches, platforms, steps, and masking screens, which can be moved about the stage and combined with curtains and cyclorama to create an almost endless variety of settings. The steps, platforms, pylons, and arch which can be seen in the illustration of a setting for Dunsany's *The Golden Doom* on page 289 are "unit" elements. These unit elements are painted a neutral grey or a slightly bluish-grey which, like the cyclorama, will be responsive to light. The colour should be somewhat darker in tone than the cyclorama.

The third type of setting consists of a "realistic" unit setting of flats or screens. These should include one or two window flats, perhaps a French window unit, one or two door pieces, and several plain flats of varying widths. If stage braces and screws cannot be used, as is the case in many schools, it is possible to hinge three flats together and use them as screens; or double hinges may be used and both sides of the flats may be covered with canvas and painted. Do not attempt to paint these canvas flats or screens in detail and perspective, as this necessitates repainting for each new play. It is much better to use the neutral grey colour suggested for the unit set. Desired effects can then be secured by skilful lighting and the use of the proper furniture.

In lighting a curtain or unit set, two types of lights are almost essential. In the first place there must be general illumination, preferably from overhead rather than from footlights. This overhead illumination can be secured from border strips which are wired in three or four circuits, each with separate control. Coloured bulbs (red, green, amber, or blue) can be used or each lamp can be placed in a compartment and covered with a slide, into which gelatine sheets of various colours can be inserted. Much simpler, more economical and effective, is the individual flood light, hanging from a batten or fastened to a standard at the side of the stage. This should be made to take from 250 to 1,000-watt lamps. It should be provided with grooves to take gelatine screens. Flood lights can be used to light the cyclorama as well as to provide general illumination.

The second type of lighting is secured with individual projectors or "baby spot" lights (250-1,000 watts). These are used for directed and "area" lighting. They should be made to accommodate coloured screens, and provided with suitable pipe clamps so that they can be fastened to battens overhead or to floor standards in either wing.

The secret of artistic and effective stage lighting is to use general illumination to secure the desired atmosphere or mood, and then to "spot" the areas where the actors are playing on the stage. This type of lighting increases the size of the stage. It is particularly effective with curtains and with a unit poetic set. The illustration of *The Golden Doom* will indicate the results that can be achieved if the above suggestions for setting and lighting plays are carried out.

NOBODY WAVED GOOD-BYE

DON OWEN

SUCCESS STORY FOR CANADIAN FILM

When *Nobody Waved Good-bye* was shown in Canadian cities in December 1964, the reviews were mildly favourable. The public showed little interest in the film, and after brief runs it disappeared from the Canadian scene. Apparently this was another of our artistic ventures that, since it was our own (and inexpensively produced by comparison with Hollywood standards), could be lightly dismissed and quickly forgotten.

Then, on April 21, 1965, *Nobody Waved Good-bye* opened in New York, and to our amazement received almost unanimously enthusiastic reviews – a rare accomplishment for any film. The *New York Journal-American* praised it for its "freshness and credibility", its "near-documentary air" and "an ending that's believable because it doesn't try for any pat solution". The *New York Daily News* liked the "spontaneous effect" achieved by its improvised dialogues: "Characters are caught unawares, spilling out their thoughts for the sound track in a novel approach to film-making."

In the *New York Herald Tribune,* Judith Crist declared, "It is a film you should not miss . . . it is a 'small' movie – and a universal one. . . . This is a movie for teen-agers and parents and anyone concerned with today's youth." She told the story of the film to the final moment when Peter's thievery has taken him on the road beyond delinquency "and it is a road he must travel alone, with arrogance, with pride, with self-involvement and without farewells. And yet the triumph of script, direction and performance is that Peter is likeable; he is every young person adults tend to dismiss as 'crazy mixed-up' but who is so large a product of our society that he cannot be dismissed."

She continued: "The dialogue is improvised – and with its hesitations and outbursts it carries the tones of truth. And the performances too are near-impromptu. There are rough edges – but one is left with the feeling that they are an integral part of the frankness and honesty of the film. And do not misread 'frankness', for there is nothing of the sensational in Peter and Julie's relationship, only a soft, almost childish groping for warmth, the sweetness of a kiss in the calm of a summer's day, the near-horseplay of affectionate hugs, the reaching out to one another for understanding. Peter Kastner and Julie Biggs, the young actors in the leading roles, are perfectly cast."

Bosley Crowther, movie critic of *The New York Times,* reviewed the film on September 17, 1964, after its showing at the New York Film Festival. He was uneasy about the film's documentary style, which he felt was too much like a case history. And he felt that "the camera never seems to get beneath the skin of the cheeky youngster that Peter Kastner plays." But he wrote, "the one set of feelings that comes through is that of a misled girl, which Julie Biggs tears from within her being and pours out through her sensitive mouth and anguished eyes."

Unlike Bosley Crowther, Joan Barthel, writing in *The New York Times* on Sunday, May 9, 1965, had no reservations about the film. In an interview with Peter Kastner, she praised the picture for its "truth", and described it as powerful and painful: "It is this texture of truth, this sense of things as they often are between parents and children that accounts for much of the power and, because nothing can hurt like the truth, all of the pain."

The big national magazines followed the example of the New York dailies in praising the film. The influential *New Yorker* (April 24, 1965) entitled its review "Breaking Free" and called *Nobody Waved Good-bye* "an exceptionally fine movie". "That family life on the split-level level frequently proves a disaster is the merest newspaper commonplace, and while *Nobody Waved Good-bye* deals with such a disaster, it brilliantly transcends its subject matter without for a moment departing from its theme. . . . What *Nobody Waved Good-bye* offers isn't a grim sociological study of the evolution of a j.d. but a *story,* commensurate in the purity of its intentions, and even in the artistry of its execution, with, say, *The Catcher in the Rye*. It is a story that is often extremely funny as well as sad, and its hero – a charming, wretched, impulsive, irritating, and highly intelligent eighteen-year-old succeeds, in the unbroken tradition of his kind, in winning our hearts as if for the express purpose of breaking them."

The entire review was written in this laudatory vein. It continued: "The form of *Nobody Waved Good-bye* is that of a documentary, and so skilfully has Don Owen written his screenplay and directed his large cast that not a word of the dialogue sounds invented and in nearly every scene one would swear that the cameras (to say nothing of the intricate botheration of the lights, the sound equipment, and the crews) not only had happened to arrive at precisely the right spot at precisely the right instant but had enjoyed the further, and crucial, advantage of being there as ghosts, unbeknownst to the actors. In brisk, cunningly broken-off episodes we watch the boy career with cocky bad manners from the harmless folly of skipping school to the theft of a car and the final, inevitable speeding away into the dark, alone and frightened, aware that in the eyes of the law and perhaps of his family as well he is already a confirmed criminal. The poignancy of his fall from a not very secure state of grace is greatly heightened by the offhand naturalness of the leading players, among them the fantastically gifted Peter Kastner, as the boy; Julie Biggs, as his girl friend; Charmion King and Claude Rae, as his mother and father; John Vernon, as a crooked parking-lot operator; and John Sullivan, as a probation officer. The love scenes between Peter and Julie are as beautiful and touching as the scenes between him and his parents are ugly and harsh." The review concluded: *"Nobody Waved Good-bye* is an almost unbearably just depiction of the pitfalls of family life; boldly, it affirms that home is the place where the child is blooded and learns to draw blood, and then it adds that, heavy as the burdens of family life may be, the heaviest of them is that it is all we have."

The reviewer in *Time* magazine, April 30, 1965, wrote that writer-director Don Owen "approaches his rusty theme the way a junk sculptor approaches a scrap heap – with zest and spirit and an evergreen appetite for discovery. Improvising action and dialogue, Owen achieves a cinema of spontaneity. His film is choked with words, yet the words effectively express the jumpy, inarticulate restlessness of youth." The reviewer praised three scenes in particular. "In one warmly accurate scene at a restaurant, Peter and his mother jockey through lunch, both full of affection but unable to find a way for the man-boy to return home and do exactly as he pleases without breaking any house rules. Actress Biggs touches the nitty-gritty core of teen-age ambivalence when she half proudly, half sorrowfully apologizes to her beau for passing a final exam: 'I got 75. I'm sorry, I had pressure from my parents. I *had* to.' Later, squatting on a deserted subway platform late at night to strum and hum folksongs, the two embrace all of a troubled generation's inchoate longings in one full, quiet moment. At such moments *Nobody Waved Good-bye* conquers its simple ideas and tangled verbiage with cool cinematic assurance, turning a problem play into a poem."

Life's review is entitled "Gem on a Shoestring". David Martin, *Life* Assistant Editor, wrote, "the picture projects an uncommon sense of immediacy and reality." As an example of the truth of the dialogue, he quoted Peter's retort to the Probation Officer who has asked him if he "goes steady" with Julie; " 'That's a pretty corny sort of term, you know. "Going steady". Sounds so . . . idiotic.' And he gives the hopeless square a look of disbelief and contempt that any adult who has ever locked horns with a smart-aleck teenager will – with a wince – instantly recognize."

Critical acclaim followed the film as it was shown across the United States. Three pertinent and interesting quotations from newspaper reviews will suffice as examples. The first two deal with the film's subject matter, the third with its style. The reviewer in *The Washington Star* (May 20, 1965) said: "It deals with a problem at least as serious as the lack of communication between nations – the lack of communication between generations. . . . It doesn't have any glib answers. But it is a film that will provoke thought as well as be enjoyed." The reviewer in *The Washington Post* (May 21, 1965) praised the film as "a statement on the difficulties of being human, of making contact on different wave lengths, of somehow accepting rules one didn't make but which bob up to thwart our erratic desires." The review in the *Boston Traveler* (May 12, 1965) concluded: "And everybody will find [in] it a fresh approach to acting and to film-making, a new freedom which is not only appropriate to the subject but captivating to the audience."

Our last two opinions come from "trade" publications, *The Film Daily* and *The Independent Film Journal.* In *The Film Daily* (May 10, 1965) Edward Lipton wrote: "Canadian film-maker Don Owen has made a low-budget, no name-star production into a beautiful little picture. It will be recognized by a good part of the American audience of today as being a mirror of their own lives." He said that the film "bubbles over with the feeling of youth". "Owen, who also wrote the screenplay, has a strong feeling for realistic dialogue and his characters are very much alive. John Spotton's camerawork helps it come alive but it is mostly Owen's direction and the acting of Peter Kastner and Julie Biggs that make a viewer recall the feelings, sights and sounds, and smells as if he were on the scene himself or reliving a memory of earlier days."

Two quotations from the review in *The Independent Film Jour-*

nal (May 1, 1965) exemplify its enthusiastic commendation of the picture. "*Nobody Waved Good-bye* is not a flawless work of the cinema, but it is a masterpiece. Made and performed by new Canadian talents, it is at all times a unique blend of the social commentary and a poignant personal story. Director-writer Don Owen has fused them by means of a youthful, documentary-like style, utilizing natural sound and lighting, a minimum of makeup and a fluid technique of scene changes. This could easily have appeared amateurish, but because his dialogue and situations are so real, *Nobody Waved Good-bye* emerges as a remarkable, organic work of art." After praising the performances of Peter Kastner and Julie Biggs, the review continued: "all the other characters are impeccably portrayed. Owen manipulates them as a master: the parents, Charmion King and Claude Rae, who are unable to understand and offer the wrong compromises; the probation officer, John Sullivan, who tries to make Kastner see that he can't change the world; the waitress, Sharon Bonin, who listens to his rambling talk."

The above critical opinions have been quoted at length to establish beyond a doubt the fact that *Nobody Waved Good-bye* is an outstanding film, a *Canadian* movie that is highly regarded by competent authorities as a fine example of film art, and as a significant statement about the problems of young people today.

From this script of one of Canada's most successful feature-length films students can learn something of how motion pictures are made and of the special qualities of this twentieth-century form of theatre. Of course not all the "shots" and specialized details of filming are recorded here – but enough are given to provide an insight into camera techniques. It is hoped that close attention will be paid to the footnotes, which have been prepared to help you understand the art of the cinema. The reading of *Nobody Waved Good-bye* should be a novel and rewarding experience, one that will help you to see and judge films in the future with new interest, understanding, and discrimination, and to think more clearly about the problems that you, as a young person, face today.

In her book *Against Interpretation*, Susan Sontag, the well-known American critic of *avant-garde* art and literature, praises the cinema as "the most alive, the most exciting, the most important of all art forms right now". She regards it as the most consistently experimental and most consistently successful of all media of expression. *Nobody Waved Good-bye* is a film that has been hailed as an important contribution to this art form – and which is Canadian, too, and has added lustre to Canada's name abroad.

INTRODUCTION

by Don Owen

Compared to the kind of feature films made in Hollywood, *Nobody Waved Good-bye* is a very simple and modest film indeed. In contrast to the large crew of technicians, the large cast of well-known actors, and the extensive filming period made possible by the million-dollar budgets typical of Hollywood productions, *Nobody Waved Good-bye* was made with a crew of five and a cast of fifteen actors, none of whom were known outside Canada. And because of the limited amount of money at our disposal, we had a shooting period of slightly over three weeks; in fact the entire cost of making *Nobody Waved Good-bye* was less than the amount often spent on costumes alone in a Hollywood film.

This meant, of course, that we could create little of the spectacle or the glamour that people are used to seeing when they go to the movies. We had to find a style of film-making that was suitable to the limited means at our disposal.

For this reason we decided to draw the material for our story from things we knew well, from our own life and the lives of people around us, and to film it in a manner that was as simple, straightforward, and realistic as possible.

The film was done on location in Toronto using the familiar streets, buildings, and parks of that city to give a feeling of ordinary, day-to-day life to our story. We tried to make use of the various activities that were taking place in the location where we were shooting; the scene in the police station, for instance, was shot at a time when the police were going about their routine work, and we simply included the general activity around the station in our story.

Although the story itself and the motivation of the characters in each scene were described in great detail in the original script, very little of the dialogue was actually written out before shooting. Instead, we talked to the actors about the motivation of the characters they were playing and had them improvise the dialogue as spontaneously as possible. In fact the whole shooting of the film was carried out in as spontaneous and improvised a fashion as possible, and for this reason we had to rely very heavily on Peter

Kastner, who played the lead, and on the very great skill of John Spotton, the cameraman.

More than most movies, *Nobody Waved Good-bye* was a collaborative effort, and if the things it had to say about growing up in a middle-class environment seem worth saying, then the entire team of crew and actors deserve the credit, as well as the National Film Board of Canada, which made the film possible in the first place.

CHARACTERS

PETER
JULIE
MOTHER
FATHER
PROBATION OFFICER
PARKING-LOT SUPERVISOR
OTHERS

Produced by the National Film Board of Canada in 1964, with the following cast:

PETER	Peter Kastner
JULIE	Julie Biggs
MOTHER	Charmion King
FATHER	Claude Rae
PROBATION OFFICER	John Sullivan
PARKING-LOT SUPERVISOR	John Vernon

Story and direction by Don Owen, photography by John Spotton, sound by Roger Hart, editing by Donald Ginsberg and John Spotton, and production by Roman Kroitor and Don Owen. The executive producer was Tom Daly.

NOBODY WAVED GOOD-BYE

SCENE: *Graveyard. Daytime.*

CAMERA PANS *through trees, following* PETER *and* JULIE, 1
walking hand in hand, past the tombstones.

VOICE (*singing*). Love is tender and love is kind,
Fair as a jewel when first 'tis new,
But love grows old and it waxes cold,
And fades away like the summer's dew.

(*The voice is* PETER'*s although we do not see him singing in the film at this point.*)

CLOSE SHOT: PETER *and* JULIE. CAMERA DOLLIES *along* 2

1. Camera pans: The word "pans" comes originally from "panoramic"; it means the sideways motion of the camera to obtain a continuous, moving, panoramic image.
2. Camera dollies: A dolly is a camera carriage with rubber wheels. A motion-picture camera can "dolly in" or "dolly out" – move toward or away from a subject – or it can "dolly with" the subject, that is, move parallel to it. For fast action, such as the shots of Peter and Julie in the car later in the play, the camera is on a vehicle that travels at the same rate as the car.

---

with them as they walk. JULIE *nuzzles against* PETER*'s shoulder. The* CAMERA MOVES *to* CLOSE SHOT *of* PETER, *then back* 3
to JULIE *as she bends down and kisses* PETER*'s hand.*

The National Film Board of Canada

Peter and Julie walk hand in hand through the graveyard.

VOICE (*singing*). The water is wide, I cannot cross o'er,
Neither have I wings to fly,
Give me a boat that will carry me thro',
And both shall row, my true love and I.

(JULIE *playfully pushes* PETER *who, responding in kind, leans over, does a handstand in the grass. He gets up and hugs* JULIE.)

3. Close shot: The term is used in this script for camera shots of one or two people taken at such close range that our attention is focused on their facial expressions.

MEDIUM SHOT: JULIE *and* PETER *walking with backs to-* 4
ward CAMERA *with their arms around each other.*

VOICE (*singing*). I put my hand into some soft bush,
Thinking the fairest flower to find.

CAMERA DOLLIES *with them.* JULIE *swings her purse at* PETER *who breaks away and jabs lightly at* JULIE. *They begin fighting playfully, laughing.* PETER *begins running, and* JULIE *follows after him.*

CAMERA DOLLIES *with* JULIE *and reveals* PETER *sitting on a tombstone.* JULIE *sits down next to him.*

CAMERA DOLLIES BACK, *as* JULIE *kisses* PETER *on the cheek, then pushes him over backwards. He falls back with his feet in the air.* JULIE *bends down to give him a hand up.*

CLOSE SHOT: JULIE *trying to pull* PETER *up. He, instead, pulls her down onto him. She rolls over onto the ground next to* PETER.

VOICE (*singing*). But pricked my finger to the bone,
And left the fairest flower behind.

(PETER *leans over and kisses* JULIE.)

CUT TO: *bridge, truck.* CAMERA PANS *with truck as it crosses*
bridge. Truck passes o.s. revealing PETER *and* JULIE *sitting* 5
on railing of bridge. CAMERA HOLDS *on* PETER *and* JULIE.

PETER. I really don't know where I want to go . . .

MEDIUM CLOSE SHOT: PETER *and* JULIE. 6

PETER. . . . and what I want to do, but I can tell you . . . I can

4. Medium shot: Midway between the close and the long shot. It is employed more frequently in the film than any other shot – over a hundred times. (The close shot is used almost as frequently – more than seventy times.) Its use here to show Peter and Julie walking together is typical. Notice that the camera, even in this medium shot, is more selective than the eye of the spectator in a theatre watching the stage.
5. Truck passes o.s.: The truck passes "off screen", or beyond the range of the camera.
6. Medium close shot: Midway between a close and a medium shot.

tell you without a minute's hesitation what I don't want to do. I don't want to get into the kind of rut that my parents are in . . . although, you know, on the surface it's fine: a comfortable house, you've broadloom, you have gold fixtures in the bathroom, you go to a good school, you dress well, your shoes are good, your pants are always pressed. (*Emphatically.*) That is what I don't want to do! I have a terrible feeling that something is happening to us and we don't really know what it is. You know, we've been living in this kind of set-up for so long that we've lost all perspective.

LONG SHOT: PETER *and* JULIE *on bridge.* JULIE *is looking* 7
very intently at PETER – *listening.*

PETER. Because you have to act in a certain way to please your employers . . .

MEDIUM CLOSE SHOT: PETER *and* JULIE.

PETER. . . . and on the surface you're secure and you've everything set up . . . but really there's no security at all, you know!

JULIE (*seriously*). Well there won't be any security if you don't have any education either.

PETER (*teasingly*). You're a hopeless case. . . . Give me a grape. I need some sustenance.

JULIE (*still serious*). I'll say you do. Sustenance for your mind!

(*She reaches into a bag in her purse and pulls out some grapes as* CAMERA PANS *with her hands, and back up to* PETER *as she puts a grape in his mouth.*

PETER. It's a sad business.

EXTREME LONG SHOT: PETER *and* JULIE *on bridge.* CAMERA PANS *with them as they walk along the bridge.* PETER *walks on railing of bridge holding* JULIE*'s hand.*

7. Long shot: One in which the camera is far enough back to show the subject *in full length* – in this case, Peter and Julie on a part of the bridge, with the vista beyond.

PETER. I've never been as happy as I am on days like today.

(PETER *begins whistling song "The Water is Wide".*)

CUT TO: *ext., car rear-view mirror. Day. The face of* PETER'*s* 8
FATHER *is seen in the rear-view mirror. He is driving the car.* PETER *is also seen following car on a motor-scooter.*

MEDIUM LONG SHOT: *car pulling into driveway with* PETER 9
following. The car is a new convertible.

MEDIUM SHOT: PETER *and* FATHER. PETER *climbs off his scooter, and goes to the door of the car, opening it for his father. His* FATHER *gets out of the car.*

PETER (*excited*). Dad, is it ever terrific! Is it ours?

FATHER. You like it? No, of course not! It's a demonstrator.

PETER (*disappointed*). Aw! (*Continues excitedly.*) It must be as powerful as anything!

FATHER. Well, I guess it's about as powerful as they can get in this particular make.

PETER. How many horsepower?

FATHER. Two hundred and eighty.

MEDIUM CLOSE SHOT: PETER *and* FATHER *talking at side of car.*

PETER. Do you think I could take it around the block?

FATHER. Now, what a silly question to ask!

PETER. Aw!

FATHER. You haven't got your licence. How will I let you take it around the block?

PETER. But who's to know! I'll just zip around and I'll be back in a second.

FATHER (*seriously, pointing a finger at himself*). I have the responsibility. Remember that?

PETER. O.K., O.K.

8. Int. and ext. are used for interior and exterior shots.
9. Medium long shot: One in which the camera is in a position roughly midway between that required for a medium and a long shot.

FATHER. How is school going?
PETER (*annoyed*). Fine!
FATHER. When are the exams?
PETER. Starting next week.
FATHER. What's the first subject?
PETER. French.
FATHER. Fine!

(PETER*'s* FATHER *puts his arm around* PETER*'s shoulder and moves towards the house.* CAMERA DOLLIES *with them as they go up the walk and into the house, talking.*)

FATHER. Let's get in.

PETER. Dad, are you sure I couldn't just take it around the block?

FATHER. *No!* That's final! When you have your licence you can take the car as many times as you want.

PETER. Yeah . . . but when do I get my licence?

FATHER. Well! Very soon now.

PETER. That's a promise?

FATHER. Right! That's a promise . . . from the old man. What have you been doing all day?

PETER. I've been going to school, what else?

FATHER. Good! Well, we'll be looking forward to those exams. After June you'll be all right. Fine!

CUT TO: *int.,* PETER*'s home.*

CLOSE SHOT: PETER*'s* SISTER, *sitting at the dinner table.*

SISTER. Dad, I have to pick my dress up tomorrow. Should I charge it or do you want to give me some money?

MEDIUM SHOT: PETER *and* FATHER *at dinner table.*

FATHER. Well, we're going to be in debt all this winter – we'll charge it.

CLOSE SHOT: PETER*'s* MOTHER *with* SISTER*'s head in foreground. His* MOTHER *is looking down at her dinner plate. She does not raise her eyes.*

SISTER. Oh! We're going to see *Cleopatra* tonight.

LONG SHOT: *family at dinner table. They speak simultaneously.*

FATHER. Oh-ho! It's forty, forty-four, or forty million dollar
MOTHER. Ooh!
PETER. Yep, four hours.
FATHER. Oh, boy!

CLOSE SHOT: PETER'*s* MOTHER.

MOTHER. Peter, what did you do this afternoon?

PETER. Mother, it's Thursday. I went to school.

MOTHER. Mr. Hardwick telephoned, Warren.

FATHER. Pardon?

CLOSE SHOT: PETER, *looks up in the air. He knows what is coming. Back to* CLOSE SHOT: PETER'*s* MOTHER.

MOTHER (*above the sound of eating*). Mr. Hardwick, the principal, telephoned and said that Peter had not been to school this afternoon or eight times in the last two months. He had skipped out . . .

CAMERA ZOOMS BACK *to* FULL SHOT *of family at dining table.*

10. Camera zooms back to full shot: With the camera on a boom (a weight-balanced steel arm), it is possible to "zoom" back from a close shot of Peter's mother to a full shot of the family at the table, showing the tension created by what she has just said. The reverse movement is used even more frequently. Find other occasions on which the camera zooms in or out, and decide why the director used the movement in each case.

The full shot – the equivalent of the stage setting – shows all the actors and the important details of a scene. It is also called the "establishing shot", because it establishes the general setting in which medium and close shots are taken. In this dinner scene the fourth shot is a long shot, which serves the purpose of a full shot, revealing the family at the table. Then after close shots of the mother and Peter the camera zooms to the full shot position. As you read the play, note the use and value of the other full shots and long shots that are employed.

PETER. Mr. Hardwick . . .

MOTHER (*firmly*). Don't interrupt when I'm telling your father something. (*Pause.*) He was terribly upset about it and he said Peter is going to have a really tough time in his exams.

PETER (*defensively*). Mr. Hardwick is a persecutor of young children and I think he must have got his names crossed.

MOTHER (*heatedly*). Mr. Hardwick is only trying to look after your own good, so you don't make a terrible mistake . . .

PETER. Mr. Hardwick is . . .

MOTHER. When it comes to writing these entrance exams . . .

PETER. . . . is a busybody.

SISTER. What were you doing instead of being in school?

PETER. Sis, never mind what! Mother and Father and I were talking . . .

FATHER. Well, let me hear the story now. We're getting into a vicious argument over something that is probably very minor. Now, what is it all about?

MOTHER (*insistently*). It isn't minor now, Warren!

FATHER. Well, what's the matter, dear?

MOTHER. If his exams are in any kind of jeopardy, it's not minor at all.

PETER. Listen, the exams are in a week and I'll be spending . . .

MOTHER. He says that your school work is not in good condition, and that if you go on missing school like this, he said your whole year is in jeopardy.

PETER. It's the usual thing . . .

MOTHER. It isn't the usual. You know what his results were like at Christmas time . . .

FATHER (*condescendingly*). Well at Christmas time they were very bad, dear. But I'm quite sure that he has picked up now. You'll certainly get through your examinations . . .

MOTHER (*insistently*). But how will he pick up if he's not there!

PETER. The last term is the longest. . . . I missed one or two days.

FATHER. One day isn't much, dear. I've done the same thing in my day . . .

MOTHER. You know perfectly well how you *wished yourself* you'd been able to go to college.

FATHER. Well, all right! That's one of those things. But this latter . . .

MOTHER. Well then don't let him make the same mistakes.

PETER (*with exasperation*). *But mother,* why do you have to be such a mother?

SISTER. What about dessert?

MOTHER. Well, there's some ice-cream in the refrigerator. Does anybody want ice-cream?

PETER. Yes, I want some ice-cream.

(*The doorbell rings*).

SISTER (*rising from the table, hurriedly*). Oh, golly! There's Ron! Mother, will you answer the door? I don't want him to see me like this.

MOTHER. I'd better get rid of these plates. You go, Peter.

PETER (*sarcastically*). I'll be happy to answer the door for the man who's going to take *her* out of this house! (*He rises from the table.*)

FATHER. All right! All right!

CUT TO: *hallway of* PETER'*s home.*

LONG SHOT: PETER, PETER'*s* FATHER, RON. PETER *is opening the door for* RON, *who enters, greets* PETER, *and walks past him to shake hands with* PETER'*s* FATHER.

FATHER. What do you think of this future brother-in-law of yours skipping school, I understand. (*To* PETER.) See you later, young man!

11. If you see the film version of the play, you will be aware that a few minor deletions and changes have been made in the text (with the consent of the director) chiefly to "tighten" the script and improve its readability. The first of these occurs after this line. Four speeches have been cut from the closing portion of the dinner scene.

(PETER'*s* FATHER *leaves. The* CAMERA FOLLOWS PETER *as he walks into the living-room ahead of* RON.)

RON. Words of wisdom, eh!

MEDIUM SHOT: PETER *and* RON.

PETER (*indignantly*). Oh! Parents! Sit down! Listen!

(PETER *sits on chair.* RON *sits down on couch across from him.*)

PETER. I mean . . . I'd like to ask you. . . . Are you happy with the set-up . . . like the way things are going for you now? (*Pause.*) Have you got what you want? (*Pause.*) Are you satisfied?

RON. No. . . . (*He pauses for a moment, thinking.*) I'm still working for it.

PETER. What exactly are you working for? You've been through college. You've got a great practice. You make a lot of money. You're putting teeth in people. Is that what you . . . is that what the whole thing was for?

RON (*smiling*). I'm doing what I want to do and I'm making a good living out of it. What's wrong with that?

PETER (*persistently*). I mean . . . did you ever stop to take a look at the kind of life you were leading? Did you ever stop to sort of consider it and consider your values and the things you were living for? Did you ever really? No, I mean, did you? Or did you sort of live without any goal or any reason for it?

(RON *does not respond. He sits looking at* PETER *indulgently, smoking his pipe.*)

PETER. I bet, that's the kind of thing . . . that's the kind of life you live isn't it? You just, I mean . . . why are you going to *Cleopatra* tonight? Why do you waste seven bucks? Just because everyone else is doing it!

RON (*irritated*). Peter, you know, you are getting a little obnoxious!

PETER. No . . . no, I mean . . . don't! Isn't it the truth? Don't you ever get that, that's what you are doing?

RON (*angrily*). No, I didn't come here to sit down and get insulted by you.

PETER (*insistently*). Listen! Why are you going to *Cleopatra* anyway? Just because of all the publicity, and the pictures all over of Elizabeth Taylor. Isn't that the reason?

RON (*patronizingly*). Peter, if you had a hard time with your parents about skipping school, don't take it out on me brother, because I don't want this . . .

PETER (*interrupting him*). I'm not taking it out on you, but, you know, I can't understand guys like you. I mean . . . I just can't understand your way of life. All you're worried about is the buck. That's all! That's all you stand on your feet all day long for . . . is to get some money, to get some more money . . . to get some more money. Isn't that what you do all day?

RON. Peter, why don't you go and study?

MEDIUM SHOT: PETER.

PETER (*angrily*). I will. I'll go and study right now.

CAMERA FOLLOWS PETER *as he rises and goes to the stairs. His* SISTER *has just come down the stairs.* PETER *gestures mockingly towards her.*

PETER (*very sarcastically*). Oh! Here's the blushing bride! I wish you both a very happy life! And I hope you make lots of money!

SISTER. What's all that about?

(RON *goes to her, takes her hand as they walk out of the house.*)

RON. Don't ask me!

SISTER. Sorry I'm late! 'Bye Mum! 'Bye Dad!

RON. 'Bye.

CUT TO: PETER'*s bedroom.*

MEDIUM SHOT: PETER. *He is sitting at his desk, an open book in front of him, trying to study, but he is unable to.*

With exasperation, he closes the book. Picks up another book, leans back in his chair, and tries to read.

CUT TO: *kitchen of* PETER*'s house.*

MEDIUM SHOT: MOTHER *and* FATHER. PETER*'s* MOTHER *is washing the dishes and his* FATHER *stands by her, drying them. They talk loudly.*

MOTHER. Good! You're phoning Hardwick, are you, tomorrow?

FATHER (*evasively*). Oh! I don't know whether it's necessary or not.

MOTHER (*emphatically*). It's necessary, believe me, Warren! It's very necessary.

CAMERA ZOOMS IN *to* CLOSE SHOT *as she talks, angrily.* 12

MOTHER. It's very necessary. The way that man spoke to me – I have never been so embarrassed in my life. I had no idea what was going on.

FATHER. Well, I don't think it . . .

MOTHER (*interrupting him*). Peter is right. He has a rather superior attitude but it doesn't negate what he had to say.

CUT TO: PETER*'s bedroom.*

LONG SHOT: PETER *attempting to study. He hears his parents quarrelling downstairs.* 13

FATHER. And I don't think it is necessary for me to talk to Hardwick. That, I refuse to do because it's one of our . . .

MOTHER. Why? (*Strongly.*) . . . because it is going to embarrass you!

12. This is the first example of the camera zooming *in* to a close shot. What is the dramatic value of this movement?
13. This long shot of Peter in his room studying, like the earlier long shot in the hallway of Peter, his father, and Ron, and the subsequent shot of Peter in the living-room, makes the house seem real and lived in.

CUT BACK TO CLOSE SHOT: *kitchen.* MOTHER *and* FATHER.

MOTHER. . . . that's the only reason. (*Very strongly.*) I want you to talk to him. Now, do that for me please!

FATHER (*controlled*). Mary, please let me make this judgment. I say that it is not necessary.

MOTHER (*shaking her head with exasperation*). But, you know, all you're doing is avoiding . . . you always avoid anything unpleasant that might put you in an unfortunate light.

CUT BACK TO: PETER'*s bedroom.*

CLOSE SHOT: PETER, *trying to study. He puts his hands up over his ears, trying to block out the sound of his parents' angry voices.*

FATHER (*annoyed*). Ah! You're upsetting me too much! How can I possibly think and talk when you are upset like this! You're like your son with his natter, natter, natter, natter. I can't get a word in edgewise anywhere.

CUT BACK TO: *kitchen.*
CLOSE SHOT: FATHER.

FATHER (*heatedly*). At the table tonight I couldn't even do it. What with Jennifer asking me about a gown . . .

MOTHER (*emphatically*). You didn't try!

FATHER. What do you mean? I try, I try, I try all the time.

CAMERA DOLLIES BACK *to* MEDIUM SHOT: MOTHER *and* FATHER.

MOTHER (*with deliberation*). You ease out of every possible situation that comes (*pause*) up. (*With strong sarcasm.*) Smiling Warren Mark!

FATHER. It's paid off! And I'm sure it will pay off . . .

MOTHER (*concerned*). Naturally it's not going to pay off if our boy turns out to be the kind of person who runs away from all kinds of work, all kinds of self-discipline. It just doesn't pay off! What kind of a life is he going to have? He's got to go to college . . . he's got to, at least, graduate from high school.

FATHER. He'll do it. I'm sure he'll do it, Mary. There's no sense getting yourself upset; you're upsetting everybody.

MOTHER (*wearily*). Yes. You're sure. (*Slowly*.) You're always sure that everything is going to work out just fine.

FATHER. It's going to work out fine! . . .

MOTHER (*shouting*). How do you know it's going to work out just fine?

CUT TO: PETER*'s bedroom.*

MEDIUM SHOT: PETER, *staring down at his desk.*

MOTHER. You won't even speak to this Hardwick. I want you to hear what he has to say about him. (*Shouting*.) I want you to share some responsibility for him for a change!

FATHER. What do you mean *for a change*? I've been sharing a lot of responsibility right in this house . . .

(*Both are now shouting at each other.* PETER *can take no more. He gets up from his desk and leaves the room.*)

MOTHER. I mean, for a change . . .

FATHER. You wouldn't have this house if I hadn't been doing a lot of work. . . .

MEDIUM LONG SHOT: *living-room.*

(PETER *enters living-room. He walks through the room. He sees the keys to his* FATHER*'s car lying on a cabinet – stops briefly, looking at them, then reaches down and grabs them and walks out the door.*)

MOTHER. That has nothing to do with it . . .

FATHER. I've done a great deal of work, my dear . . .

MOTHER. You would do that anyway.

FATHER. I don't know why you get yourself so upset – (*Insistently*.) there's nothing to worry about.

MOTHER (*shouting*). There is *everything* to worry about! It's the boy's whole future!

(*Door slams.*)

CUT TO: *ext., front steps of* JULIE*'s house.*

MEDIUM CLOSE SHOT: JULIE, *sitting on the front steps of her house, reading a book. She hears a car pull up in the driveway, and gets up as she recognizes* PETER. CAMERA PULLS BACK *and* FOLLOWS *her as she walks over to the car.*

JULIE. Hi!

PETER. Hi! Let's go.

JULIE. I'm studying, Peter.

PETER (*impatiently*). Come on. Just round the block. It'll take five minutes. Come on in.

JULIE. Oh, all right! Where did you get the car?

PETER. My dad's demonstration model. Do you like it?

(JULIE *gets in the car.* CAMERA DOLLIES BACK *to show car pulling out of driveway, and driving away.*)

CUT TO MEDIUM CLOSE SHOT: PETER *and* JULIE *as they drive along in the car.*

PETER. Let's have some music. Turn on the radio.

JULIE. All right! What do you want to hear?

PETER. I don't know. Find something fast and watch us go! (*He laughs.*)

JULIE (*a little uneasy*). Peter! (*Loud rock-'n'-roll music is heard.*) Oh, come on Peter! Not too fast, eh?

PETER. This is the only way to drive a car.

JULIE (*strongly*). It isn't!

PETER. It is!

JULIE. The only way to kill yourself.

PETER. Oh, come on. . . . This is terrific!

JULIE (*sharply*). Peter be careful! . . . (*Apologetically.*) I'm sorry.

PETER. With you in the car, you can be sure I won't have any accidents. You're too precious to lose.

JULIE. Go a little slower and make me feel precious.

PETER (*laughs*). Right now we're in the fast lane.

JULIE. Well turn.

DISSOLVE TO: *int., car.* CAMERA LOOKS SQUARELY *through*

window next to PETER, *at the fast-moving highway. The window is dotted with raindrops.*

PETER. My mother's decided that she's going to . . . it's the Reformation . . . she's going to take matters into her own hands. She's going to . . . (*Wearily.*) I'm fed up! Just fed up!

CUT TO: *ext., car on highway. Early evening.*

MEDIUM LONG SHOT: CAMERA DOLLIES *ahead of car facing it coming down the highway. It is raining slightly, and the convertible top raises up and covers the car as it moves.*

PETER. Don't you ever get the feeling that your parents are sort of working on the opposite team . . . from you?

JULIE. Yes, I *know* they are!

PETER. It's the truth! Listen! I'm going to write my exams, and I'm going to write them for my parents. Then afterwards, I'm going to start living for myself.

CUT TO: *int., car.* CAMERA LOOKS OUT *onto moving highway through rain-dotted window.*

PETER. I'm going to get a job, doesn't matter what kind, so long as it pays me well enough, so that I can get out of this town as soon as possible.

CUT TO MEDIUM CLOSE SHOT: PETER *and* JULIE.

JULIE (*seriously*). What about me then? What about us?

PETER. I want you to come with me.

JULIE. I can't go running off like that!

PETER (*angrily*). *Why not*? Why can't you do what you want to do? You're almost twenty . . . and people all over the world are doing whatever they want to do, regardless of what their parents think. All we have to do is work during the summer and earn a couple of hundred dollars. It'll just be enough to get us away from this town.

JULIE. It's awfully easy to say, but what am I going to do? (*She shrugs her shoulders.*) I've never had a job before.

PETER. Well, get a job. Go down to Murray's. They hire inexperienced girls as waitresses.

JULIE. Yeah, but I'll be working at nights. Would you like that?

PETER. The point is you'll be working for *us*. We're not just working because our parents tell us to work. We're working because we've got something we want to do together. Makes a difference.

CUT TO: *ext., car driving down highway. Night.*

LONG SHOT: CAMERA DOLLIES *evenly ahead of car as, facing towards* CAMERA, *it drives down highway.*

JULIE (*alarmed*). Peter, you just went through a red light.

PETER (*anxiously*). Are you kidding?

JULIE (*strongly*). I'm not!

PETER (*shrugging it off*). It doesn't matter anyway. There's nobody watching these intersections.

JULIE. You don't know!

PETER (*knowingly*). Ah! It's true! All the cops are in the middle of the city.

(*Car continues on down the highway. Blinking lights of police car are seen following* PETER.)

VIEWPOINT SHOT: JULIE. *Car passes large truck parked along side of the road.*

LONG SHOT: PETER *and* JULIE *in car, travelling down highway.* CAMERA IS DOLLYING *in front. The police car is seen now travelling alongside* PETER*'s car.* CAMERA FOLLOWS *police car as it pulls ahead of* PETER *and* JULIE.

MEDIUM SHOT: PETER *and* JULIE *in car.*

MEDIUM LONG SHOT: PETER *and* JULIE *in car, and police car. The police car is seen in front, pulling onto the shoulder of*

14. This is our first viewpoint, or point-of-view (p.o.v.) shot. We have had the camera dollying evenly ahead of the car, and we have seen the approach of the police car. Suddenly the camera switches to Julie's point of view; with her, we watch the large parked truck on the roadside move into and out of view. Subconsciously we begin to identify with her in the crisis that is approaching.

the road. It stops. PETER *and* JULIE *have pulled over to the shoulder.*

MEDIUM SHOT: *police car, with lights flashing. The policeman gets out of the car.* CAMERA PANS *with him as he walks over to* PETER'*s car, and opens the door.*

OVER SOUND OF HIGHWAY TRAFFIC:

POLICEMAN. Will you step out of the car, please?

(PETER *gets out of the car.*)

PETER (*apologetically*). Officer, I left my wallet at home.

POLICEMAN. Got your driver's licence?

PETER. I haven't got a thing on me.

POLICEMAN. Nothing whatsoever? Any identification?

PETER. No, I haven't.

POLICEMAN. Is this your car?

PETER. It's my Dad's.

POLICEMAN. Dad's car. Is this a girl friend of yours?

PETER. Yes, it is, sir.

POLICEMAN. Will you please step out, miss?

JULIE. Yes officer.

CAMERA TILTS DOWN *and* ZOOMS IN *as* JULIE *steps out of* 15
the car. CAMERA FOLLOWS *her up into* MEDIUM CLOSE SHOT *of the three of them.*

POLICEMAN (*to* PETER). Put your hands on top of the car will you?

(*The* POLICEMAN *frisks* PETER.)

PETER (*nervously*). We were just going for a drive.

POLICEMAN (*matter-of-factly*). Were you? . . . Well, I started following you on Bayview Avenue. You went through two red lights.

15. Camera tilts down: The motion picture camera can pan, not only horizontally, but up and down in "tilt" shots. Here is one use of the tilt shot – to follow Julie from a sitting position in the car in a continuous action to a standing position in the group that includes Peter and the police officer.

PETER (*alarmed*). Two red lights?

POLICEMAN. You turned down the 401 at a speed of seventy miles an hour.

PETER. I must have got talking or something.

POLICEMAN. Well, I'm placing you under arrest for dangerous driving.

PETER (*trying to make light of the matter*). We were just taking it around for a . . .

POLICEMAN (*cutting him off quickly*). Yeah! Well, we'll talk about it at the station.

CAMERA ZOOMS BACK *to* MEDIUM LONG SHOT *of the* POLICEMAN. JULIE *and* PETER *stand on the highway.*

CUT TO: *int., police station.* MEDIUM CLOSE SHOT: PETER, JULIE, *and* POLICEMAN.

PETER *and* JULIE *look at each other, briefly.*

POLICE SERGEANT (*professionally*). What is your name please?

(PETER *looks very unhappy, and slightly frightened.*)

PETER. Peter Mark.

MEDIUM SHOT: POLICE SERGEANT. *He is seen in profile, stern, looking down. He is writing down the information solicited from* PETER.

MEDIUM SHOT: PETER, JULIE, *and* POLICEMAN. PETER *has his arm around* JULIE*'s shoulder.*

POLICE SERGEANT. Your age?

PETER. Eighteen.

POLICE SERGEANT. Born in Canada?

PETER. Yes.

POLICE SERGEANT. Your occupation?

PETER. I'm in high school.

POLICE SERGEANT. Student?

PETER. Yes.

POLICE SERGEANT. Single, I suppose?

PETER (*looks first at* JULIE, *then answers*). Yes.

POLICE SERGEANT (*to* POLICE OFFICER). Dangerous driving?

POLICE OFFICER. That's right, sergeant.

MEDIUM LONG SHOT: PETER, JULIE, POLICEMAN, *and* POLICE SERGEANT.

POLICE SERGEANT. Take him along the back.

PETER (*frightened, but trying to control his fear*). Where am I going?

POLICE SERGEANT. You're going into the cells.

PETER. I want to call my father first.

POLICE SERGEANT. I said I would call your father.

POLICE OFFICER (*to* JULIE). Like to take a seat over there, miss, please?

PETER (*holding on to* JULIE'*s hand*). Why couldn't she stay with me?

POLICE OFFICER (*pulling* PETER'*s hand away from* JULIE, *he turns him around to lead him off to the cells*). Because she's not going into the cells . . . you are!

(PETER *resists the policeman, who puts his arms around* PETER, *pushing him in the direction of the cells.*)

PETER (*struggling*). I'm not going into the cells. (*Thoroughly frightened.*) Oh, *no*!

CAMERA STAYS ON PETER *and the* POLICEMAN *as* PETER *struggles to get away. The* POLICE SERGEANT *comes over to help restrain* PETER. *He takes him by one arm; the* POLICEMAN *holds the other.* CAMERA DOLLIES *with them as the* POLICEMAN *and* POLICE SERGEANT *pull the struggling* PETER *down a corridor towards the cells.*

PETER (*desperately*). I want to call my father first . . . (*Shouting.*) I want to call my father!

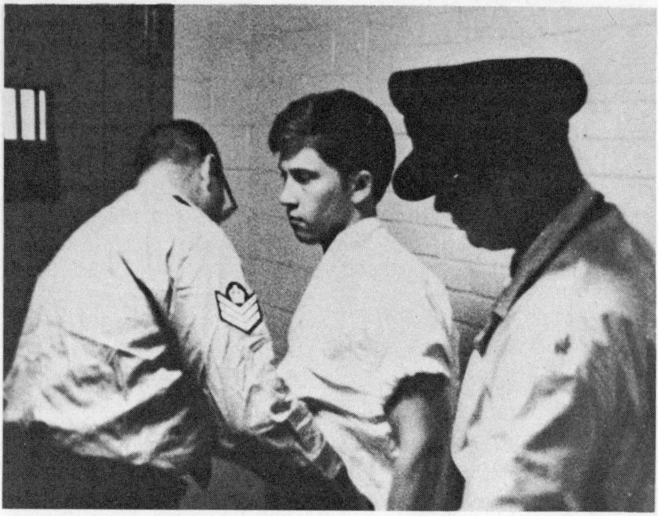

The National Film Board of Canada

Peter is searched before he is taken to a cell.

MEDIUM SHOT: PETER, POLICEMAN, *and* POLICE SERGEANT. CAMERA DOLLIES *with them as* PETER *is pushed through a door, into another room adjacent to the cells. They stop, and the* POLICEMAN *holds* PETER*'s hands behind his back as the* POLICE SERGEANT *goes through* PETER*'s pockets.*

CUT BACK TO: JULIE, *sitting in other room.* CAMERA DOLLIES *from* MEDIUM SHOT *to* CLOSE SHOT *of* JULIE, *looking sad and helpless.*

CLOSE SHOT: PETER. CAMERA DOLLIES IN *even closer, as* PETER, *eyes down, watches the* POLICE SERGEANT (*who is o.s.*) *search him.*

16. Some authorities on screen playwriting distinguish between the close shot and the close-up. They define the close shot as one that reveals the figure from the shoulders up; it may also include some other details for compositional or story purposes. The close-up shows only the head, or some part of the face, such as the eyes, or some important detail or action which will heighten the emotional

PETER. How long will it be before my father gets here?

POLICE SERGEANT. Probably up to him. I'll call him as soon as I get back out there and let him know.

MEDIUM SHOT: POLICE SERGEANT *and* PETER. POLICE
SERGEANT *finishes searching* PETER. CAMERA FOLLOWS *him*
as he takes out key and goes to door to open it. PETER *is still*
in frame. CAMERA DOLLIES IN *to* MEDIUM SHOT *of* PETER *as* 17
he stands watching him open the door. PETER *looks completely*
drained. CAMERA FOLLOWS PETER *as he walks slowly towards*
the door. The SERGEANT, *who is standing by the door, takes*
his arm and leads him into the other room containing several
cells. CAMERA DOLLIES *with them in* MEDIUM SHOT. *The* SER-
GEANT *opens a cell door and guides* PETER *into the cell.*
CAMERA DOLLIES *to position in back of* SERGEANT, *and we*
see PETER *from p.o.v. looking over* SERGEANT*'s shoulder as*
the cell door is closed in front of him.

CLOSE SHOT: PETER. *His face is seen looking helplessly out from behind the bars. He is fighting back tears. He leans his head against his hand which is resting on the bars.*

impact of the scene. Here we have had a close shot of Peter, and the camera dollies in closer to reveal his fear and anxiety as he is being searched. There are four examples of the use of the hands to initiate important sequences which you should look for: the hand on a book, on a door buzzer, on a floor-number indicator in an elevator, and on a coin box in a laundromat. These are examples of close shots which authorities also regard as close-ups.

If you have an opportunity to see the film, you will find it a fascinating project to see how many of the seventy-odd "close shots" are close-ups by these standards. The important thing to note is that it is the close shot (and the close-up), perfected by the great innovator D. W. Griffith, which, more than anything else, has made the motion picture the important art form that it is today – a form completely different from the theatre. Visually, the artist-director has in his hands, in the camera, an instrument that is unique in achieving for us a new and authentic dramatic experience.

17. In frame: Peter is still "framed" in the camera shot.

MEDIUM SHOT: POLICE OFFICERS. *Office of police station. Two officers are seen talking on the phone. The following lines are heard.*

OFFICERS. When did it happen, Madam?
Ah, we'll have to lay charges . . .
Herbert Young.

(*All the background noise associated with a police station is heard in the background.* PETER'*s voice is heard shouting faintly, from the distance.*)

PETER. Let me out of here. I want my father. Let me out of here . . . let me out!

MEDIUM SHOT: *ext., police station.* JULIE *walks slowly, sadly, and alone out the door of the police station.*

MEDIUM LONG SHOT: *int., police station.* POLICEMEN *are lined up in hall for briefing.* POLICE OFFICER *stands in front of them reading a notice.*

MEDIUM LONG SHOT: POLICE SERGEANT *and* TWO POLICEMEN. *Front desk of station. One* POLICEMAN *stands holding his gun in one hand and his papers in another, being checked by the* SERGEANT *before going on duty. Behind them* PETER'*s* FATHER *walks in the door of the station.* CAMERA PANS *with father as he walks up to the desk. He looks very self-conscious and uncomfortable.*

CUT BACK TO MEDIUM SHOT: POLICE OFFICER. *Hallway. We see the* POLICE OFFICER *reading from a bulletin.*

OFFICER. On September 16th and September 17th, a five minute talk . . . a ten-minute film on cancer research. You've all seen the bulletin on the memo book.

18. The following scene, in which Peter's cries, Julie's departure, the father's arrival, and Peter's approach are set against a background of the noises, conversation, and routine "business" of the police station, is characteristic of film art; it would not be attempted in the theatre. Why is it effective, both visually and dramatically?

MEDIUM LONG SHOT: POLICE SERGEANT *and* FATHER. *Front desk of station.*

POLICE SERGEANT. Yes, of course, sir. Sit down a moment, will you, please?

FATHER. Thank you very much.

CAMERA PANS *and* DOLLIES *with* FATHER *as he walks over to a near-by chair and sits down. He does not look angry – just tired.*

MEDIUM LONG SHOT: OFFICER *and* POLICEMEN *in hallway. The briefing is completed, and the* POLICEMEN *turn together and march out of the hallway.*

DUTY OFFICER (*to* POLICEMEN). Left turn. To your posts. And sign your log please.

(PETER, *held by the* POLICE SERGEANT, *is led down the hallway, past them. They walk towards* CAMERA; CAMERA PANS *with them as they pass and walk through the door into the office of the station.*)

VIEWPOINT SHOT: PETER *and* POLICE SERGEANT. *They are seen walking into station office from* FATHER'*s p.o.v.* CAMERA DOLLIES BACK *with them, revealing* FATHER. PETER *greets his* FATHER *happily.*

PETER. Hi Dad.

FATHER. Hello Peter! (*Firmly.*) All you can do is smile. I told you not to use that car, didn't I? You haven't got your licence. Do you realize how much trouble you are getting me into?

PETER (*quickly – wanting to avoid the impending scene*). Dad, can we . . .

FATHER (*angrily*). The car is not mine. The car belongs to the business. You could have got yourself into a lot of trouble. You could have got that car smashed up. Do you realize that?

CLOSE SHOT: PETER'*s* FATHER. *He looks coldly and angrily at* PETER.

PETER. But there's nothing wrong with the car, Dad.

FATHER (*disillusioned*). I don't care! There's something wrong with you when you can do a thing like that.

MEDIUM SHOT: PETER, FATHER, *and* POLICE SERGEANT.

PETER (*anxiously*). Can we talk about it at home, Dad?

FATHER. Two hundred dollars I have to have in my pocket, the officer tells me, with five hundred dollars . . .

POLICE SERGEANT. Property.

PETER. But you'll get it back!

FATHER. I haven't got it – I know that.

CAMERA ZOOMS IN *to* CLOSE SHOT *of* PETER'*s face*.

FATHER (*to* POLICE SERGEANT). Take him back.

MEDIUM SHOT: PETER, *his* FATHER, *and* POLICE SERGEANT.

PETER. But . . . er . . . Dad!

FATHER. I told you not to touch that car, didn't I?

PETER. But what does it matter?

FATHER (*strongly*). It means a great deal. How about Jennifer? . . . and your mother? What do you think they are going through right now?

PETER (*anxiously*). What about me? Are you going to let me stay here all night long?

FATHER. I wish you had used your sense before getting into the car and driving like you were.

PETER (*to the* POLICE SERGEANT, *sarcastically*). The guy is my father! He won't even take me out of the station for the night.

FATHER. Officer . . .

PETER. It will only cost you two hundred bucks. What's the matter with you? Are you cheap?

FATHER. Officer, I think . . .

PETER. You can call up ten guys and they'll have the money for you in a second.

FATHER. Will you be quiet and let me do the talking. . . . You've been doing too much.

CAMERA ZOOMS *to* CLOSE SHOT: PETER.

FATHER (*coldly, to* POLICE SERGEANT). Take him back. Maybe the night would do him a lot of good.

CAMERA ZOOMS BACK *to* THREE-SHOT *of* PETER, FATHER, *and* POLICE SERGEANT *as* POLICE SERGEANT *goes over to* PETER *and takes him by the arm.*

FATHER. I don't want anything more to do with him anyway.

(*The* POLICE SERGEANT *pulls* PETER *by the arm and pushes him in front of him towards the hall. The* CAMERA PANS *with them. As they move in front of* CAMERA, CAMERA DOLLIES *with them down the hall.* PETER, *in front of the* POLICE SERGEANT, *tries frantically to talk to his* FATHER *as he is pushed down the hall.*

PETER (*alarmed*). Dad, what are you doing? Dad it's just two hundred bucks. He's my father. . . . (*Shouting.*) Dad!

CUT TO MEDIUM SHOT: PROBATION OFFICER. *His office. Day.*

PROBATION OFFICER (*quietly*). Ah! You're on probation. You signed a voluntary arrangement whereby you will come in here every week and we'll talk about things, and we'll try to help . . . best we can . . .

MEDIUM SHOT: PETER. *He sits rocking back in his chair, looking very uncooperative.*

PROBATION OFFICER. What about the charge?

(PETER *smiles. He is trying to look very "cool" – unperturbed by the situation.*)

PROBATION OFFICER. This car business . . . how did that all come about?

PETER (*trying to sound casual*). Well, haven't you ever gone through a red light?

PROBATION OFFICER. Yeah.

PETER. Well, that's how it came about.

PROBATION OFFICER. Well, we're not talking about that. It's . . . was it your car?

PETER (*glibly*). Well, it was my father's car, but, you know . . . it's in the family. Some magistrate just decided he was going to play the social worker . . .

PROBATION OFFICER. Peter, look, I agree with you. It's a little offence, but, nevertheless, it is an offence.

PETER (*smiling*). O.K. What else is new? I mean . . . well, I'm perfectly happy to come down here. Well, I mean . . . as a matter of fact, I'm not. I mean I've better things to do. But it's O.K. I'll come down. (*Evasively.*) But I really don't think I need any help, you know! I don't come from a broken home . . . my father doesn't drink . . . I'm a very nice boy and I come from nice parents . . . and . . .

PROBATION OFFICER. Well, if you really don't need any help as you say, what are you doing here?

(PETER *looks up at the ceiling, briefly. Then, smiling, looks back at the* PROBATION OFFICER.)

PETER. I mean, Mr. Sullivan . . .

MEDIUM SHOT: PROBATION OFFICER.

PROBATION OFFICER. Is there something terribly wrong with me? Do I bother you in any way?

PETER. No. I feel perfectly comfortable with you . . .

PROBATION OFFICER. All right! Then, let's be comfortable. Let's use it.

MEDIUM CLOSE SHOT: PETER. *He drops his forced joviality. He looks sullen.*

PROBATION OFFICER. How long have you and this girl Julie been going around together?

PETER (*directly*). We've been seeing each other for about a year now.

PROBATION OFFICER. She goes to the same school? Same class? Or what?

PETER. Well, she's in the same school but, you know, some of our classes we take together and some we don't.

PROBATION OFFICER. You're going steady now?

PETER. Well that's a pretty corny sort of term you know!

PROBATION OFFICER. What other term is there?

PETER. Well, I prefer not to say. It's even hard to say, *going steady*. Sounds so . . . idiotic!

PROBATION OFFICER. Can I ask you a personal question?

(PETER *smiles. He has assumed his "forcedly relaxed" pose once again.*)

PETER. Yes.

PROBATION OFFICER. How intimate are you with her? 19

(PETER *has a big smile on his face. He looks down for a moment, then back up at the probation officer.*)

PETER (*aloofly*). But that's a little too personal.

CLOSE SHOT: PROBATION OFFICER.

PETER (*quickly*). What kind of money do you make in this job?

PROBATION OFFICER. Oh . . . adequate.

PETER. I don't know. I'm not so sure about that! If you're so good at helping people, you know, you'd be the head of the division, don't you think so? You'd be the supervisor . . .

PROBATION OFFICER (*smiling*). I may be! I may be!

PETER (*strongly*). Well, you're not yet! I think you're sitting in that seat just because it's a job. You've got to get up at nine and do it to make your buck, just like everybody else.

PROBATION OFFICER. You're exactly right.

PETER. Well then, you're not qualified to help me at all!

PROBATION OFFICER. I certainly am qualified. At least I think I am. I may not be able to help you. No guarantee . . . no promises.

CLOSE SHOT: PETER.

PETER. All you're worried about is . . . you want me to behave myself. You want me to be a good boy. Not get into any trouble. And I'll do that. Simple – enough? (*Lightly.*) I'll come to you every week and I'll make my little report and tell

19. The wording of this line has been changed.

you where I've been and what I've done . . . and I will . . . there'll be no trouble . . . I'll be a very good boy.

CUT TO MEDIUM LONG SHOT: PETER *and* JULIE. *Bookstore. Day.* PETER *and* JULIE *are looking at books, each on either side of the aisle with their backs to each other, in a large bookstore.* PETER *takes a book off the rack, walks towards* CAMERA *away from* JULIE. *He looks around, and then slips the book under his belt into his pants. Trying to look casual, he walks slowly around the aisle looking at books.* JULIE *follows after him.*

CLOSE SHOT: PETER'*s hand on book.* PETER *takes the book* The Wizard of Oz *from the shelf.*

PETER (*to* JULIE). Did you ever read this – *The Wizard of Oz*?

MEDIUM SHOT: PETER *and* JULIE. *They are looking at the book.*

JULIE. Yes. It's lovely. It's just like the film. Have you seen the film?

PETER. About twenty times. . . . Let's go!

MEDIUM LONG SHOT: PETER *and* JULIE. PETER *pulls* JULIE *by the hand towards the door.* CAMERA PANS *with them.* JULIE *stops at the cashier to pay for a book she has.* PETER *walks past the cashier, o.s.*

JULIE. Peter, I want to buy this book.

PETER (*urgently*). Come on, let's go!

LONG SHOT: *ext., bookstore.* PETER *walks out of the store.* CAMERA PANS *with him as he walks hurriedly down the street.* JULIE *runs out of the store after him.*

LONG SHOT: *street.* PETER *and* JULIE *run down the street towards* CAMERA. CAMERA DOLLIES BACK *as they approach revealing* PETER'*s motor-scooter parked on sidewalk. They go to the scooter.*

20. Why is this scene in the bookstore placed right after the scene with the probation officer?

JULIE. Are you going to start it first?
PETER. O.K. Will you hold this please?

(PETER *hands her the stolen book.*)

JULIE. Where did you get this, Peter?
PETER (*flatly*). Stole it.
JULIE. Oh, come on! Where did you get it?
PETER. No, I just felt like stealing a book. Don't you ever do things on impulse?
JULIE (*perturbed*). You can do . . . get kicks out of other things besides stealing books.
PETER. But who does it hurt anyway? (*Annoyed.*) Aw come on! Is this a gag or something?

(JULIE *looks at him seriously.* PETER *starts the scooter.*)

PETER (*shouting as they move off*). Bookshops are made to be stolen from.

CAMERA PANS *with them as they drive off down the side-walk.*

MEDIUM CLOSE SHOT: PETER *and* JULIE *on motor-scooter.* CAMERA DOLLIES *with them as they ride.*

PETER. You know that all automobile drivers have an instinctive hatred of scooter drivers. (*Laughing.*) It's true! They try to take . . . I don't know what it is. . . . They envy our freedom or something like that. They try to force us off the road.
JULIE (*lightly*). They want to see us splattered all over the countryside.
PETER. Yeah! (*He shouts.*) *H-e-r-e we . . . go!*

(*They both shriek.*)

MEDIUM LONG SHOT: PETER *and* JULIE *on scooter. They travel happily down the street, towards* CAMERA. JULIE *has her arms wrapped tightly around* PETER, *leaning her head on him.*

DISSOLVE TO: *ext., river. Day. P.o.v. from inside boat.* CAMERA *shows trees and riverbank as it* DOLLIES *along river.*

PETER. Forward!

JULIE. All right! One . . . (*She starts to laugh.*)

PETER. Two, three.

MEDIUM SHOT: PETER *and* JULIE *in canoe. They sit together paddling happily.*

PETER. O.K. now? Heave!

JULIE. One, two, three . . .

PETER. Come on! Heave! . . . and . . .

JULIE (*joyfully*). Heave! (PETER *joins in.*) *Heave! Ho!*

PETER (*laughing*). What are we turning to the left for? We're supposed to be turning to the right.

CLOSE UP: JULIE *paddling.*

PETER. Here we go!

JULIE. You know paddling isn't that easy . . .

PETER. Here we go! That's the way! That's the way!

JULIE (*hurt*). Peter! Ouch!

(JULIE *has hurt her hand. She brings it up to her mouth.* PETER *bends over, takes her hand and kisses it.*)

PETER (*tenderly*). Is that O.K.?

(JULIE *kisses* PETER.)

JULIE. Um.

PETER. Forward! Forward!

JULIE (*sings*). *Onward into battle . . .*

LONG SHOT: *trees, park along riverbank.*

PETER. We can't seem to get forward when we want to get forward.

21. In a "dissolve", one shot fades, or dissolves, into the next. This is a particularly effective dissolve – from the motion and excitement of the scooter ride to the beauty and tranquillity of the river and its shore.

JULIE. What's that sand bank?

P.o.v. from inside the canoe. CAMERA DOLLIES *along river.*

PETER. Yes, that's the sand bank . . . we're heading right for the sand bank.

MEDIUM SHOT: PETER *and* JULIE *in canoe.* CAMERA DOLLIES *in front. They face* CAMERA.

PETER. Oh that's how you do it! (*Seeing an object ahead.*) What is it? What is it?

JULIE (*curiously*). I don't know! Let's pick at it.

PETER. It's like a mattress. (*Delighted.*) No, a sofa! Look, it's a sofa. *It's a sofa!*

CAMERA PANS *over water to show old, decrepit sofa floating in the water.*

JULIE. We can make the house here!

PETER. (*Laughs.*)

MEDIUM LONG SHOT: PETER *and* JULIE *in canoe.* CAMERA FOLLOWS *them from riverbank as they slowly paddle down the river towards a bridge.*

PETER. You know this is all an escape.

JULIE (*softly*). That's not so.

PETER. Ah-la-la-la.

JULIE. You should go and climb that tree.

MEDIUM SHOT: PETER *and* JULIE *in canoe. They face towards* CAMERA. *They both look very happy and content.* PETER *bends down and kisses* JULIE*'s head.*

PETER. O.K.

JULIE (*intimately*). O.K. boss.

PETER. Um . . . O.K.

CLOSE SHOT: JULIE *in boat. She is leaning against* PETER*'s chest. His arms encompass her. He is slowly paddling.* JULIE *looks up at* PETER. *He kisses her forehead tenderly.* CAMERA TILTS UP *to* CLOSE SHOT *of* PETER *as he gently caresses* JULIE*'s forehead.* CAMERA ZOOMS BACK *to show them in*

MEDIUM SHOT: PETER *raises* JULIE*'s head and kisses her long and tenderly.*

MEDIUM SHOT: *River. P.o.v. from the boat. The sun and trees are reflected in the gleaming water.* CAMERA DOLLIES *along river.*

LONG SHOT: PETER *and* JULIE *on motor-scooter driving up to* JULIE*'s house. Day. They come down the street towards* CAMERA *and stop at* JULIE*'s house.*

PETER. Here we are! Home!

JULIE (*sadly*). Oh, Peter, we don't want to be home.

PETER. Yep. Every day we have to come home.

JULIE. I know!

PETER. The burden of all modern teen-agers. Here we are . . . Responsibilityville!

MEDIUM SHOT: PETER *and* JULIE. *In front of* JULIE*'s house.* JULIE *climbs off the scooter.*

JULIE. Are you coming in for a coke?

PETER. No.

JULIE. Please!

PETER (*softly*). No, I've got to go. No! It was a terrific day, eh?

JULIE (*tenderly*). It was! It's wonderful!

PETER. Better than school eh?

JULIE. Um-m-m . . .

PETER. Are you coming out with me tonight?

JULIE. No, I can't. I have to study . . .

PETER (*surprised*). What are you talking about? You have to come! . . . And you are coming.

JULIE (*firmly*). I'm not going out tonight.

PETER. I'll be here at eight o'clock. . . . O.K.?

JULIE (*quietly*). Really, I'd like to . . . but no!

(JULIE*'s* MOTHER *is seen coming out of the house.*)

JULIE. Peter, come on in for a coke, please.

PETER. No. I've got to go. No, but my parents are going out tonight.

JULIE'S MOTHER (*calling*). Julie!

(*She walks towards* PETER *and* JULIE. *It is very obvious that* PETER *is anxious to get away. He starts up his scooter.*)

PETER. There is your mother. Listen. I've got to go. (*In a low voice.*) One start and I'll start it. (*Trying to start the scooter.*) I'm calling you tonight. O.K.?

(JULIE *stands looking after* PETER *disappointedly as he drives off.*)

PETER. Hi, Mrs. Martin! I'll see you!

JULIE. Fine!

MEDIUM SHOT: JULIE *and her* MOTHER. *They both stand at the curb looking after* PETER. JULIE'S MOTHER *looks angry.*

MOTHER. Well where have you been, my girl?

JULIE. School.

MOTHER (*annoyed*). Look Julie! It's one thing to do something that you know is wrong, and another thing to lie about it.

JULIE (*defensively*). I'm not lying.

MOTHER (*controlled*). I happen to know that you weren't at school today. The school phoned this morning. So let's start all over again, shall we? Where have you been?

JULIE. I was out with Peter.

MOTHER. I can see that! But where were you, and what did you do? . . . Nothing to smile about, Julie!

JULIE (*sullenly*). I'm sorry!

MOTHER. I don't know what's happening to you anymore, since you started to go with Peter.

JULIE (*indignantly*). Nothing's happening to me since I've gone . . .

MOTHER (*anxiously*). I don't know what kind of person you are . . . what you think . . . how you feel . . . anything! Your father and I are worried about you . . . and we try to be fair . . . and we've tried to let you have your own friends, but we've got to put our foot down with this relationship you have with Peter.

(JULIE *looks sullen. She lowers her head. Her* MOTHER *turns and walks towards the house.* JULIE *follows her, reluctantly.*)

MOTHER. I don't want to talk about it anymore. Your father is waiting for his dinner. (*Firmly.*) But we are going to talk about it later and there are going to be some new rules.

MEDIUM SHOT: *int., coffee house.* PETER *and friends. Night.* PETER *sits with several friends around a table. One of the boys is playing the guitar and singing.*

CLOSE SHOT: *singer.* CAMERA STAYS ON *singer for a few moments, then* PANS *along the group at the table to several boys and girls in* CLOSE SHOT, *also singing. They are enjoying themselves.*

CLOSE SHOT: PETER. *He is singing also. Several* CLOSE SHOTS *of the young people and* PETER, *singing and laughing, follow in rapid succession.*

MEDIUM SHOT: PETER *and friends.* PETER *gets up to go.*

PETER (*hurriedly*). Here listen! I've got to go. My mother's going to kill me when I get home.

GROUP (*overlapping*). Here. Stick!

SINGER. Stick around. Let's sing *Oleanna.*

GROUP (*coaxing*). Come on!

(PETER *sits at the table again.*)

GROUP. . . . One last song. Start it up! Come on, eh? Start it up!

MEDIUM SHOT: *int.,* PETER'*s house. Night.* PETER'*s* MOTHER, *dressed in her bathrobe, stands leaning at the bar, waiting for* PETER. *She is smoking a cigarette. She has just finished drinking a cup of coffee, and the empty cup is in front of her. She hears him enter and walks towards the door.* CAMERA TILTS UP *to follow her and reveals* PETER *entering the house, carrying his banjo. He moves towards the stairs.*

MOTHER (*ominously*). Peter, come down here.

MEDIUM SHOT: *den.* PETER'*s* MOTHER, *back towards* CAMERA, *enters the den.* PETER *follows her. She sits down near the fireplace.* PETER *stands, facing* CAMERA, *leaning on the fireplace.*

MOTHER (*firmly*). Sit down.
PETER. I'll stand.
MOTHER. Do you know what time it is?
PETER (*sighs*). Around four o'clock.
MOTHER. Where have you been?
PETER. I was at a hoot.
MOTHER. A what?
PETER (*nonchalantly*). A hoot. . . . Bunch of kids, playing and singing.

(PETER *stands stiffly, arms crossed.*)

MOTHER. Now I think . . . You sit down here while I talk to you. I've asked you to sit down. (*Strongly.*) I want you to sit down right now. Where have you been till this hour?

CAMERA TILTS DOWN *with him as he sits in chair next to his* MOTHER. *He does not face her.*

PETER. Out.
MOTHER. Answer me, Peter!
PETER (*directly to her*). *Out! Out! Out!*
MOTHER. What were you doing?

CLOSE SHOT: PETER. *He is looking away, sullen. He does not answer.*

MOTHER (*mockingly*). Nothing! Nothing! Nothing!
PETER (*annoyed*). Do you have to have an interrogation every night when I come in? I was out seeing some people.
MOTHER (*calmly*). You were supposed to be in at twelve o'clock. Were you with Julie?

MEDIUM SHOT: PETER *and* MOTHER.

PETER. No I wasn't with Julie.
MOTHER. Peter?

PETER (*firmly*). I wasn't with Julie! Anyway, what have you got against her?

MOTHER. I just don't want you getting involved with anybody. You've got a great deal to do in the next few years . . .

MEDIUM SHOT: PETER *and* MOTHER.

MOTHER. . . . and it would be too ridiculous for you to get involved with anybody.

PETER. Just what have you decided that I'm going to do in the next few years, Mother?

CAMERA ZOOMS IN *on* PETER.

MOTHER (*positively*). You are going to go to the university . . .

CLOSE UP: PETER.

MOTHER. . . . and you are going to be a lawyer, and you're going to set yourself up in a decent career. . . . That's what you are going to do!

PETER (*with a mocking smile on his face*). That would make you very happy, wouldn't it?

MOTHER (*emphatically*). It certainly would! I'd be very proud of you. You'll fulfil all the things that I ever wanted you to do. And you are going to do that!

PETER. I am not going back to school in the fall, Mother.

CLOSE SHOT: PETER'*s* MOTHER. *She is momentarily stunned by what has been said. Her expression changes very quickly. She is very angry.*

MOTHER. Oh yes, you are! What do you mean you're not going back to school in the fall?

MEDIUM SHOT: PETER. *He is controlled.*

PETER (*resolutely*). Exactly what I said! I'm not going back to school in the fall.

MEDIUM SHOT: PETER'*s* MOTHER.

MOTHER (*refusing to take him seriously*). Well, that's ridiculous! We'll talk about that sometime later.

MEDIUM CLOSE SHOT: PETER.

PETER (*insisting*). No! Let's talk about it right now!

MEDIUM CLOSE SHOT: MOTHER.

MOTHER (*defiantly*). *No!*

MEDIUM CLOSE SHOT: PETER.

(*They are both shouting.*)

PETER. I've got my matriculation. I can start whenever I want to . . . I don't want to start . . .

MEDIUM CLOSE SHOT: MOTHER.

MOTHER. You don't know whether you have your matriculation, as a matter of fact!

MEDIUM CLOSE SHOT: PETER. *He looks away, disgusted.*

MOTHER. And the way you are behaving in this past term, I think it is highly questionable.

PETER (*flatly*). I don't care any more!

MEDIUM CLOSE SHOT: MOTHER.

MOTHER (*insisting strongly*). But you should care! You don't care about anything. You're *bored* with life.

MEDIUM CLOSE SHOT: PETER.

PETER (*hotly*). I'm bored with *this* kind of life! That's the kind of life *I'm* bored with. For thirteen years you've been telling me what I should do . . . where I should go . . . what school I should go to . . . what time I should come home . . .

MEDIUM SHOT: MOTHER *and* PETER.

MOTHER (*shocked that* PETER *is unappreciative of her role*). But, of course, I have to! I'm your mother.

PETER. Well . . . I'm . . .

MOTHER. You're only a little boy.

PETER (*openly*). When . . . when exactly will I become a big boy, Mother?

MOTHER (*curtly*). When you begin to act like one.

PETER (*sullenly*). The vicious circle! Well I'm going to start to act like one right now. O.K.? You can go to bed . . . you can just forget all about me. I'm going to get a job . . . I'm going to find a place of my own. . . . You won't have to worry when I come home . . . and if I eat the right meals . . . and I should have a job by the end of the month and then you'll be free of me . . . and you'll be free of all your troubles . . .

MOTHER (*coldly*). Don't wait until you get a job. Go now! If you feel so responsible for yourself, go now and try it. You'll find out what it's like! And get this . . .

(*His* MOTHER *gets up.*)

MOTHER. . . . but don't wait till you get a job.

(*She turns and leaves the room.* PETER *stands with his hands on his hips watching her.*)

CUT TO LONG SHOT: PETER'*s bedroom.* PETER *enters the darkened bedroom. He turns on the light, and closes the door.* CAMERA PANS *with him as he crosses the room and sits down on his bed.* CAMERA ZOOMS IN *to* CLOSE SHOT *of* PETER'*s face. He looks tired and emotionally drained.*

DISSOLVE TO EXTREME LONG SHOT, HIGH ANGLE: *park and Toronto skyline. Early morning.* CAMERA LOOKS DOWN *on park framed by the downtown sky-scrapers.* CAMERA PANS *across the park and* ZOOMS IN *to a* MEDIUM LONG SHOT *of* PETER *lying asleep on a park bench. His scooter, with a banjo case and suit-case resting on it, is parked beside the bench.*

CLOSE SHOT: PETER *is asleep on the park bench, his head resting on his hands. It is very early. The sound of birds and a passing train is heard.* PETER *turns slowly and looks up, squint-*

22. The angle at which a shot is taken is important. These shots of the Toronto skyline and of the park, framed by the sky-scrapers, are most effective in the film. The high-angle shot gives us the feeling that we are superior beings looking down at man and his troubles. The low-angle shot gives unusual dramatic effects, making the figure loom larger than life.

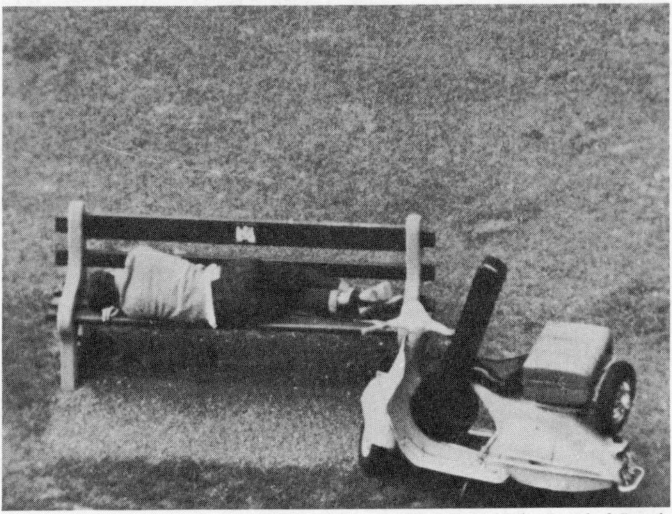

The National Film Board of Canada

Peter asleep on the park bench, his scooter beside him.

ing in the morning light. CAMERA ZOOMS BACK *to* MEDIUM SHOT *and* TILTS UP *to follow* PETER *as he sits up. His face clearly conveys the discomfort of a night spent sleeping on a park bench.*

CUT TO CLOSE SHOT: *ext., door buzzer. A hand comes up and presses the buzzer.* CAMERA ZOOMS BACK *to* MEDIUM LONG SHOT *of* PETER *standing at the door of a rooming-house. His banjo and suitcase are beside him. The* LANDLORD *opens the door.*

LANDLORD. Yeah?

PETER. I'm looking for a room. I was told that you rent out rooms here.

MEDIUM SHOT: LANDLORD. *A very sleepy-looking man, dressed in a bathrobe and holding a cat, stands at the door.*

LANDLORD (*somewhat irritably*). Why did you have to come so early?

PETER. I know. I'm sorry, but you know, I just got in. I haven't got a place to stay.

LANDLORD. But who told you about it?

MEDIUM SHOT: LANDLORD *and* PETER. *They are standing at the door.*

PETER. The girl who works out at the Uptown Lunch – Sharon – you know! The tall girl from . . .

LANDLORD. Oh yes!

PETER. How much for the room?

LANDLORD (*pointing to the banjo case*). What's that? What's that?

PETER. It's a banjo.

LANDLORD. You don't play late at night, do you?

PETER. No, I don't.

LANDLORD. Well, come and look at the room then, eh?

MEDIUM SHOT: PETER. *He picks up his baggage and enters the house.*

MEDIUM SHOT: *int., boarding house.* LANDLORD *and* PETER *are coming up the stairs.* CAMERA ZOOMS BACK *to* MEDIUM LONG SHOT *as they round the top of the stairs and walk towards the* CAMERA *down the hall. The* LANDLORD *enters a room and* PETER *follows him.*

LANDLORD. Do you come from out of town?

PETER. Well, my parents have a place at Etobicoke – that's out of town.

MEDIUM LONG SHOT, HIGH ANGLE: *room.* PETER *and* LANDLORD *enter the room.* PETER *looks around briefly.*

LANDLORD. I was going to redecorate this room, but I haven't had time.

PETER. Oh no. That's fine! I'll take it. It's? . . .

LANDLORD. It's eight dollars in advance. No rule of the house, but as long as you're quiet after eleven . . . because of the people who work in offices and things.

PETER. O.K. Eight.

(PETER *hands him eight dollars.*)

LANDLORD. Eight . . . Thank you!

PETER. Thanks very much.

(*The* LANDLORD *exits from the room.* PETER *closes the door after him, crosses to the bed, and lies down wearily.* CAMERA DESCENDS *to* CLOSE SHOT *of* PETER*'s face as he lies with eyes closed on the bed.*

VOICES OVER: PETER *on bed.* 23

PERSONNEL DIRECTOR. Peter Mark. . . . Is that Mark?

PETER (*voice over*). Yes sir.

CUT TO: *ext., employment office. Day.* MEDIUM SHOT *of* PETER *walking on the street towards the entrance of a building.* CAMERA DOLLIES *behind him up to the entrance and holds on the door, displaying the words "National Employment Bureau". Street noises are heard.*

PERSONNEL DIRECTOR (*voice over – reserved*). You live at 68 Williams Lane. . . . Where's that?

PETER (*voice over*). In Etobicoke, sir.

MEDIUM LONG SHOT: *employment office.* CAMERA PANS *across room. People are seen standing in long lines leading up to the counter. Sounds of voices, typing, etc.*

23. This scene is a typical film sequence – clear, interesting, and meaningful on the screen, but not easily followed when transposed to the printed page. Two things are happening at the same time. Our *ear* is hearing the interview between Peter and the Personnel Director. This is marked "voices over" or "voice over". Meanwhile our *eye* watches Peter in bed, approaching the Employment Bureau, standing in line in the Employment Office, walking down the street toward the commercial building where he is to be interviewed, in the elevator of the building, at the receptionist's desk, and finally in the Personnel Director's office. Thus eye and ear come together for the climax of the interview – the last seven speeches – to show us Peter's first disappointment: his first glimpse of the truth that in the eyes of the world he is a nobody.

PERSONNEL DIRECTOR (*voice over*). You might have put that down in your application. So have you completed your senior matriculation?

MEDIUM SHOT: PETER *in employment office. He stands waiting in line.*

PETER (*voice over*). Well I finished my exams and the results should be coming out in about three weeks or so.

MEDIUM SHOT: *ext.*, PETER *on street.* CAMERA DOLLIES *with* PETER *as he walks down a busy street. He stops in front of a building.*

PERSONNEL DIRECTOR (*voice over*). Well, of course we *did* ask specifically for senior matriculation.

PETER (*voice over – confidently*). Yes, I realize that, sir, but I . . . there's really no question about my passing the exams.

CUT TO MEDIUM CLOSE SHOT: *int., commercial building, lobby elevator.* CAMERA PANS QUICKLY *along the wall to the floor indicator above the elevator door. The words "This Car Up" are seen above the numbers indicating the floors.*

PERSONNEL DIRECTOR (*voice over – cautiously*). Mr. Mark, these qualifications look reasonable to me . . .

CUT TO CLOSE SHOT: *int., floor number indicator inside elevator. Floor 6 is indicated.* CAMERA TILTS DOWN *to reveal elevator doors opening.* PETER *walks in front of* CAMERA, *out through the doors.* CAMERA DOLLIES *with him as he walks to the receptionist's desk in a large office. He speaks to the receptionist, and she points o.s. Peter walks off in the direction indicated.*

PERSONNEL DIRECTOR (*voice over*). . . . but I must warn you that this position isn't exactly a very high-paying one, at the moment. What we need is a junior in the office to assist the sales officer, Mr. Bertrand.

MEDIUM LONG SHOT: PETER *and* PERSONNEL DIRECTOR *in the latter's office.* PETER *sits facing* CAMERA *in front of* PER-

SONNEL DIRECTOR'*s desk.* CAMERA ZOOMS IN QUICKLY *to* CLOSE SHOT *of* PETER.

PERSONNEL DIRECTOR. I would say that we could offer you forty dollars a week to start.

(*Expression of disappointment crosses* PETER'*s face.*)

PETER (*disappointed*). Forty dollars. How long would I be earning that? Is there no prospect of augmentation in salary?

PERSONNEL DIRECTOR. Oh, we might increase it in two or three years.

PETER. Two or three years.

MEDIUM CLOSE SHOT: PERSONNEL DIRECTOR.

PERSONNEL DIRECTOR (*reassuringly*). I think I can promise you that there'll be security. There'll be a pension plan. You'll . . .

PETER. I really wasn't . . . I was thinking about earning money now. Actually I was expecting something higher . . . the future . . .

PERSONNEL DIRECTOR (*decisively*). I see! I must say I'm not too taken with your attitude, Mr. Mark. . . .

CLOSE SHOT: PETER. *He looks down with embarrassment.*

PERSONNEL DIRECTOR. I suggest you contact us again . . .

MEDIUM LONG SHOT: PETER *and* PERSONNEL DIRECTOR.

PERSONNEL DIRECTOR. . . . when you have the results of your matriculation. Come in and we can consider the matter then. (*Curtly.*) Thank you very much.

CUT TO MEDIUM SHOT: *int., tray of dirty dishes, restaurant kitchen. Day. The tray of dirty dishes sits on the sink counter. Figure comes into view and reaches for dishes.* CAMERA ZOOMS BACK *to* MEDIUM LONG SHOT *revealing* PETER *standing at the sink, washing dishes. Waitress enters carrying another tray of dishes. She places them on counter.*

WAITRESS. Hi Peter!

PETER (*lightly*). You're bringing me in such dirty dishes.

WAITRESS. Yes, a few of them you know.

MEDIUM SHOT: PETER, *seen over shoulder of* WAITRESS.

WAITRESS. How's everything going?

PETER. Well I'm the best dishwasher in town and maybe in the province and who knows!

MEDIUM CLOSE SHOT: WAITRESS. *She smiles at* PETER'*s remark.*

PETER. How's your daughter?

WAITRESS. She's fine. Went over to see her the other day. She comes out with the funniest remarks. My sister said, "Why don't you go and see your mother?" She said (*imitating a young child's voice*), "I don't want to see my mummy." You know! She's so funny now.

PETER. How old is she?

WAITRESS. She's three.

PETER. She's only three! (*Jokingly.*) You had better watch out for that kid!

WAITRESS. I'm just waiting for her to walk out of the door and say "Good-bye".[24]

(PETER *laughs.*)

PETER. What does she do all day when you're . . .

WAITRESS. Oh she stays with my sister all week. I find it best. It's very hard for a child to move around.

BACK TO MEDIUM SHOT: PETER.

WAITRESS. So where are you going to go tomorrow?

PETER (*wearily*). I don't know. I'll just check the ads – again. Really the trouble is that I don't know how to do anything. Either that or you need grade thirteen . . . you know.

MEDIUM SHOT: WAITRESS.

PETER. What about you? Are you staying here?

WAITRESS. Oh just for a little while.

24. Why does this line have a special meaning for Peter?

PETER. I don't know anything about office work.

WAITRESS. Don't you?

PETER. I don't know the first thing.

WAITRESS (*trippingly on her tongue*). Just clerking, clerking, clerking!

MEDIUM SHOT: PETER.

PETER. This is all I know. If we went into the restaurant business, we could, I think, make a fairly good deal on it. . . . What do you say?

WAITRESS (*laughing*). All right.

MEDIUM LONG SHOT: WAITRESS *and* PETER.

WAITRESS. I could cook.

PETER. You could do that.

WAITRESS. O.K., that would be fun.

PETER. And we'd be the only two salaried people and we'd take all the money.

WAITRESS. O.K.

PETER. I think we owe it to ourselves. You draw in all the 25
customers. They only come in here because of you. The food is lousy. I watch them when they sort of walk by, look at the menu, and then they see you and they decide to come in.

WAITRESS. Oh yeah, oh yeah.

PETER. It's true!

WAITRESS (*hurriedly*). Anyway, I'd better rush back. He's going to get mad at me. O.K. 'Bye, we'll see you later . . . Do you want a coffee?

PETER. O.K. . . . I'll see you later!

(*She exits.*)

MEDIUM SHOT: PETER. *He returns to washing the dishes.*

CUT TO MEDIUM SHOT: *ext., street corner. Person holding newspaper. A newspaper is held, then opened to classified*

25. Minor changes and deletions were made in the dialogue in this speech.

advertising section. CAMERA TILTS UP *to reveal* PETER *looking at the paper.*

CUT TO LONG SHOT, HIGH ANGLE: *large parking lot in the city.* CAMERA PANS *across lot and* ZOOMS IN *on two figures walking between a row of parked cars.*

PARKING-LOT SUPERVISOR (*gruffly*). *What made you choose* this particular lot, kid?

PETER. Well I answered the ad, and I went down to Adelaide Street, and they told me there was a place out in this lot.

MEDIUM SHOT: PETER *and* PARKING-LOT SUPERVISOR. CAMERA PANS *as they walk along lot towards the ticket booth. A man occupies the booth.*

SUPERVISOR. How long do you figure you are going to stay on the job?

MEDIUM SHOT: PETER *and* SUPERVISOR *stand next to the doorway of ticket booth. Attendant is working in the background.*

PETER. Well, as long as I'm making money I'm happy, you know.

SUPERVISOR. You got to make some money, eh?

MEDIUM SHOT: PETER *and* SUPERVISOR *stand outside ticket booth, talking, their backs to the booth.*

SUPERVISOR. How bad do you need it?

PETER. Well, I need it, you know . . . I thought . . . I was working as a dishwasher . . .

SUPERVISOR. Yeah. . . . That's no good.

PETER (*casually*). You know I figured it's the Caddies and the Lincolns and that sort . . . where you pick up the money.

SUPERVISOR. Ah . . . humm. Ah . . . humm.

PETER. And then you could work long hours.

SUPERVISOR. There are a few ways you could make it.

26. Eight speeches were omitted here involving the supervisor, Peter, and the attendant in the booth.

PETER. Yeah. Like what?

SUPERVISOR. Watch Charlie!

MEDIUM SHOT: CHARLIE *working in the ticket booth. Customer comes up to the booth.* CHARLIE *stamps his ticket, takes his money, and gives him change.*

SUPERVISOR (*knowingly*). Just keep an eye on him.

MEDIUM CLOSE SHOT: SUPERVISOR. *He stands looking down, passing his fingers over his lips.* CAMERA PANS *over to* PETER. *He has a puzzled expression.*

SUPERVISOR. Now Peter . . . afterwards we'll ask him how much change he gave.

PETER (*not comprehending*). What do you mean?

SUPERVISOR. Why, it's as simple as anything. The old business of short-changing!

PETER (*uneasily*). Well, I know, that's a little different. I was thinking about tips . . . and working hours, you know.

SUPERVISOR (*bluntly*). You want money or not?

PETER. Well, yeah. I got certain plans and . . .

SUPERVISOR. It's part of the business.

PETER (*surprised*). You mean everybody does it?

SUPERVISOR. Some people . . . what do you need the money for?

PETER. Well, I just got a place of my own and . . . I want to support myself.

SUPERVISOR. Any chick there waiting for you? You are pretty young for that, eh?

CLOSE SHOT: PETER. *He smiles embarrassedly.* SUPERVISOR *pats* PETER *on the head.*

PETER. No, I mean, I'm not that young. . . . Don't laugh.

CAMERA TILTS UP *to* CLOSE SHOT *of* SUPERVISOR *leering.*

SUPERVISOR (*laughs teasingly*). She's expensive, eh? Eh?

PETER. No it's me. . . . It's me that I want to support.

CAMERA TILTS DOWN *to* CLOSE SHOT *of* PETER. *He looks down uncomfortably.*

SUPERVISOR. You don't have to support her? Does she have a job too? (*Reassuringly.*) Peter, my boy! You see you've come to the right spot!

CLOSE SHOT: SUPERVISOR *smiling.*

CUT TO CLOSE SHOT: PETER *playing banjo. Plaza. His hand only is seen playing the banjo. The music is heard.* CAMERA ZOOMS BACK *to reveal* PETER *and* JULIE *in* MEDIUM SHOT *sitting alone at a table by a fountain. The plaza is located in the centre of an indoor shopping complex. Stores and people are shown in background.* JULIE *and* PETER *are totally oblivious to anything else but themselves. He is singing to her only.*

PETER (*singing*). Ah, love is tender and love is kind,
Fair as a jewel when first 'tis new,
But love grows old, and it waxes cold,
And fades away like the summer's dew.

MEDIUM LONG SHOT: PETER *and* JULIE. CAMERA DOLLIES *from behind post. P.o.v. is that of a person viewing* PETER. *He sings to* JULIE *as they walk around the plaza.*

PETER (*singing*). The water is wide, I cannot cross o'er,
Neither have I wings to fly,
Give me a boat that will carry me thro',
And both shall row, my true love and I.

CLOSE SHOT: JULIE.

PETER (*singing*). I leaned my back up against some young oak,

MEDIUM CLOSE SHOT: PETER *and* JULIE. *He sings to her. The fountain is seen splashing in the background.*

PETER (*singing*). Thinking it was a trusty tree,
But first it bended, and then it broke,

HIGH-ANGLE LONG SHOT: PETER *and* JULIE *near fountain.* CAMERA LOOKS DOWN *at them, from above.*

PETER (*singing*). And thus did my false love, my false love, to me.

Ah, love is tender and love is kind,
Fair as a jewel when first 'tis new,
But love grows old, and it waxes cold,
And fades away like the summer dew.

CLOSE SHOT: JULIE. *Her expression is one of love mixed with sorrow.* CAMERA ZOOMS BACK *as* JULIE *and* PETER *stand up.* CAMERA DOLLIES *with them as they walk off.* 27

PETER. Come on, let's go.

JULIE (*warmly*). That was nice.

CUT TO FULL SHOT: *ext., subway sign – entrance to subway. Night.* CAMERA TILTS DOWN *and* ZOOMS BACK *to* MEDIUM LONG SHOT *of* PETER *and* JULIE, *walking through the entrance to the subway.* PETER'*s banjo hangs around his neck.*

PETER. It's early in the morning.

FULL SHOT: *int., subway platform.* PETER *and* JULIE. CAMERA DOLLIES *with them as they walk along the platform of the almost empty station.*

JULIE (*laughing*). Not very late. Look. We've got the whole place to ourselves.

PETER (*shouts*). *Hello . . . o . . . o.*

JULIE. There's no echo.

PETER. *Hello . . . o.*

JULIE (*shouts*). *Peter!* It's back there, isn't it? If we stand absolutely in the centre, would we get an echo from both sides?

PETER. I don't know. Let's try.

JULIE. Is that centre?

PETER (*shouts*). *Peter and Julie.* (*Echo.*)

JULIE. Hey, there it is!

PETER (*mischievously*). Actually there's no echo at all. There's a little man hiding up at that end of the station . . . and a little man hiding down at that end of the station.

27. Why is Julie's expression one of love mixed with sorrow?

FULL SHOT: PETER *and* JULIE. JULIE *sinks down wearily on the floor.* PETER *sits beside her.*

JULIE (*whining*). Ah, Peter, I'm tired.

PETER. Oh . . . h.

JULIE. Play to me.

PETER. Thank you.

JULIE. Play to me.

CAMERA TILTS DOWN *and* ZOOMS IN *to* MEDIUM CLOSE SHOT *as* PETER *begins singing.*

PETER (*singing – hamming it up*). Show me the way to go
home, (JULIE *joins in.*)
I'm tired and I want to go to bed,
I had a little drink about an hour ago,
And it's gone . . . right to my head.
Right to my . . . ooh . . .

JULIE (*complainingly*). Oh, Peter, where's the train?

LONG SHOT: *subway train. Train rushes into the station.* CAMERA PANS *along with it. It stops in front of* CAMERA. *Through the windows of the train, we can see* PETER *and* JULIE *standing on the opposite platform. The following dialogue is over the sound of the train arriving, stopping, and departing, and persists until the sound of the train* PETER *and* JULIE *want replaces it.*

PETER (*shouting*). You're on the wrong side of the track, mister. We want a train on this side of the track.

JULIE. Oh, Peter, *hush*!

PETER. We'll yell together. *A train on this side of the track.*

JULIE. One, two, three, four.

PETER (*less strongly*). A train on this side of the track.

CLOSE SHOT: *train. It leaves the station.* JULIE *and* PETER *are now seen standing on the platform in* LONG SHOT.

PETER (*singing*). *A train on this side of the track . . .*

JULIE. You're not supposed to sing. Aren't you tired of singing?

PETER. Not supposed to sing!

JULIE (*irritably*). You've been singing all night.

LONG SHOT: PETER *and* JULIE. *They see their train coming.*

JULIE. (*She imitates a train.*)
PETER. Right here!

(*Train crosses and stops in front of* CAMERA.)

JULIE (*calling*). Hello!

MEDIUM SHOT, REVERSE ANGLE: PETER *and* JULIE. CAMERA 28
DOLLIES *with them as they enter the train, walk down the aisle, and sit down.* JULIE *puts her head on* PETER*'s shoulder.*

JULIE (*relieved*). At last! I thought this train would never come. (*Sympathetically to* PETER.) You must be tired, you've been working all day.

CLOSE SHOT: JULIE *in train.*

PETER. Think you'll go out looking for a job tomorrow?

JULIE (*beginning doubtfully*). I was thinking of . . . I don't know. Yeah. Yes, I will.

PETER. That's better. (*Seriously.*) No really, we got to do something.

CAMERA PANS *over to* PETER.

JULIE (*defensively*). But it's only been a few weeks, Peter.

PETER. Yeah, but money isn't coming in as fast as I expected.

JULIE. I haven't been able to find a good job.

PETER (*impatiently*). But where have you looked for a job?

JULIE. I've looked at the coffee houses and a few shops and down around Avenue Road.

PETER (*annoyed*). Coffee houses. You can't get money at the coffee houses.

CLOSE SHOT: JULIE.

28. Medium shot, reverse angle: In a reverse-angle shot, the camera is turned 180° and faces in an opposite direction from its original position.

JULIE (*hurt*). Well, you told me to look there. Don't blame me, for God's sake!

PETER. Did I tell you to look there? Anyway . . .

JULIE. Yes. (*Sarcastically.*) You'd think I was going to provide most of the income or something.

PETER. Oh, come on! There's no cause for sarcasm. I just am not making as much money as I expected to. (*Calmly.*) But if you want to go away you'll need money – that's all.

CAMERA ZOOMS BACK *to* FULL SHOT *and* PANS *with them as they get up and walk to door of train.*

PETER. Julie, do you know how important it is? The fact that *how* important money is?

JULIE (*sullenly*). Yes, I know. But if we want to go away together, I've got to get a job and I've got to make some money.

PETER. Well, we'll be earning twice as fast. This way I'm hardly saving anything at all.

JULIE (*flatly*). Well, don't take me out so much.

MEDIUM SHOT: PETER *and* JULIE. CAMERA DOLLIES *with them as they get off train and walk down subway platform.*

PETER. You'll look tomorrow?

JULIE (*irritably*).Yes, I'll look tomorrow.

PETER (*bitingly*). I mean, there's jobs around the city if you want them.

CUT TO LONG SHOT: *ext.,* PETER *in ticket booth of parking lot. Day.* PETER *is now working as an attendant. He stands in the booth. A man walks up to him.*

PETER. Your number please, sir.

CUSTOMER. P 52914.

PETER (*lightly*). P-5-2-9-1-4. Lovely morning, isn't it?

CUSTOMER. Just what I was thinking.

PETER. Yeah . . . yeah . . . O.K.

(*The man walks off and a lady with a small boy comes up.*)

PETER. Ah-ha-ha! (*With mock authority, he directs his statement to the little boy.*) What's your licence number please, sir?

LADY (*to her child*). Well, what is it? All right?

PETER. He doesn't even know his own licence number!

LADY. No. I don't think he even knows his own name!

PETER (*laughing*). Don't think he even knows how to drive!

MEDIUM SHOT: *int.,* PETER *in ticket booth. His back is towards* CAMERA. PETER *stands whistling as a* CUSTOMER *approaches. The* CUSTOMER *comes up to the booth and* PETER *takes his ticket.*

PETER. Thirty cents please, sir.

(*The* CUSTOMER *hands* PETER *money.*)

FULL SHOT, REVERSE ANGLE: *ext.,* PETER *and* CUSTOMER. *The* CUSTOMER*'s back is now towards* CAMERA. *We see* PETER *as he counts out the change and hands it to the* CUSTOMER.

PETER. Thirty . . . forty . . . fifty. . . . (*He pauses.*) And one. I think that's better. . . . There really are efficient attendants working . . . er . . .

CUSTOMER. What?

PETER. There really are some efficient lot attendants.

CUSTOMER. I see!

(CUSTOMER *turns and leaves.* PETER *thumbs his nose at him. He stands there whistling.* JULIE *walks up to the booth.*)

PETER (*hamming it up, joyfully*). Well, well, well, miss.

JULIE (*imitating* PETER). Hello, handsome.

PETER. What is your licence number, please?

JULIE. Pardon! (*She leans against the door.*)

PETER. What is your licence number, please?

JULIE. Um . . . JK 15732 . . . oh! (PETER *has opened the door slightly and* JULIE *starts to fall towards him.*)

PETER. Oh, yeah. See, this is built to trap girls who lean against it.

JULIE. How many have you trapped?

PETER. Well, I was only hoping to trap you.

(*A woman comes up to the booth.*)

PETER (*recognizing the woman*). Oh!

WOMAN (*surprised*). Peter, how are you?

PETER. Not bad! And yourself, too?

WOMAN. I'm all right.

PETER (*reading number from ticket she has handed him*). 011. You never knew I'd fallen this far, did you?

WOMAN. Have I been wanting to talk to you, and what a time to say it because I'm in such a darn rush. What the hell are you doing here?

PETER. Well, I've got to make a buck, you know!

WOMAN. Are you going to be here for a while? I mean I have to go and . . . I'm coming back, because I've lots I want to talk to you about. How are your parents?

PETER. Not bad. Not bad.

WOMAN. See you in a few minutes.

PETER. O.K.

(*Woman leaves.*)

CLOSE SHOT: JULIE. *She tries to act nonchalantly.*

PETER. So what's new?

JULIE. I got my report today.

MEDIUM SHOT: PETER *and* JULIE *as before.* PETER *looks worried.*

PETER. What do you mean?

JULIE. My report.

PETER (*disbelievingly*). But – ah – the marks don't come out till next week.

JULIE. They came out this morning. I got mine anyway and you got yours. . . .

(*Man walks up to booth.* PETER *continues talking to* JULIE *as he works. He is obviously concerned.*)

PETER. Your number please, sir.

CUSTOMER. N 14552.

PETER (*to* JULIE). I got mine? (*Referring to his marks.*)

JULIE. Eh . . . hum. (*She avoids answering him.*)

PETER. N 14 . . . (*His mind is not on his work.*)

CUSTOMER. 552.

PETER. 552. I . . . I'll be . . . right? (*He stamps the ticket.*) What . . . eh?

CLOSE SHOT: JULIE.

JULIE (*flatly*). You failed three.

MEDIUM SHOT: PETER *and* JULIE *as before.*

PETER (*gloomily*). Three?

JULIE. Yes, but you'll be able to pick them up very easily.

PETER. What three?

JULIE. Chemistry, trig., and geometry.

PETER (*annoyed*). Oh, the damn maths!

(*They both look unhappy.*)

JULIE. Don't you think you'll be able to?

(PETER *sighs.*)

JULIE (*hopefully*). Don't they have any exams through correspondence schools, or night schools, or something you could take . . . and get them?

PETER. What did you get?

JULIE. Seventy-five. (*She says this with obvious pride but mixed with a reluctance to wound* PETER'*s ego.*)

MEDIUM SHOT, REVERSE ANGLE: *int.,* PETER *and* JULIE, *as seen from inside booth.*

PETER (*amazed*). Seventy-five!

JULIE (*apologetically laughing nervously*). I'm sorry. Peter, I had pressure from my parents. I had to. I think it's silly having examinations . . . I don't see how you can judge by that; but just the same, what about picking up those three?

PETER (*forcefully*). No! I'm finished . . . I'm finished . . . I'm finished!

JULIE. Peter, you could sit at them any time.

CAMERA ZOOMS IN *to* CLOSE SHOT *of* JULIE.

JULIE (*pleading with him*). You could do them once . . . a couple of weeks . . . please.

PETER (*firmly*). By the time these subjects are supposed to be written, I'm going to be out of this place. I mean you still want to go ahead with the plans we made, don't you?

JULIE (*looking down and speaking reluctantly*). Yeah . . . sure!

MEDIUM SHOT: *ext.,* PETER *and* JULIE, *as seen from outside ticket booth.*

PETER. I guess she was pretty mad, eh? . . . My mother?

JULIE. She was upset. (*Emphatically.*) She wasn't mad! She was just very upset because she thought you'd be able to do it.

CUT TO: *int., restaurant foyer. Day.* FULL SHOT: PETER *as he walks into restaurant towards* CAMERA. *He looks around.*

LONG SHOT, REVERSE ANGLE: *restaurant. Many tables, occupied by patrons, are seen.* CAMERA ZOOMS IN *on table to* MEDIUM SHOT *of* PETER'*s* MOTHER. *She sits looking serious and unhappy. She looks up and smiles as she sees* PETER. *He sits down at the table. The following dialogue is heard over the natural restaurant sounds.*

MOTHER. Hello, Peter.

PETER. Hi, Mum.

MOTHER. Sit down.

PETER. Thanks.

MEDIUM SHOT, REVERSE ANGLE: PETER *and* MOTHER *at table. They are both trying to act happy.*

PETER (*warmly*). Say, I love your hat! You changed your hair.

MOTHER. Do you like it?

PETER. Yes, it's very nice.

MOTHER. How have you been?

PETER. Well I miss your cooking.

MOTHER (*laughing*). Ha – ha. Are you hungry?

PETER. Yeah, I am.

MOTHER. Oh . . . we'll have some service.

PETER. How are things?

MOTHER. Fine . . . marvellous! We miss you.

PETER. Oh, I miss you too!

MOTHER. Do you?

PETER (*seriously*). Well it isn't . . . hasn't worked out the way I thought it would be. Not exactly, you know!

(WAITRESS *comes to table.*)

MOTHER. What are you going to have, dear?

PETER. Um. I'd like a chicken pie, if I can have it.

MOTHER. O.K.

PETER. And maybe a glass of milk.

The National Film Board of Canada

Peter and his mother in the restaurant.

WAITRESS. Have it.

MOTHER. And I think I'd like those little sandwiches.

WAITRESS. Egg sandwiches. . . . Cream and coffee?

MOTHER. Yes please.

(*As* WAITRESS *leaves,* CAMERA ZOOMS IN *to* CLOSE SHOT *of* PETER.)

PETER. How's Dad?

MOTHER. Fine, very well dear.

PETER. Yeah. And Jennifer? She isn't ours anymore.

MOTHER. Ah-ha-ha! Why . . . she phones me every day . . . and I talk to her.

PETER (*laughing*). It's the first married sister I've ever had.

MOTHER (*seriously*). I miss you very much, Peter, and I'd love to have you come back.

CLOSE SHOT: MOTHER. *She suddenly appears serious.*

PETER. Well, I miss you too.

CLOSE SHOT: PETER. *He looks embarrassed. He changes the subject.*

PETER. So, everything is O.K. at home, eh?

MOTHER. Yes, just fine! (*Crestfallen.*) Except for . . . we got the . . . results of your exams in today.

PETER. Oh yeah. . . . I was talking to Julie. Did she call you?

MOTHER. Yes . . . yes, she did.

PETER. It's funny. (*Earnestly.*) There was a time when I really believed that I was going to pass.

MOTHER. I thought you would too and . . .

PETER. I want to . . . know those . . . I was just . . . I knew I wasn't going to do well in those subjects, but I thought I'd make it. Oh, well.

CLOSE SHOT: MOTHER. *She broaches the subject "delicately", trying not to anger* PETER.

MOTHER. Your father and I talked it over and we thought that we'd like to get you a tutor . . . if you'd come back. We'd have him come every day and you could try the supplementary exams. . . .

PETER. Supps?

MOTHER. Yeah.

MEDIUM SHOT: PETER. CAMERA ZOOMS IN SLOWLY *to* CLOSE SHOT *as* PETER *talks.*

PETER. Well it would require a fair amount of work . . . but a tutor is a pretty expensive set-up . . .

MOTHER. Oh, well, we wouldn't mind that! (*Hopefully.*) Would you consider that?

PETER. Moving back?

MOTHER. Yes.

(PETER *jumps at the offer. He looks very happy.*)

PETER (*eagerly*). It's a great idea. . . . I'd be eating well. . . .

MOTHER. (*Laughs.*)

PETER (*laughing*). I'd have someone to fight with all day long.

MOTHER (*laughs*). Oh, no, we wouldn't – I'd try not to. Really!

PETER. Oh, we'd love that!

MOTHER. And we won't fight. We really won't!

PETER. You believe that?

MOTHER (*strongly*). I do. I do believe it!

PETER. (*Laughs.*)

MOTHER. I thought a lot about it, Peter.

MEDIUM SHOT: MOTHER. CAMERA ZOOMS IN *to* CLOSE SHOT *as she talks.*

MOTHER. I think maybe if we could analyse what's happened and we could get back on a different footing . . . I know I treated you like a little boy and I didn't realize you're eighteen. I still can't. But I think both your father and I would be . . . very willing to meet you more than halfway. If you could, you know, simply concentrate on your work and give up everything else. We . . .

FULL SHOT: PETER *and* MOTHER. PETER'*s mood changes as he hears his* MOTHER *talk. He looks down at his food.*

SLOW ZOOM IN *to* CLOSE SHOT *of* PETER. *He looks uncomfortable.*

PETER (*fearful of her intent*). No, I . . . what do you mean, "give up everything else"? I like to feel that I still had . . . you know . . . that I could go where I wanted to.

MOTHER (*assuredly*). Oh. We wouldn't interfere with that, except that I think we would . . . (*Qualifying her statement.*) As you say a tutor is really quite expensive, and, for your own good, we'd want you to spend *most* of your time studying, and . . . oh, well . . . maybe give up your social life for just that period of time. . . . I know that you have been seeing quite a bit of Julie and . . .

CLOSE SHOT: MOTHER. *She continues talking, relating all her plans to* PETER, *completely unaware that she is again alienating him as before.*

MOTHER. . . . you know, for this period of time it would be marvellous if you could just concentrate on your studies. And she would certainly understand that, and . . .

PETER. You mean . . . not see her for five weeks?

MOTHER (*forcefully*). But yes!

CLOSE SHOT: PETER. *He is getting angry.*

MOTHER. Just put your nose to the grindstone and get the exams and then, of course, you do whatever you want.

PETER. You can't just stop a relationship like that for a month and then start it up four weeks later.

MOTHER (*persuasively*). Oh, but I'm sure she'd understand. She'd want you to get the exams.

PETER (*self-confidently*). No, but would I want to . . . but what about what I want to do, I mean? I don't think that it's really necessary at all to think in those kind of terms.

CLOSE SHOT: MOTHER. *She has nothing to say.*

CLOSE SHOT: PETER.

PETER. I mean I've been living away and I've a different

kind of life and I'm sort of used to it you know. I mean I'm my own man. I can do what I want to do.

CUT TO: *int., laundromat.* PETER *and* JULIE. 29

CLOSE SHOT: JULIE*'s hand pushing lever of coin machine.* CAMERA ZOOMS BACK *to* MEDIUM SHOT *of* PETER *and* JULIE. CAMERA PANS *and* DOLLIES *as they walk over to washing machines.*

PETER. Whoa.
JULIE (*pointing to machine*). Isn't that nice?
PETER. Yes, sure.
JULIE. Just stuff it in here.
PETER. Is it empty?
JULIE. Yeah! Look. (*She puts clothes in machine.*)

CLOSE SHOT: *washing machine. Clothes being washed are seen through glass door of machine.*

JULIE (*reading directions*). Step 5 – when amber light appears, add soap. It says to wet first.
PETER. Well, it's wetting it.

CUT TO: *int., supermarket.*

MEDIUM SHOT: PETER *and* JULIE *are selecting materials for making spaghetti from a shelf.* 30

CUT TO: *int.,* PETER*'s rooming-house. Evening.*

MEDIUM SHOT: PETER, *opening a bottle of wine. The pop of the cork is heard. And* JULIE *imitates the sound.*

MEDIUM SHOT: PETER *and* JULIE *stand together, each having an arm on the other's shoulder, glasses filled with wine raised up.*

PETER. To us!
JULIE. To us!

29. Why is this scene in the laundromat placed immediately after the scene between Peter and his mother? What is its purpose?
30. A sequence of ten speeches was deleted here.

PETER. To spaghetti!
JULIE. No. To us!
PETER (*after he sips the wine, winces*). Ugh!
JULIE (*laughing*). It's fierce, isn't it?
PETER. Let's finish the spaghetti.

CUT TO: *int., coffee house. Night.* PETER, JULIE, *and* JACQUES.

MEDIUM SHOT: PETER *and* JULIE. PETER *is talking to* JACQUES.

PETER. Your struggles are on a sort of provincial level.

MEDIUM SHOT: JACQUES, *a young French Canadian.*

PETER. Well, you and all your talk is about identity on a sort of – Quebec, Quebec – we're French Canadians.

The National Film Board of Canada

Jacques, Julie, and Peter in the coffee house.

FULL SHOT: PETER, JULIE, *and* JACQUES. JACQUES *sits across from* PETER *and* JULIE. *A chessboard is between them.* PETER *moves one of the pieces.* JACQUES *stops him.*

JACQUES (*quickly*). Wait a minute. I haven't moved yet.
PETER (*proudly*). I have my own character. I have my own needs. I have my own desires and those are very specific, and

I'm not ready to lose myself in a mass of English Canadians so that I can say: *we*. Like you say: *we*. Like the French Canadians. My identity is important.

JULIE. To have your own individuality – to be an individual, you must give yourself to others . . . receive from them.

PETER. No, I don't. I think that's a very corny . . .

JULIE (*interrupting*). You can't stand alone in this world, Peter. You should know that.

MEDIUM CLOSE SHOT: JACQUES.

JACQUES (*facetiously*). You don't think it is selfish at all?

JULIE. I think he will . . .

PETER (*interrupting*). Selfish! It's a moralist's term!

JACQUES (*argumentatively*). But you agree that you maintain your identity as an individual when you adopt all those American . . . (*He pauses, searching for the right word.*)

MEDIUM SHOT: PETER *and* JULIE.

PETER (*firmly*). I don't adopt them.

JACQUES. All this American way of life – you're taking it.

PETER. But that's exactly it, I don't adopt them. When you say that, your criticism becomes a broader one, a more general one. You're criticizing an influx of American culture, but I have my own standards, and I have my own values.

JACQUES. What are they?

CAMERA ZOOMS IN *to* CLOSE SHOT *of* PETER.

PETER (*derisively*). They are certainly not transistor radios!

MEDIUM SHOT: JACQUES.

JULIE *and* JACQUES (*together*). What are they?

JACQUES. I'm not asking you what they are not; I'm asking you what they are.

CLOSE SHOT: PETER. *He looks slightly uncomfortable. He does not say anything.* 31

31. Why is this scene in the coffee house important?

CUT TO: *ext., parking lot – ticket booth. Day.*

MEDIUM LONG SHOT: PETER, *working in ticket booth, and* CUSTOMER. FIRST CUSTOMER *hands* PETER *his ticket and a dollar bill.* PETER *stamps the ticket.*

MEDIUM SHOT: FIRST CUSTOMER. *The* CUSTOMER *stands with his palm outstretched.* PETER *places the change in his hand.*

CUSTOMER. Thank you.

CAMERA PANS *with* FIRST CUSTOMER *as he walks away. He stops suddenly and comes back to the ticket booth as* CAMERA PANS BACK *with him.* CAMERA ZOOMS BACK *to* MEDIUM SHOT *of him and* PETER.

CUSTOMER. Did you say thirty?
PETER. Yeah.
FIRST CUSTOMER. You gave me sixty cents here.
PETER. Oh, I'm sorry, sir.
FIRST CUSTOMER. That's seventy cents.

(PETER *hands him the additional money awkwardly.*)

FIRST CUSTOMER. That's right. Thank you.
PETER. Thank you.

JUMP CUT TO MEDIUM LONG SHOT: PETER *in booth with* SECOND CUSTOMER. PETER *is giving change to a man.*

SECOND CUSTOMER. Is that twenty?

(PETER *hands him additional change.*)

PETER. Er . . . yeah.

JUMP CUT TO MEDIUM LONG SHOT: PETER *in booth and* THIRD CUSTOMER. *Man approaches booth.* CAMERA ZOOMS IN *to* MEDIUM SHOT *of him and* PETER *as he gives* PETER *the*

32. Jump cut: One in which continuous action is broken by a violent "jump". In this scene, three jump cuts are used to separate Peter's encounters with the four dissatisfied customers.

ticket and money. PETER *gives him some change and turns around.*

THIRD CUSTOMER (*with alarm*). You're cheating me!

PETER (*indignantly*). Cheating – cheating – this lot doesn't cheat. (PETER *gives him the rest of his change. The* CUSTOMER *turns and leaves.*)

JUMP CUT TO CLOSE SHOT: PETER *and* FOURTH CUSTOMER. *Man takes his change from* PETER, *counts it, then steps back to look up at a sign on the ticket booth o.s., which apparently lists the hourly parking-rates.*

FOURTH CUSTOMER (*questioningly*). Fifteen, isn't it? (*Meaning fifteen cents an hour.*)

PETER (*vacantly*). Oh, I'm sorry!

FOURTH CUSTOMER. Yeah!

CUT TO MEDIUM SHOT: *int.,* PROBATION OFFICER *at his desk in his office. Day.*

PROBATION OFFICER (*intensely*). I'm concerned about you. You are one of the few kids who comes in here who has anything at all up here. (*He points to his head.*) Something that could be used. Now, why don't you use it!

CLOSE SHOT: PETER. *He appears unconcerned.*

PROBATION OFFICER (*continuing*). Look! Will you accept something graciously and not as an accusation or anything like that?

PETER. Sure. What?

PROBATION OFFICER (*hesitantly*). You're not . . . you wouldn't do anything foolish down there. And I mean *really* foolish?

PETER (*smugly*). Well, ah . . . I don't know. Nickels and dimes aren't foolish.

PROBATION OFFICER. Well, nickels and dimes are foolish.

PETER (*unconvincingly*). Well, how can you get into any kind of trouble when you're only . . . you know, a guy comes in and pays twenty cents for staying . . .

EXTREME CLOSE SHOT: PROBATION OFFICER. *He interrupts* PETER. *He is determined to try to reach him.*

PROBATION OFFICER (*with great deliberation*). Now look! I'm going to tell you something very seriously, and you listen, please. You've got a choice to make here and it's – and it's the most important choice you've ever made in your life.

MEDIUM SHOT: PETER. *He leans back in his chair, looking off in the distance, disinterestedly. He sighs.*

PETER (*defensively*). It's five cents, ten cents every day . . . that's all.

PROBATION OFFICER. Just a little thing again, you know. . . . (*Strongly.*) Like driving a car.

PETER. Yeah. A little thing.

PROBATION OFFICER. But this is far more than driving a car. This is a *big* thing whether you realize it or not. And it is a big thing where you're concerned . . . and you'd better get with it and realize it. Open your eyes and take a look around. Look at yourself occasionally.

PETER (*hotly*). O.K. Thank you very much. You've told me. O.K.? The interview is at an end.

REVERSE ANGLE SHOT: PETER. PETER *stands up, back towards* CAMERA, *and exits, revealing the* PROBATION OFFICER *in* MEDIUM SHOT *sitting at his desk.*

PETER. Good-bye, I'll see you next week.

PROBATION OFFICER. Peter! Watch your step!

(*He looks after him. His expression is one of deep concern.*)

CUT TO: *int., pool hall.*

33. This is another example of an extreme close shot. Why is it used here?

EXTREME CLOSE SHOT: *Cue ball on pool table. Cue, from* 34
o.s., thrusts into frame and hits ball.

FULL SHOT: SUPERVISOR *and* PETER *standing at pool table.* SUPERVISOR *is playing pool as he talks.* PETER *stands watching him.*

SUPERVISOR. You've never played this game, eh, Pete?

PETER. No, I haven't. No.

SUPERVISOR (*lightly*). Your old man hasn't got one in the basement?

PETER (*with mock sarcasm*). Ah-ha.

SUPERVISOR. You should invest in one.

PETER. Must be pretty expensive, eh?

SUPERVISOR (*slowly – while playing a shot*). Oh, yeah . . . yeah. Several hundred dollars at least.

(SUPERVISOR *leans down to make a shot and* CAMERA TILTS DOWN *to* CLOSE SHOT *of the action.* CAMERA TILTS BACK UP *to* SUPERVISOR.)

SUPERVISOR. You like your work, Peter?

PETER (*flatly*). Yeah . . . it's O.K.

SUPERVISOR (*inquiringly*). Making any money?

(SUPERVISOR *continues to play.* PETER *doesn't answer.*)

SUPERVISOR. U-m-m-m?

PETER (*cautiously*). Ah . . . I've got about forty bucks saved.

SUPERVISOR. Ah-ha! How much from . . . (*he pauses*) from dividends?

CLOSE SHOT: PETER. *He looks very serious.*

34. The text-book authorities referred to above would call this a close-up. A significant detail – a cue ball – first appears; then the cue thrusts into the frame and hits it. Visually, the shot is unusual and exciting; dramatically, it creates interest and suspense.

PETER (*trying to sound convincing*). No . . . you can just forget about that, John, because I'm not having anything to do with that stuff. I told you the first day I came on the lot.

MEDIUM SHOT: PETER *and* SUPERVISOR.

SUPERVISOR. Peter . . . (*He now speaks ominously, but still continues playing.*) A couple of regulars have been complaining.

PETER. Who?

SUPERVISOR. Mrs. Schwartz . . . Harry Bancroft. (*Firmly.*) I told you, Peter, there are lots of ways to make it – but leave the regulars alone.

PETER (*innocently*). No. But I don't know anything about Mrs. Schwartz, really!

(*The* SUPERVISOR *looks directly at* PETER.)

SUPERVISOR (*strongly*). Don't hand me that nonsense. *Three times,* she says!

PETER (*unmoved*). No, it must have been a mistake. I didn't have anything to do with her.

MEDIUM SHOT: PETER, *as* SUPERVISOR *moves in foreground.*

SUPERVISOR (*very sure of himself*). You know what I'm talking about. And you know what – my cut from now on, Peter, is three bucks a day.

PETER. *Three bucks a day!*

SUPERVISOR. That's right.

PETER (*protesting*). One hardly makes three bucks a day . . . you know that.

SUPERVISOR. What are you saying?

PETER. Well, I mean . . . you know . . .

LONG SHOT: *pool hall.*

PETER (*correcting himself*). . . . most days.

CLOSE SHOT: PETER.

PETER (*assertively*). I don't have to stay and work with you, I can . . .

SUPERVISOR (*interrupting him – threateningly*). Oh, yes you do.

PETER. I can get a job on any other lot in town.

SUPERVISOR. Well, I happen to like it the way it is . . with you here.

PETER. What can you do about it?

SUPERVISOR. I want my cut.

PETER (*resolutely*). I'm telling you, you might just as well forget about that because I'm not going to have anything to do with that stuff.

SUPERVISOR (*slowly, deliberately – while playing his shot*). You know what Mrs. Schwartz said? She said, "Look, I'd like to register a complaint" . . . through me . . . to the authorities.

PETER (*matter of factly*). So, you fire me, that's all.

SUPERVISOR (*coldly, deliberately*). Oh yeah! We'll fire you, you bet! But the police has got hold of your hand.

CLOSE SHOT: SUPERVISOR. *He looks threateningly at* PETER.

SUPERVISOR. Now, you got that straight? You are in a little too deep, daddy.

CLOSE SHOT: PETER. *He bites his lip.*

SUPERVISOR. A little too deep!

PETER (*anxiously*). Listen, John! Why don't you lay off of here about the whole thing. O.K.?

SUPERVISOR (*unmoved*). Sure . . . sure . . . I'll lay off. But I just want my cut. That's all! So no more of this stuff. Leave the regulars alone and three bucks a day. O.K.?

PETER (*protesting*). Yeah, but listen . . .

CAMERA ZOOMS BACK *to* MEDIUM SHOT *of* PETER *and* SUPERVISOR. PETER *picks up cue stock and leans over pool table.*

SUPERVISOR. Shoot!

CUT TO HIGH-ANGLE FULL SHOT: *int., stairs of* PETER'*s boarding house. Early morning.* JULIE *enters from o.s., running up the stairs. She carries a small suitcase.* CAMERA FOLLOWS *her. She stops at the head of the stairs.* CAMERA

ZOOMS IN *to* MEDIUM SHOT. *She stands there undecidedly – nervously – then moves suddenly to* PETER'*s door as* CAMERA ZOOMS BACK *with her, keeping her in* MEDIUM SHOT.

JULIE (*calling, as she knocks on his door*). Peter.

MEDIUM SHOT: PETER'*s* ROOM. PETER *is in bed, asleep. He wakes at the knock.*

JULIE. Peter.
PETER (*sleepily*). Coming.

MEDIUM SHOT: *door,* PETER'*s room. The door opens and* JULIE *enters. She looks very serious.*

PETER (*yawning and stretching, as he lies in bed*). Good morning. Ah . . . I hate getting up in the morning. (*He yawns again.*) Eh, what's the suitcase?

JULIE (*quietly*). I left home. (*She puts down her suitcase, crosses to the bed, and sits down beside* PETER.)

PETER (*laughingly*). Oh, you left home. When did that happen?

JULIE. Only this morning. Peter, *stop laughing*. . . . It's very serious . . .

CAMERA ZOOMS IN *to* CLOSE SHOT *of* JULIE.

PETER (*laughs*). What do you mean? Ah . . . why don't you move in here?

JULIE. My parents have nothing . . . (*She stops, then chidingly.*) Oh, don't be an ass.

PETER. Listen! I think . . . I think . . .

JULIE (*interrupts*). I just left home, that's all. They were fighting . . .

PETER. We've got enough troubles . . . take the bag and tell your mother you love her and won't see me any more . . . and you know . . .

JULIE (*firmly*). I told her I wouldn't see *her* any more and I love *you* very much and I left. And Peter . . .

CAMERA PANS OVER *to* PETER *as he lies back on bed.*

PETER (*unbelievingly*). No . . . no! Tell your mother you love *her* and you wouldn't see *me* any more, and go back home. What do I need a girl with a suitcase for? I got enough troubles on the parking lot . . . o-h-h!

CAMERA PANS BACK *to* JULIE.

JULIE (*mixed resolution and disappointment*). Well, I'm leaving, Peter. And I'm leaving Toronto. And if you don't care about the girl with the suitcase, you don't have to.

PETER (*dismissing her*). We'll go in September. Listen! If you knew what's happening on that parking lot . . .

JULIE (*strongly, interrupting him*). You're the one that has been talking about going away. Great plans! Let's go away. (*Shouting at him.*) Well, why don't we *go*?

PETER (*insisting*). But . . . I can't go away. I haven't enough money now.

JULIE (*angrily*). Well that's a stupid reason. You could borrow it.

PETER. From whom? I could borrow money?

JULIE. One of your friends . . . your father . . . anybody!

CLOSE SHOT: PETER *lying on bed.*

PETER (*softly*). Borrow two hundred bucks from my Dad?

JULIE. Yes.

PETER (*sarcastically*). Sure.

JULIE. Yes, it's not that much.

PETER. Sure.

MEDIUM SHOT: PETER *and* JULIE.

JULIE. Oh, Peter, stop it. You could try, and you could ask him.

PETER. He'd never give me the money.

JULIE (*urging*). Peter, *try*!

PETER. Do you think that he would give me two hundred bucks?

JULIE (*after a pause, threateningly*). Yes. If you don't get the money I'm not going to see you any more. No, I'm not kidding. Get the money, or I don't see you.

PETER. Is it blackmail?

JULIE. No, it's not blackmail.

PETER (*imitating her threatening tone*). Two hundred bucks or else?

JULIE. Yes, that's right.

PETER (*coaxingly*). Julie, come on!

JULIE (*withdrawing*). No, don't try and soft-soap me. It's no good.

PETER. I'm not trying to soft-soap you, just . . .

JULIE (*interrupting, speaking with finality*). If we don't go away that's it, Peter, and if you don't get the money that's it!

(PETER *pulls the blankets up over his head.*)

PETER. I'm going back to sleep. No, really!

MEDIUM SHOT: JULIE. *She jerks blankets down.*

JULIE (*with exasperation*). *Peter.*

PETER (*feigning surprise*). What's the matter?

CAMERA ZOOMS BACK *to* MEDIUM SHOT *of* PETER *and* JULIE.

JULIE. Don't you care what happens to me at all?

PETER. Yeah, I do! But I . . . (*He sits up.*)

JULIE. But you can't.

PETER. I just think the . . .

JULIE (*thoroughly aggravated*). You sit back and pull your damn sheet over you and sure, go and fly girl, I don't care . . .

PETER (*annoyed*). Well, why did you change all of a sudden? Why did you have to leave in a hurry?

JULIE. Because there was a great fight! They're thinking of sending me away to a school. I don't want to go . . .

PETER (*firmly*). Oh, come on. They are always making threats about school. Listen. Work it out. We can't afford to leave now. That's all there is to it.

JULIE. But, I'm leaving. I can afford to.

PETER. What did you have a fight for, like that? What did you have to . . .

JULIE (*violently*). What do you mean, what do I have to have a fight for? For you, anyway!

PETER (*angrily*). To put yourself in a position where you . . .

CAMERA ZOOMS BACK *and* PANS *with* JULIE *as she gets up angrily and crosses to her suitcase.*

JULIE. Oh, shut up! Stop screaming at me.
PETER. Listen, I'm not screaming at you. I . . .
JULIE. I don't care what you do!

(JULIE *picks up her suitcase and goes slamming out the door.* PETER *rushes to the door and brings her back into the room.*)

PETER. Julie come in . . . listen. All right. Put the suitcase down.

(*She re-enters room. Her face is expressionless.*)

PETER. I'll go and talk to my father. O.K.?
JULIE (*dubiously*). You will?
PETER (*with determination*). Yes, I will.

CAMERA ZOOMS IN *to* CLOSE SHOT *of* JULIE *and* PANS *with her as she crosses to the bed and sits down.*

JULIE. If you don't get the money?
PETER. Well, I'll get the money.

(JULIE *is looking down at the floor, not at* PETER.)

MEDIUM SHOT: *int., car showroom where* FATHER *works. Day.* PETER *stands with his arms crossed, waiting impatiently to talk to his* FATHER. FATHER *is o.s. His voice is heard talking to a customer.*

FATHER. . . . on our popular options and accessories, so we have the change over to the Fordomatic, automatic, the whitewall tires and the transistorized push-button radios . . .

LONG SHOT: FATHER *and* CUSTOMER, *as they stand talking by a new car.*

FATHER. And I might mention here also that this little trunk – it looks little – but there's 23.7 cubic feet in it.

CLOSE SHOT: PETER. *He is very tense.*

FATHER. It's a lot for a compact car I would say!

CUSTOMER. Yeah. Yeah, that's very nice. Yes, I stayed a little longer than I intended to.

MEDIUM SHOT, REVERSE ANGLE: FATHER *and* CUSTOMER, *with* PETER *standing in background.*

CUSTOMER. Nice to have met you. I'll call you . . . right away . . . tomorrow.

FATHER (*enthusiastically*). Fine. We are looking forward to it.

CUSTOMER. I'm pretty sold on it. 'Bye.

FATHER (*shakes hands with customer*). Ah-ha. Thank you, sir.

CUSTOMER. Good-bye.

FATHER. Thank you for dropping in.

PETER. Hey, Dad. (*Walks over to his father.*) Have you got a minute, Dad?

FATHER (*somewhat annoyed*). It's a fine way to come down here to see me, for a minute.

PETER. Well it's something special.

FATHER. Well, when it's something special, at least you can put something on to come down here to see me. (*He looks at* PETER *disparagingly.*) Some clothes that . . .

PETER (*interrupting him – quietly*). I'm sorry. But, really it was a last-minute thing and I had to see you. It's something special. Just a second.

FATHER. Well, I have to get a haircut. . . . (*Firmly.*) And I don't like this!

CUT TO: *int., barber shop. Day.*

MEDIUM SHOT: BARBER. CAMERA ZOOMS BACK *as the* BARBER *puts cape on* PETER'*s* FATHER, *who sits in the chair. Continues* ZOOM *in* FULL SHOT *of* BARBER *and* FATHER (*backs towards* CAMERA) *and* PETER *who stands facing his father.*

PETER (*apologetically*). Dad, I'm sorry about dropping in, in the middle of a business day.

FATHER (*more gently*). I'd like you to have some decent clothes, coming down to my place. It's stupid . . .

PETER. Yeah, I'm sorry about that too. But you know I got up, and I'm just going down to work this afternoon . . .

MEDIUM SHOT: PETER, FATHER, *and* BARBER. PETER *stands*
next to the mirror, and we see, in the mirror, his FATHER 35
having his hair cut, as PETER *talks.*

PETER. Well, you know things haven't been going too well with us lately. The business with the car . . . and then . . . and now Sullivan, the probation officer.

FATHER. Yes.

PETER (*sincerely*). . . . and (*sighs*) I'm sorry about that too! I know it's not great having a son who gets into trouble and has to go and see the probation officer every week and . . . but I don't know, you know. . . . It isn't that I set out to do something to hurt you or anything. . . . It's just that . . . that . . .

FATHER (*flatly*). You did hurt me, that's all.

PETER (*expressing himself with some difficulty*). Well, well it's a funny time you know when you are as old as I am. And things aren't as clear as they are when you are older . . . you know I . . . I just am not sure where I'm going and what I'm going to do. Well, since it's probably just a stage, you know . . . it's probably just a matter of . . . I'm not finding a direction. I thought it would be a good idea if I . . . sort of . . . went away for a year. I just want to try something else. I want to see places and . . . I've been going to school for thirteen years, and I thought it would be a good idea to take a breather now. Then when I come back, if I want to start again, I can always do it. I can always get the three papers that I missed . . . and go to school . . . and go to university if I want to. But just to sort of work and be on my own for a year. Away from the city. And all I need is something . . . just something to start on. (*Hopefully.*) Can you loan me some money? Can you loan me three hundred bucks to start with?

35. When before have we had a "mirror shot" of Peter's father?

FATHER (*quietly*). Three hundred dollars?

PETER. I know it sounds crazy, but it's just a start. . . . It's like a fund, you know. Three hundred bucks.

FATHER. How long are you going to be away?

PETER. A year.

FATHER (*straightforwardly*). Look, Peter, I'm a business man. Three hundred dollars is three hundred dollars. Now don't give me that jazz that I've got all kinds of money . . .

PETER (*uncomprehendingly*). Yeah, you're a business man, but I'm your son. It's not a business proposition. It's a loan. . . . It's a favour. . . . It's a gift from father to son . . . can't you do that?

FATHER. I wonder how many sons just go to their fathers all the time and say: *"Dad I want three hundred bucks."* I wish I'd been able to do it.

PETER. Well, but . . . you didn't have you for a father, did you?

MEDIUM SHOT: FATHER. BARBER*'s hands are seen cutting his hair. Sound of* BARBER*'s scissors.*

PETER (*bitingly*). How long does it take to earn three hundred bucks anyway? You sell one car and you make three hundred dollars commission.

FATHER (*tellingly*). You know how much work it is to sell one car.

PETER. You were sweet-talking that guy in there pretty good. He'll probably come back tomorrow and buy the car and with that money . . . you can give it to me.

FATHER (*simply*). No.

MEDIUM SHOT: PETER, FATHER, *and* BARBER. PETER *is angry.*

PETER (*frustrated*). You know you're a bloody poor excuse for a father. I'm telling you that much. Who needs you anyway? You talk about money and that you're . . . (*Vindictively.*) You're just a money-grabbing old bastard, that's what you are.

MEDIUM CLOSE SHOT: FATHER.

FATHER (*furious*). Now listen! Don't you dare start talking to me like that! I've been listening to you for a long time now. You're not worth three hundred dollars. Your life is so mixed up, Peter, you wouldn't know what to do with it. You're a bad investment. . . . (*He reaches over and grabs* PETER. *Then, threateningly.*) And until such time as you get your life unscrambled, don't you come anywhere near me. You get the hell out of here! Get out! Now! (*He flings* PETER *past* CAMERA *towards the door.*)

CAMERA ZOOMS BACK *to* MEDIUM SHOT *of* FATHER *and* BARBER. *We see* PETER *leaving the shop in the mirror.*

CUT TO MEDIUM SHOT: SUPERVISOR *in ticket booth. Day.* PETER *runs up to the booth and goes inside. The* SUPERVISOR *ignores him.*

SUPERVISOR. (*Humming.*)

PETER. I'm sorry I'm late, John! Is everything O.K. here?

SUPERVISOR. (*Humming.*)

PETER. John?

SUPERVISOR. Yeah, yeah. Look, Peter! (*Sighs.*) No more lates, eh? Yeah, come on now . . .

PETER. I was just held up. I'm sorry.

SUPERVISOR. Yeah. All right. Look there's about a hundred bucks and a half here. This is the monthly pay . . . this part of it . . . I'll pick up the rest tonight, eh?

PETER. O.K. What time are you coming around?

SUPERVISOR. O.K. Late on. Making any money?

PETER (*bluntly*). Not enough.

SUPERVISOR. Not enough, eh? Give it a little extra try, eh? (*Flatly on leaving.*) Don't be late any more Peter. O.K.?

PETER. No. I won't, I'll see you, eh?

(*The* SUPERVISOR *leaves.*)

MEDIUM LONG SHOT: CUSTOMER. CAMERA PANS *with man as he walks from his car to the ticket booth. We see him and* PETER *in* MEDIUM SHOT.

PETER. Coming in, sir?

CUSTOMER. Yes. Four hundred and six sixty-two.

PETER. Four hundred and six sixty-two. Yes, sir! (PETER *hands him his ticket and he walks off.*)

CUSTOMER. Thank you.

MEDIUM SHOT, REVERSE HIGH ANGLE: PETER *in booth. He goes to the cash register and takes out a stack of bills.*

CUT TO MEDIUM LONG SHOT: *two women approaching booth.*

LADY CUSTOMER. 79 . . . er . . . 599.

MEDIUM SHOT: PETER. *He gives change to the customer o.s. They leave, and* PETER *stands for a moment looking around to see if anyone else is coming. Then he goes back to the cash register, takes out bills, and shoves them in his pocket.* CAMERA DOLLIES *with him as he rushes out of booth and runs over to a parked car. He tries the door of one and finds it locked. He runs around to the driver's door of the next car, finds it open, and gets in. He starts the car, and* CAMERA PANS *with him as he drives away.*

MEDIUM SHOT: *car driven up to boarding house. Stops.*

CUT TO: *int., stairs and foyer of* PETER*'s boarding house. Day.*

FULL SHOT: *foyer and stairs.* LANDLORD. *The* LANDLORD *is in the foyer and walks to the bottom of the stairs to meet* PETER *as he descends stairs carrying banjo and suitcase.*

LANDLORD. Ah. Peter . . . er . . . where are you going?

PETER. I've got to go. I'm going out of town.

CLOSE SHOT: PETER *and* LANDLORD. PETER *crosses o.s. in front of* CAMERA.

PETER. I can do nothing really, I'm sorry.

36. The "er" in three of the landlord's speeches suggests the halting way in which they were spoken, expressing his feelings of surprise, dismay, and annoyance.

LANDLORD (*perplexed*). You may say there's nothing you can do, but somebody called me for a room last night. I said I didn't have a room.

PETER (*urgently*). I'm really very sorry but I have to go, and I have to go now.

(LANDLORD *stands, looking amazed at* PETER'*s actions.*)

LANDLORD (*astounded*). Er . . . but you didn't give me any notice!

PETER. Oh, I'm sorry! I just have to go. . . .There's nothing I can do.

LANDLORD. That's not very fair really, I mean . . . er . . . (*Door slams cutting off his words.*)

CUT TO: *int., car.* PETER *and* JULIE. *Highway. Dusk.* CAMERA FACES OUT *front window of car. We see the moving highway, and* PETER'*s hands on the wheel. It is raining.*

UNDER: *driving and street noises.*

JULIE (*disbelievingly*). But who would lend you a car for doing him a few favours by working for him a few times?

PETER (*insistently*). Somebody did lend me a car. There's this car in the lot . . .

JULIE (*impatiently*). Oh come on! It's not a very likely story.

MEDIUM SHOT: *p.o.v. back seat.* PETER *driving. He is tense.*

MEDIUM SHOT: *p.o.v. back seat.* JULIE.

JULIE (*persistently*). Did you steal it, Peter?

PETER. No, I . . .

JULIE. You did, didn't you?

PETER (*evasively*). Can't we just sort of think of . . .

JULIE (*strongly*). No, we can't!

PETER. . . . where we're going, and what we want to do . . .

JULIE (*upset*). You stole the car.

MEDIUM SHOT: PETER. *He does not look at* JULIE.

JULIE. Come on now – tell me the truth!

PETER (*quietly*). The car was sitting in the lot and the keys were in the . . . in the ignition, so I took it.

LONG SHOT, HIGH ANGLE: *ext., car on highway. The car is seen driving along.*

CUT BACK TO MEDIUM SHOT: *p.o.v. back seat.* PETER *and* JULIE. PAN *to* JULIE.

PETER (*insisting*). We haven't got the money to leave by train . . .

JULIE. I thought you borrowed some money.

PETER. No. I saw my father this afternoon, and he wouldn't give me any money.

JULIE (*also insisting*). But you told me on the phone you had some money.

CLOSE SHOT: PETER.

PETER (*quietly*). I have some money.

JULIE. Where did you get the money?

PETER. I got the money from the cash register.

JULIE (*coldly*). So you stole the money as well!

PETER (*pleading*). Listen! Get off my back and just let's forget about it . . .

JULIE. Peter!

PETER. . . . until we get down there.

CLOSE SHOT: JULIE.

JULIE. I want to go home.

PETER. What do you mean – you want to go home?

JULIE (*with determination*). I want to go home. I want to turn round and go back.

CLOSE SHOT: PETER.

PETER (*sarcastically*). Remember all the times, and all the things we said . . . and all the plans we made. And then it was all fine. . . . Put your head on my shoulder and you'd say "Yes" . . .

JULIE. Yes . . . and you didn't tell me you were going to start stealing, did you?

PETER (*insistently*). But, but . . . what difference does that make?

CLOSE SHOT: JULIE.

JULIE (*firmly*). All right. If you won't take me home, stop the car and let me out.

CLOSE SHOT: PETER. *He does not say a word. He looks to the side quickly to see if he can pull over.*

JULIE (*insisting*). Stop the car and let me out!

PETER (*urgently*). Listen! We'll drive and we'll stop tonight and we'll think about it over the night and . . . we'll talk about it tomorrow.

JULIE (*unmoved*). No, I don't need to think about it, Peter.

CUT TO LONG SHOT, HIGH ANGLE: *ext., car pulls over to side of highway.* CAMERA ZOOMS IN *to* FULL SHOT *of car as it stops facing* CAMERA.

JULIE (*urgently*). Peter, will you listen to me? You've stolen a car and you've stolen the money . . .

MEDIUM SHOT: *int.,* PETER *and* JULIE *in car.* CAMERA FRAMES *them through* JULIE'*s side window.*

PETER. Yes I know. We went over it all before . . .

JULIE (*deeply concerned*). Your only chance is to go back. And . . . they might not have missed it yet . . .

PETER (*coaxingly*). Julie, let's go, and we'll talk about it . . .

JULIE. Well, listen! They might not have missed it now, or otherwise, they'll let you off extremely lightly . . . either a short term in jail, or . . . you know . . . a heavy fine . . .

PETER (*firmly*). I don't want to think about it. Let's just get on the road. O.K.?

JULIE (*dryly*). I want to think about it because . . .

CLOSE SHOT: JULIE.

JULIE. . . . because I'm going to have a baby. . . . And a baby can't be brought up like this.

MEDIUM SHOT: PETER *and* JULIE. CAMERA ZOOMS IN SLOW-

LY *on* PETER*'s face. He looks at* JULIE *as if he thinks she is play-acting.* JULIE *is intense and serious.*

PETER (*shocked*). You're kidding!

JULIE (*worriedly*). No. And a child can't be brought up in this kind of life . . .

PETER. (*Laughs, embarrassed.*)

JULIE. You must see that. . . . He's got to have security! Now I was hoping that we'd get married and have a good start. This isn't any start at all, Peter.

PETER (*nervously*). No, but . . . why didn't you tell me yesterday?

CLOSE SHOT: JULIE. *She looks down.*

JULIE (*honestly*). I didn't want to tell you because . . . I thought quite possibly you'd go away because of the baby, and that you'd take me with you and marry me because of the baby . . . and I didn't want that.

PETER. Gee, I . . .

JULIE. That's not the point!

PETER. That's crazy!

JULIE. It's up to you, what you want to do. You've got t decide.

(*She reaches for the door.*)

JULIE (*sadly*). Best of luck.

(*Car door opens.*)

MEDIUM SHOT: *ext., side of car as* JULIE *climbs out.* CAMERA ZOOMS BACK *and* TILTS UP *to* FULL SHOT *of* JULIE. PETER *gets out of the car after her, grabs her by the arm, and tries to pull her back in. She struggles.*

PETER. Into the car!

JULIE. No, I'm not getting into the car!

PETER (*forcefully*). Come on . . . into the car!

JULIE (*shouting*). No!

PETER. But it's different now. We . . .

JULIE (*fiercely*). It isn't different!

(PETER *stops his attempts to force her into the car. they stand by the car door.* CAMERA ZOOMS IN *to* MEDIUM SHOT *of them.*)

PETER (*pleading*). Please get in . . . and sit down . . .

JULIE. No! You go away, you think about it . . . you either come back or go on. It's up to you.

PETER (*protestingly*). But Julie . . .

(JULIE *moves away from* PETER. CAMERA FOLLOWS *her in* MEDIUM SHOT.)

JULIE. *No!*

PETER. Give me a minute to think about it.

JULIE. No! Go away and think about it, without me. (*With finality.*) It's your decision, Peter!

MEDIUM CLOSE SHOT: PETER. *He looks at* JULIE, *with sad frustration, not knowing what to do.*

MEDIUM SHOT: PETER *and* JULIE. PETER *stands looking at* JULIE, *back to* CAMERA. CAMERA FOLLOWS *him as he turns sharply and climbs into the car, closing the door.* CAMERA PULLS BACK *to* FULL SHOT *of car as* PETER *quickly starts the engine.*

(*Music of "The Water is Wide" – played on banjo.*)

CLOSE SHOT: JULIE. *She stands looking sadly after* PETER. *It is no longer raining, but the wind blows her hair around her face. She turns slowly, as* CAMERA ZOOMS BACK *to* FULL SHOT *and she walks away from* CAMERA, *down the shoulder of the road.*

CLOSE SHOT: PETER *driving. He is filled with emotion, staring at the road ahead.*

LOW ANGLE SHOT: *highway lights passing by.* CAMERA LOOKS OUT *front window as car passes briefly under a bridge.*

CLOSE SHOT: *p.o.v. of* PETER. *Highway at night as car travels on.*

CLOSE SHOT: PETER. *Slowly the feeling welling up inside* PETER *comes out. He starts to cry helplessly.*

PERFORMING THE PLAY

The film does not lend itself readily to stage performance because the visual element – the contribution of the camera – is so important. Normally, in a classroom reading, students will be assigned parts and will read some of the scenes, particularly the longer ones. If special importance is attached to the class reading, the parts can be prepared in advance, with some rehearsal and attention to costume, and perhaps with memorization.

If an over-all production is attempted, the best plan will be to prepare a narrator's part that will condense the visual material to the essentials needed to introduce each new group of actors and to enable the audience to visualize the changing scenes. In such a production the parts might be read (perhaps at microphones as in a radio performance) or memorized, rehearsed, and prepared following traditional stage procedures.

We are fortunate in that the film is immediately available across the country, so that the reading and study of the text can be complemented by a viewing and appraisal of the picture itself. At the time of publication, the five offices of the National Film Board in Vancouver, Saskatoon, Toronto, Montreal, and Halifax, or local film libraries, can supply the 16 mm. film, and Columbia Pictures the 35 mm. copy. Prices will vary for the 16 mm. according to the rates charged by the local film libraries; and for the 35 mm., the rates will depend on the number of seats in the hall, the admission prices charged, and other factors.

The beautiful folksong "The Water is Wide" is included in the *Joan Baez Songbook* (Ryerson Music Publishers) and in *Songs of Man,* compiled by Norman Luboff (Prentice-Hall). Several recordings of the song are available.

THINKING ABOUT THE PLAY

1. "Julie shows a strength Peter cannot match." Discuss this comment.

2. One critic maintains that Peter is too intelligent, and comes from a background with too much common sense to go as far astray as he does. Do you agree or disagree? Give your reasons.

3. Below are listed four of the comments made about *Nobody Waved Good-bye* by critics (chiefly in Canadian newspapers

before the picture was a success in New York). Consider each of these comments in turn. The weight of critical evidence is strongly against them, as shown in the quotations from the reviews cited before the play. Use your judgment in making up your own mind about each of them, basing your conclusions on a study of the text, and, if possible, on a viewing of the film.

(a) The improvisation of dialogue tends toward "pretentiousness and awkwardness", particularly when the "rebels-without-a-pause" indulge in philosophical discussions.

(b) The improvisation is also "painfully obvious" in the scene with the waitress in the restaurant.

(c) The luncheon scene between Peter and his mother is "a bit thick". His scenes with his parents at home are "sticky" and have "a cardboard unreality" to them. His parents "emerge as not much more than caricatures".

(d) "The camera never seems to get beneath the skin of the cheeky youngster that Peter Kastner plays."

4. The basic issue, and the one around which your discussions will centre, is that of responsibility. Who is at fault in Peter's delinquency? Let us examine the question on two levels. In the story as told, can we place the blame on Peter's parents, or does it rest largely on his own shoulders? Then, in a deeper sense, is society to blame? Are our values in life wrong?

Clyde Gilmour, movie critic for *The Telegram,* Toronto, criticized the picture because the cards are "too clearly stacked" against the parents. Archer Winsten, in the *New York Post,* wrote: "His parents, the totally permissive father, who never went to college, and the nagging mother, who insists he must go to college, have battles over him that are book lesson one as contributing factors." Certainly his father, for the most part, is too lenient. His mother is too possessive; she refuses to acknowledge that he has grown up, and "predigests" his life, demanding that he fulfil her wishes and hopes, and not his own.

On the other hand, the film makes the point very clearly (particularly in the coffee-house scene with the French-Canadian boy) that Peter, while he ridicules money-oriented people, has no values of his own to substitute for their materialism. He is a rebel with no cause but a rejection of his parents' affluence and way of living. He is more than thoughtless and selfish in his rebellion. Likable and intelligent as he is, he goes from petty to grave wrongdoing in following the road that leads "beyond delinquency".

In his interview with Joan Barthel, which appeared in *The New York Times,* Peter Kastner insisted that no one is "fingered" as being the villain. "I think the director goes out of his way to say it's nobody's fault. The alienation is a thing that happens. . . . A kid's rebellion is not a planned kind of thing. He'll say things to his parents that he doesn't necessarily believe, and he'll justify it by saying that he has to stand on his own feet."

Kastner agreed that Peter Mark had no values of his own. "He didn't have the answer. I think that holds true for a lot of young people. They don't have a specific replacement – they haven't come up with a system of coherent values. But I think they work out their values by first rejecting the worst of the old. The film just deals with the anarchy part; it doesn't go into the next stage which, hopefully, comes."

Is society the real culprit? One reviewer suggested that it is more difficult for young people to "communicate" with their parents when there are no money worries in the home. The reviewer in *The Independent Film Journal* wrote: "The subject is youth, the well-fed, disturbed, middle-class youth of the present who refuse to accept the materialism of their parents; the ones who become disillusioned with the lust for things, and in their quest for meaning try for independence in the society that does not understand why they need something more." Finally, the reviewer in *America* magazine on May 1, 1965, made the following comment: "It [the picture] simply presents the baleful interplay between the well-meaning but confused and ineffective parents and the arrogant youth, who has understandably rejected his parents' standards but has unknowingly been so corrupted by affluence and lack of discipline that he has nothing of value to espouse in their place. The total effect seems a chillingly accurate enactment of a prevalent contemporary situation."

Here are three "guidelines" for your discussion. Is society at fault? Are our values wrong? What is to be done about Peter Mark?

5. The initial reception accorded *Nobody Waved Good-bye* by Canadian critics and audiences raises the question: Does the work of our performing and creative artists have to win approval abroad before it is accepted in Canada? Can you give other examples, apart from this film, to show that this is the case? Can you point to instances that indicate that the situation is improving?

THE WESTERN HERO

GERALD WEALES

A TELEVISION DOCUMENTARY DRAMA

Our second play is a documentary drama. It is a documentary because it "explores" the Western and its hero; it is a drama because the hero is an actor, consistent in his characterization, who explains his roles in Westerns to a boy visiting the television set. In doing so, he acts out scenes (in a series of plays within the play) to show the boy the changes that have occurred in the Western, and also its unchanging basic character.

In his comment that follows the play, Vincent Tovell explains how television drama is increasingly making use of motion-picture techniques. Even in 1960, the techniques of the two forms had much in common. Mr. Tovell has described, in his clear and interesting stage directions, what viewers who watched the show on the evening of October 5, 1960, saw on their screens. He has not employed the technical terms used in the stage directions in *Nobody Waved Good-bye,* but you can imagine the cameras being employed in much the same way, with the same range and variety of shots: close, medium, long, panning, tilt, and angle shots.

Those of us who saw the production of *The Western Hero* have an advantage over the rest of you: it is the advantage that all who have seen and heard a play enjoy over those who have to visualize it as they read it. The stage directions, however, will help you to relive in the theatre of your imagination the experience we had. Visually, there was always something interesting happening: for example, the Cowboy and the Boy stole along the set, play-acting, while the Cowboy was talking in the opening sequence. Dominating the whole performance was the warmth, eagerness, and vitality of Don Francks as the hero, and the amusing, appealing friendship between him and the Boy. All the actors joined in the make-believe, in the serious "fun" of the show. If you are interested in ideas and use your imagination, you will learn a great deal about Westerns as you read *The Western Hero*. And you will enjoy yourself as the actors and producer did, and as the author did when he wrote it.

Much of the fun in the play, of course, comes from its satirical flavour, particularly the "spoofing" of the new Westerns, which show the influence of the theories of psychologists and psychoanalysts. I am sure you know enough about these theories, and have seen enough of the new heroes in action, to enjoy these satirical episodes.

Above all, after you have read the play with interest and understanding, you will begin to be an authority on Westerns. You will have standards by which to judge those you have seen and will see, both motion pictures and television serials. You will know something about their history, and the changes that have occurred in them throughout the years. You will be familiar with what the critics say about them: that they are adult fairy tales, simple folk legends or morality plays, escape entertainment for the masses – all the "jargon" of the Intellectual Man in the play. Take all the facts and opinions into consideration, matching them with what you have learned from your own experience, and make up your own mind about Westerns. Be sure you are able to support your point of view intelligently. There are no satisfactions like those of the reasonable, well-informed person, who keeps an open mind, is eagerly interested in all aspects of knowledge, and searches continually for his own truth. Be prepared to make your own judgment on Westerns.

HOW THE PLAY CAME TO BE WRITTEN

by Gerald Weales

CBC's *Explorations* was an unusual television series, one that was bound by no restrictive pattern. Any subject in the arts or sciences was a possibility and any approach worth considering. I no longer remember the precise steps by which I became involved with *Explorations*. Sometime early in 1960, Robert McCormack, a CBC program organizer, one of the men who helped plan the show, got in touch with me to discuss an idea about television heroes – why people liked them and how they were related to the heroes in other literary, dramatic, or musical forms. The three most popular kinds of programs at that time were the Western, the private-eye, and the family show, and we agreed that we would "explore" the hero of each of them. The usual approach with such a program would have been to call in a commentator – a sociologist, perhaps, or someone like me who writes about pop-culture – and let him lecture the audience while the camera occasionally left him to look at visual material or staged scenes that proved his point. I decided – and Robert McCormack agreed – that it might be more fun if the commentator were the hero himself, if we let him step in and out of scenes, sometimes explaining, sometimes performing. Never having written for television before, I was worried about what could and could not be done technically, but Ted Pope, who was to produce and direct all three shows, turned me loose by telling me to do anything I wanted and that he would find a way to get it onto the screen.

Just before the first of the three, *The Western Hero,* was done, Ted Pope was killed in an automobile accident. At this unhappy point, another CBC producer, Vincent Tovell, an old friend of mine, and a fine television producer, stepped in to finish the job. Although he had had no part in the planning of the series nor in the discussions that preceded my writing, he – with the indispensable help of Don Francks, who played all three heroes – put together shows that were remarkably like what I had in mind.

INTRODUCTORY NOTE

by Vincent Tovell

Once, and very recently, Westerns were about the most popular programs on television. You could see them night and day, old-fashioned fairy tales with plenty of riding, shooting, and tall heroes in white hats who hadn't much to say (though they could sing), or new-fashioned fairy tales with fancy talk and villains with psychological problems. The styles changed along with the heroes' hats, but not enough to confuse anyone for long. The old clichés we loved endured. The heroes remained heroes, and right, in the end, was still might.

The Western Hero isn't a Western; it is about Westerns. It takes place on a television set where actors earn good money playing out these familiar North American myths for the cameras. A Western set, of course, has to have a dusty main street, a saloon with swinging doors, a stable, a newspaper office, rows of plain board storefronts, a bank, a jail, and, for special occasions, a white church with a spire. We had some of these familiar landmarks in this production. Since we're on a set, most of the characters we meet are actors dressed up for work in Westerns. But now and then they are interrupted by visitors – tourists – who wander by to watch a television show being done. And some of them get caught up in the action. That is what the Boy is doing there. He is finding out about Westerns from a television cowboy, and who could tell him more? Of course a real cowboy would tell a different story.

The script as presented here has been adapted slightly for publication to make it more easily read. Minor changes have been made both in the original text and in the production version.

CHARACTERS

THE COWBOY
THE BOY
THE GIRL
THE INTELLECTUAL MAN
THE YOUNG MAN
THE VILLAIN
THE SIDEKICK

Produced for the Canadian Broadcasting Corporation by Ted Pope and directed by Vincent Tovell. Telecast on the television series *Explorations* on October 5, 1960, with the following cast:

THE COWBOY	Don Francks
THE BOY	Rex Hagon
THE GIRL	Corinne Conley
THE INTELLECTUAL MAN	George Luscombe
THE YOUNG MAN	Jeremy Wilkin
THE VILLAIN	Rick Hart
THE SECOND MAN IN BLACK	J. Frank Willis

THE WESTERN HERO

CLOSE UP: *a gun in a holster. A hand reaches for it, a boy's hand. The* BOY *draws and shoots – several times. It is a cap gun.*

We hear a COWBOY *singing. While he sings, the titles are shown.*

There was a cowboy,
An *Explorations* cowboy,
He rode the range by day, by night
To punish wrong, to uphold right.

And, oh, this cowboy,
This *Explorations* cowboy
Sought to erase the smallest fault,

1. Those who saw the television production will remember this haunting ballad – beautifully played and sung. It established the mood of the presentation perfectly.
2. *Explorations*: See the introductory note by the playwright, Gerald Weales, on p. 101.

For such a search was his Gestalt, 3
This cowboy,
This *Explorations* cowboy.

The CAMERA PULLS BACK *to show a* BOY *about ten years old, dressed in a cowboy hat and rig. He is firing his cap gun at another boy on a "Western" street. The* BOY *then starts down the street by himself and finds an actor who is also dressed up in cowboy regalia. He has a white hat, and he is perched on the wooden railing of a store veranda reading a Western comic book. The shots haven't bothered him much, so the boy goes up to him and tugs at his trousers.*

BOY. Mister, are you a Western hero?

COWBOY. What are you doing on the set, son?

BOY. Ma and me were taking the tour. Are you a Western hero?

(*The* COWBOY *pauses long enough to imply that he is thinking.*)

COWBOY. Yep.

BOY. Is it easy?

COWBOY. It gets harder and harder all the time.

BOY. Yeh? (*This is not sarcastic, just a question.*)

COWBOY. Yeh. Let me explain what I mean.

(*The* COWBOY *pulls a bag of tobacco from his shirt pocket, takes out some cigarette papers, and begins a one-handed cigarette roll – ineptly. We see in the background a crowd of studio tourists wandering around the set, led by a studio guide.*)

COWBOY. You see, son, in the good old days it was easy to tell who was who in a Western. The hero always wore a white hat . . . like mine.

(*The crowd spots a* VILLAIN *on the set. He has a black hat, a black coat, a string tie, and a brocaded vest,*

3. Gestalt: a school of psychology that regards the whole as greater than the sum of its parts. Here the word applies to the hero's overriding interest or concern: the "dynamic" of his existence – his means of self-fulfilment.

which make him look a little like a banker in an old-fashioned movie. He also has a black moustache.)

COWBOY. The villain always wore a black hat – like that guy. The hero was always clean-shaven – like me. The villain always had a moustache – like him.

(*The* COWBOY *and the* VILLAIN *eye one another, and then another actor – all in black – appears. He nods to the* VILLAIN *in a friendly way.*)

The Second Man in Black appears, adding to the Cowboy's confusion

C.B.C. Television

COWBOY. But nowadays everything is mixed up. (*He looks at the two men in black.*) You can't tell one from another. It gets so I don't know from one day to the next just who I got to shoot. Right, kid?

(*The* BOY *nods judiciously. The* COWBOY *gives up trying to roll his own cigarette in disgust.*)

COWBOY. Kid, you got a cigarette?

(*The* BOY *shakes his head.*)

COWBOY. No? Oh, well, that's the spirit. Straight-shooters always win; law-breakers always lose.

(*He suddenly jumps down from the railing, and both stroll off together, along the veranda of the store and around the corner into the main street. They keep on talking, but as they go, they play a game: the* COWBOY *clings close to the outside walls of the stores motioning the boy to do the same behind him and they slink along stealthily – guns at the ready – just in case.*)

BOY. What kind of line is that?

COWBOY. Straight-shooters always win; law-breakers always lose. That's the way Westerns are made, son. Even today.

(*Looking through a window upstairs over one of the stores we can see the whole street stretched out below us. It is empty, except for the* COWBOY *and the* BOY *who are clinging to the shelter of the storefronts and peering cautiously around every corner before running to the next shelter.*)

COWBOY. These new Westerns with the hats all mixed up and all the talk. Give me the good old days ever'time, I can tell ya. Still and all, they come out the same in the end. Straight-shooters always win; law-breakers always lose. You know whose line that was, don't you? Tom Mix. That's who, Tom Mix.

BOY. Who's Tom Mix?

COWBOY. Who's Tom Mix?

(*The* BOY *nods.*)

COWBOY. Well I'll be a hog-tied tumbleweed.

(*He fumbles in his pocket for a wallet. He flips it open and in the plastic picture-folder, where there is usually a girl's picture, there is, instead, one of Tom Mix. He offers it reverently.*)

COWBOY. Now you just lookee here, kid, and I'll show you who's Tom Mix.

(*We see the photo.*)

COWBOY. He's like William S. Hart, he is. Just one of the all time greats, that's all. Stick around, boy, and I'll educate you. Lookee here, the Wild West ain't all *Bonanza* and *Gunsmoke*. It is older than old, believe me. Why folks was already readin' Westerns when Wyatt Earp was a boy. 'Course, things never really got started till Owen Wister wrote *The Virginian*. Here, let me show you.

(*They've arrived on the edge of the set where there is an open sports car – the* COWBOY'*s – hidden behind one of the false fronts of the stores. He takes a book out of the glove compartment. It is a well-worn copy of* The Virginian.)

COWBOY. There you are, take a peek at that. Now the Western hero really got underway when the Virginian came moseyin' into the public eye and said . . .

(*A voice is heard – from beyond.*)

VOICE. When you call me that, smile!

COWBOY. Hey, want a root beer, boy?

BOY. Sure.

(*They are at the saloon by now. The* BOY *nods.*)

COWBOY. Ever since then, us handsome, silent types been comin' in off the range and settin' things to rights.

(*They start into the saloon through the swinging doors. There are a few others in there sitting quietly.*)

COWBOY. Folks has such a cryin' need to have things set to rights, that they been readin' about us ever since, and seein' us in the movies, and watchin' us on television.

BOY. You mean they don't listen just to hear the guns go off?

(*Suddenly the* BOY *whips out his cap pistol, yelling and firing. He lunges about riddling invisible enemies all around him.*)

BOY. Pow, pow, pow, pow!!!!

(*He catches a bullet in the belly, drops his pistol, clutches himself, staggers about for awhile, and then falls down. The* COWBOY, *the* BARMAN, *and a few other guests watch him pick himself up calmly, retrieve his pistol, and walk to the fountain, dusting himself off a little.*)

BOY. You mean they don't watch just to see all that?

COWBOY. Well, that's part of it. Folks do like all that shooting.

(*They sit. The* COWBOY *takes the* BOY'*s cap pistol from the holster and blows out the barrel.*)

COWBOY. Don't treat your piece like that, son. You gotta take care of a pistol like it was your right arm. Two root beers, Pop. . . . As I was sayin', folks do like all the shootin', a' course. Like ever'body wants to watch a good fight. Or to go to a wreck. But there's more to it than that. It's me. How I come in and save the town when it needs me. Here, ask Pop here. (*To the* BARMAN *who also serves soft drinks on this set.*) Pardon me, Pop, just why do you like Westerns?

POP. I like all the shootin'. (POP *makes a pass at a nonexistent holster with his thumb and fore-finger poised, ducks down below the counter, and begins shooting.*) Pow, pow, pow, pow!!!

(*The* COWBOY *leans over and puts his hand gently on the man's shoulder and quiets him.*)

COWBOY. We've done that bit.

(POP *shrugs and goes back to wiping glasses.*)

COWBOY. He's an exception, son. He just ain't thought it out.

(*There is a young fellow sitting along from them – one of the extras on the set.*)

COWBOY. Let's ask this guy. Pardon me, stranger, why do you like Westerns?

YOUNG MAN. Well . . . ah . . . well . . . cause . . . well . . . gee . . .

COWBOY. Y'ever save a child from a runaway horse, mister?

YOUNG MAN. Nah.

COWBOY. Y'ever want to?

YOUNG MAN. Sure.

COWBOY. Y'ever jump from the back of a movin' horse and drag the villain off his?

YOUNG MAN. Nah.

COWBOY. Y'ever want to?

YOUNG MAN. Sure.

COWBOY. Y'ever . . . but why go on? Now, mister, are you sure you can't say why you like Westerns?

YOUNG MAN. Well . . . ah . . . well . . . cause . . . well, gee . . .

(*The* COWBOY *looks at the* BOY, *the* BOY *looks at the* COWBOY, *and they both look at the* YOUNG MAN. *The* COWBOY *shrugs and they go out the swinging doors to the street.*)

COWBOY. You get it?

BOY. I get it. He's like me. He wants to be a Western hero when he grows up, only he's already grown up.

(*The* YOUNG MAN *is staring at them through the swinging doors still trying to explain.*)

COWBOY. That's the stuff, kid. Everybody wants to be a hero, even second-hand.

(*There are tourists in the studio street, including a young* LADY *with a big hat, sun-glasses, and a camera. She sees the* COWBOY *and immediately starts to take snapshots of our "hero". He is very obliging, putting on his serious cowboy look for her.*)

BOY. Ladies too?

COWBOY. Let's ask this lady. Pardon me, ma'am, why do you like Westerns?

LADY. My husband can't even put a washer in the kitchen tap without making a mess of it. It's nice to think that there might be a man who could protect a water-hole without

4. Protect a water-hole: protect it from Indians or villains. Water is essential to the survival of settlers and their livestock.

getting his hands dirty.

(*The* LADY *walks off with the crowd down the street.*)

COWBOY. There you are, son, same story. Different angle. Well, are you convinced that it's more than just the shootin'?

(*The* BOY *looks a little dubious. A tourist appears. He is obviously an intellectual because he has heavy-rimmed glasses.*)

COWBOY. We could ask some more people. Him, maybe? . . . Well, one more for the road.

(*The* COWBOY *stops him.*)

C.B.C. Television

The Intellectual Man is questioned by the Cowboy.

COWBOY. Pardon me, sir, why do you like Westerns?

INTELLECTUAL MAN. Who said I like Westerns? Adoles- 5

5. Adolescent compensation images: images or picture experiences that compensate adults for the loss of their youth and help them to maintain the mood and viewpoint of childhood.

cent compensation images.

COWBOY. When you call me that, smile.

INTELLECTUAL MAN. Ah, yes, the historical analogue.

COWBOY. What I mean to say, stranger, is why do most folks like Westerns?

INTELLECTUAL MAN. Variation on the ritual dance. Fleshing out of the mythos. Each man's deep urge for a saviour, the mysterious ordering stranger who rights wrongs and protects the innocent. Also each man's longing to be that saviour. Vicarious armchair identification with heroic adventure.

COWBOY. I couldn't have put it more clearly myself.

INTELLECTUAL MAN. Globally speaking, Western culture is sprinkled with amusing equivalences to the Western hero.

COWBOY. Hold on, stranger, you've gone far enough. You sound like a narrator on a documentary show. Git along.

(*He pushes him out. The* INTELLECTUAL MAN *gits.*)

BOY. What was that fellow trying to say?

COWBOY. He was tryin' to say that us Western heroes are like the knights of old who used to kill the dragons and save the princesses from evil dukes. He was tryin' to say that ever'body watches us 'cause they either want to kill a dragon or they got a dragon they want killed.

BOY. And isn't that the truth?

6. Historical analogue: an analogue is a comparable word or thing; for example, a species or type of one period that is similar to a species or type of a different period. The words "When you call me that, smile" (spoken by the hero in *The Virginian*) are analogous to, or similar to, the expressions used by the heroes of modern Westerns and suggest similar heroic types.
7. Variations . . . dance: in primitive tribal dances the basic struggle between good and evil was acted out, as it is in Westerns.
8. Fleshing . . . mythos: mythos (or mythus) means myth. In myths supernatural figures or archetypal images are involved in actions that are usually larger than life. The Western "fleshes out", or embodies in physical action, the myths of larger-than-life struggles between figures representing good and evil.

COWBOY. Sure, that's the truth.

BOY. Then why did you make him git along?

COWBOY. To save the show, son. If he had kept on talkin' there wouldn't have been anything left for me to do.

BOY. And what *are* you going to do, mister?

COWBOY. *I'm going to show you* how it used to be, son. 9
And how it's changed.

(*From the top of the store we can see the street at high noon. The shadows under the roofs and the verandas look inviting but the* COWBOY *and the* BOY *are sitting on some steps in the sun. The* COWBOY *takes a stick and draws a circle in the dirt.*)

COWBOY. Now, look here, boy, you see this circle. That's the Western town. (*He gestures all around the town.*) This here town, for instance. Closed in. Self-contained. Self dependent. That was the West, boy. That's what livin' on the frontier meant. (*He draws two more circles.*) A bunch of circles. (*He draws lines to link them.*) Joined by a stage-coach line maybe. Crossed once in a while by a wanderer. But mostly closed in so that one man could control the whole circle, the whole town.

(*The circle he has just drawn is suddenly covered with a shadow – the shadow of the black-hatted, black-moustached man we saw before.*)

COWBOY. Hey, you. . . . You be the villain for us here.

VILLAIN. What do I have to do?

COWBOY. Not much until you get shot. Look sure of yourself. Sneer a little. (*He leads the* VILLAIN *over to the front of the bank.*) Lounge right over here. Clean your fingernails with a silver pocket-knife. That'd be a nice touch.

(*The* VILLAIN *leans just where the* COWBOY *has put him and starts to clean his nails with a little silver pocket-knife.*)

9. Why is this an important transitional speech? What has the author dealt with thus far? What does he propose to do now?

COWBOY. You're the banker. And you own that saloon there. And most of the land around here. You run the town. So you gotta be a little genteel. Clean nails would show that.

VILLAIN. Is this the idea?

COWBOY. That'll do it.

VILLAIN. But who does my dirty work for me?

COWBOY. You got tough guys working for you . . . like these.

(*He is referring to two men who have appeared from inside the saloon – one young, one older. The younger is the bit part player we met in the saloon before. They are wearing gun belts.*)

YOUNG MAN. But I wanted to be a hero.

COWBOY. Don't push. You gotta start somewhere. O.K., now, let's see how you are at it.

(*The* YOUNG MAN *draws his gun and fires towards the camera several times.*)

YOUNG MAN. Dance, dang ye, dance. (*He laughs happily.*)

COWBOY. That'll be fine. Now, we gotta give you some helpless opposition.

VILLAIN. Wait a minute. How come I have to be a banker and a rich man? How come the rich are always villains in Westerns?

(*The scholarly tourist approaches and watches.*)

COWBOY. The rich is always villains ever'where. Except in sophisticated comedies, where they marry poor girls.

BOY. The Cinderella bit.

COWBOY. That's it, boy. Except for the Cinderella story, the rich is always villains. It's easier to sort out the good and the bad if you can do it by income and property holdin's.

VILLAIN. O.K. (*Snorts.*) I'll be the banker, but I must say I don't see why politics has to come creeping in everywhere.

INTELLECTUAL MAN. Economics, too. Politics and economics, and *not* creeping. They're in because they belong in. They're like . . .

(*The* COWBOY *suddenly covers the* BOY'*s ears.*)

COWBOY. Spell it.

INTELLECTUAL MAN. P-s-y-c . . . why do I have to spell *psychological determinism*? 10

(COWBOY *smiles sheepishly to the camera. Whispers.*)

COWBOY. I thought he meant sex. That's in everywhere, too. (*He releases the boy. The others turn and stare at him, as one. To the* INTELLECTUAL MAN.) It's all your fault. Always buttin' in when nobody wants you. We're tryin' to get a little demonstration together and we're lookin' for . . . hey . . . wait a minute . . . why didn't I think of that before? . . . We're lookin' for you – that's who. (*He claps the* INTELLECTUAL MAN *on the back.*) You can be our crusadin' editor. The only voice in this town raised against the banker's control. . . . Now, you git along to your office, editor. We're almost ready to go. . . . Wait, we got to find you a daughter. (*He points to the* LADY *in the group who took his picture before.*) Slip into a sunbonnet, will you honey, and be the spunky daughter of the crusadin' editor?

(*She slips into a sunbonnet and walks to the* EDITOR'*s office.*)

COWBOY. Now, we're ready to begin.

BOY. What about me?

COWBOY. You? Oh, you. You just sit there by the hitchin' post and smile. Take your hat off. Ever'one who hitches up will muss up your hair. Except the villain, a' course.

10. Psychological determinism: determinism is the doctrine that character and events are "determined" by a chain of causes. In the new Westerns, writers and directors follow the psychologists in telling us that the villains are not really bad men, that they do what they do because they are not well or because they have been brought up in unfortunate home conditions and environment. In other words, they follow the psychologists in suspending moral judgment on the villains. They see their problem as one of mental health rather than morality.

C.B.C. Television

The Cowboy finds an Editor and an Editor's Daughter to complete his cast.

(*The* CAMERA *moves up to the window of the newspaper office and looks through. The* EDITOR *is setting hand type. His* DAUGHTER *hovers about.*)

COWBOY (*voice over*). The story begins, as it always does, when the villain, tired of puttin' up with the editor, sends his thugs to teach him a lesson.

(*We see the two tough guys from the saloon tap on the newspaper office window and motion for the* EDITOR *to come out. One man grabs him as he appears – the other begins to pistol whip him. His* DAUGHTER *screams – but silently as in a silent movie. She is helpless to stop them. The* COWBOY *is lounging at the saloon corner near the boy, watching.*)

COWBOY. At about that time, son, I come ridin' into town. All by myself.

VOICE (*from within the saloon*). Hold on now, podner.

(An old, toothless character with a scruffy hat, who looks like the last prospector from the gold rush, appears through the swinging doors.)

COWBOY. Oh, I forgot about you. You see, boy, although us Western heroes are loners, as like as not we have an old guy with us. He's what they call a comic sidekick. Don Quixote had 11
one, you remember? Right, comic sidekick?

SIDEKICK. Right, podner.

COWBOY. Mostly they just say funny things.

SIDEKICK. Tarnation, podner, I'm so hungry I could eat a No. 10 can of pork and beans, tin, rim, glue, paper, and all.

(He spits. The COWBOY *has a pained look on his face.)*

COWBOY. Very funny things like that. Meanwhile . . .

(Outside the EDITOR's *office, the* DAUGHTER *is leaning over him, trying not to cry. The* COWBOY *is still with the* BOY *in the street.)*

COWBOY. We don't get there till the beatin's over, natcherly. Too early for a showdown.

(The COWBOY *saunters to the* EDITOR's *office – mussing the* BOY's *hair as he passes him. The* SIDEKICK *comes along too.*

COWBOY. Trouble, ma'am?

DAUGHTER. Why won't anyone stop them? You're as bad as all the rest. I wish I were a man.

(The COWBOY *walks back to the* BOY.*)*

COWBOY. Course I quiet her down after a spell. She don't trust me at first – me bein' a stranger and all – but after a fist-fight, a chase on horseback, and some more funny things from my comic sidekick . . .

11. In Cervantes' great novel, *Don Quixote,* the knight's constant companion was his squire, Sancho Panza, who has been called "the most humorous creation in the whole range of fiction".

SIDEKICK. Tarnation, podner, I'm so hungry . . .

COWBOY. . . . funny things like that, there is a showdown with the villain, the town is saved, and I ride away again.

BOY. Don't you marry the girl?

COWBOY. Sometimes I do, sometimes I don't. Classic cases, I don't. You know those changes I was tellin' you about. Changes that come over the Western the last few years. This girl business is as good a way as any to show you what I mean. Now take the old days. At first, I didn't love nobody but my horse.

(*A horse is tied up by the saloon. The* COWBOY *takes its head between his hands and looks into its eyes.*)

COWBOY. There, girl. There's a good girl. How's my sweetheart today? Got the sweet tooth, have you, girl baby? Well, let's see what I got here. (*He begins to feel in his pockets – takes out a sugar cube and holds it towards her.*) How does that look to you, girl? That's a good girl. There, girl. (*Turns to the* BOY.) That, boy, was my only love. The knight and his steed, alone against the world.

SIDEKICK. Hold on now, podner.

COWBOY. And his honest squire. Savin' one princess after another, but leavin' them rattlin' around their castles as soon as they was saved.

(*The* LADY *walks into the picture.*)

COWBOY. But then this new-fangled idea came along.

LADY. New-fangled, my sunbonnet. Even the Virginian got the girl.

COWBOY. O.K. O.K. Right from the start they was two kinds of ends. Girl and no girl. No girl was my kind of end. Kept me free to come ridin' in any time I wanted to save a town. The girl-gets-cowboy end was another matter.

LADY. Not that it looked all that different. Let's show him.

(*The* COWBOY *and the* LADY *stand facing each other with the horse between them. She is shorter than he is so that he leans down a little awkwardly.*)

COWBOY. Well ma'am, I guess that takes care of your little problem. . . . Wait, somethin's wrong.

(*The* LADY *looks around.*)

LADY. No bodies.

COWBOY. Must be that. Would you mind?

(*The* COWBOY *motions to the* VILLAIN *who happens to be near by. The* VILLAIN *shrugs obligingly. The* COWBOY *shoots him, and he falls at their feet.*)

COWBOY. That's better. Well, ma'am. I guess that takes care of your little problem. . . . I'll be headin' off now.

LADY. Must get kinda lonesome out there in the desert.

COWBOY. I got my horse, ma'am, and I got my comic sidekick.

SIDEKICK. Tarnation, podner, I'm so hungry . . .

LADY. That ain't what I meant. You must get mighty lonesome for a little home-cookin', for a place to take off your boots and set, for . . . for . . .

COWBOY. For a little girl like you, ma'am.

(*He holds out his hand. She takes it. They kiss briefly. He turns to* BOY.)

COWBOY. So there it is, son, the domestication of the Western hero.

LADY. I wouldn't put it that way.

COWBOY. How else would you put it? It was done for you anyway. The men in the audience could go home feelin' heroic, but the ladies could only go home with the settin' sun in their eyes, watchin' him ride off. So that first thing you know, they're ridin' with him.

SIDEKICK. On my horse. Nobody ever really looked at the major problem of Westerns, podner. . . . Whatever happened to all the comic sidekicks of all the Western heroes who rode off into the sunset with the girl?

COWBOY. We ain't gonna solve that problem on this show neither. The real trouble with the girl end is that it puts the hero out of business. Soon as a hero settles down to ranchin' and raisin' a family and all that, he ain't got time to go traipsin' around the countryside savin' folks from villains.

(*The* VILLAIN, *still lying in the street, comes to life with a grin.*)

VILLAIN. Speaking of whom, can I get up?

COWBOY. Sure.

(*The* VILLAIN *gets up, brushes himself off, and walks out of the scene.*)

COWBOY. Once he's corralled, the hero is just another guy who has to set at home and take care of the store.

LADY. And so he should, too. Plenty of others to go around saving towns.

COWBOY. Ain't that just like a woman. Always wantin' a hero and always wantin' him to quit bein' heroic. I declare to mercy I was better off with my horse.

LADY. Unless you like girls.

COWBOY. Well, the new Western has solved that – what they call the ay-dult Western. You ready, ma'am? Lookee-here.

(*He goes to the saloon door. We are in the saloon. It is now full of people. Someone is playing an old piano and there is plenty of laughter and shouting. The* COWBOY *strolls through the smoke and the crowd to the bar. A dance-hall girl – the* LADY – *comes swinging down the stairs and goes up to him at the bar.*)

DANCE-HALL GIRL. Well, if it ain't . . .

COWBOY. It is, honey. Why I ain't seen you since Virginia City.

DANCE-HALL GIRL. I ain't changed.

(*The* COWBOY *takes dance-hall girl into his arms and kisses her passionately.*)

DANCE-HALL GIRL. And you ain't changed neither, big boy. Why don't you come over to my place when we close the saloon? I'll make you a cup of coffee and we can . . . talk.

COWBOY. Sorry, I can't wait, honey. This is only a half-hour show.

(*The* COWBOY *steps out of picture, leaving her standing sadly against the bar. The* COWBOY *returns to the* BOY *out in the street.*)

COWBOY. There you are. That's what has happened to the Western hero.

BOY. That's bad?

COWBOY. Not exactly bad, son. Just symptomatic. When the Western hero developed an eye for the ladies and a taste for hard liquor, as like as not he bought himself a ruffled shirt.

(*The* SIDEKICK *steps forward and holds up a dickey, ruffled front, black tie attached, which the* COWBOY *steps into.*)

COWBOY. And black coat. (SIDEKICK *helps him into a coat.*)

COWBOY. And a black hat. . . . He gets culture. (*The twang has gone. Now whenever he is in this outfit, he speaks in a cultured voice.*)

COWBOY. I can't even draw my pistol from its holster without first involving the muses:

"Stern Daughter of the Voice of God! 12
O Duty! if that name thou love
Who art a light to guide . . . ."

You know the rest. Wordsworth. Not one of the really great poets of course. No Shakespeare. No Blake. Still he does sometimes speak to us here on the frontier. So the hero becomes a poetaster – the longing for culture. He becomes a gourmet – the longing for good living and the correct thing. He becomes a gentleman – the longing for status. And that's just the half of it.

(*The rich* VILLAIN *enters.*)

12. These are the opening lines of Wordsworth's "Ode to Duty". Why does Wordsworth, particularly in the "Ode to Duty", *speak to* cowboy heroes?

BOY. What's the other half?

VILLAIN. I'm the other half. Turns out I'm not just greedy any longer. I have a power complex, it's true, but as likely as not it comes from the fact that I married out of my class and have been trying ever since to make it up to the girl.

(*In the background we see the two men who were the* VILLAIN*'s henchmen before.*)

VILLAIN. Or my son doesn't understand me. Or my father didn't.

(*The* YOUNG HENCHMAN *comes forward.*)

YOUNG MAN. Or maybe I become the villain. Only I'm not really bad. I'm misunderstood. There was no kids my age for me to play with as I grew up. Or else, there was, and it was sibling rivalry. Or my father married again. So I shoot six people, but I'm just an upset kid.

COWBOY. You see where that leaves me. I have to bone up on psychology. I never draw my gun until analysis fails. But here, help me out of these feathers and we'll show you the old ending and the new ending of that story about the banker and the editor with the sunbonnety daughter.

(*Several people – some of them tourists – help him to take off his black coat and vest. We are at the* EDITOR*'s office again where the two tough guys are still pistol whipping the* EDITOR, *as they did before. The man holding the* EDITOR *lets go and he falls in a heap at their feet. The* YOUNG MAN *kicks him in the face.*)

YOUNG MAN. That'll learn ya.

(*The* COWBOY *walks in at the end of the beating.*)

COWBOY. I thought I told ya to keep yer hands off that good old man. Now draw.

(*Both men turn, drawing as they turn, but before their*

13. Sibling rivalry: rivalry between children for the attention and love of their parents.

guns are out of their holsters, the COWBOY *has fired two shots and they collapse, holding their sides. The boy sees trouble coming and shouts.*)

BOY. Look out, cowboy!

(*A bullet breaks a window in the* EDITOR*'s office. The* COWBOY *whirls around, gun in hand. He sees the* VILLAIN *coming down the street.*)

COWBOY. All right, mister, this is the end for you in this town.

(*The* VILLAIN *ducks into the shadows of the saloon veranda.*)

VILLAIN. Let's just see about that.

(*They start the classic confrontation in the village street. The slow walk. The draw. The firing. The* VILLAIN *collapses slowly. The* COWBOY *walks to the body and looks down. The* LADY *runs up and stands beside him.*)

COWBOY. Well, ma'am, I guess that takes care of your little problem. . . .

(*A crowd has gathered, including the* BOY.)

COWBOY (*to the* BOY). Well, we don't have to go through all that again. (*He holds out his arms and two men come forward with the fancy dickey and coat.*) Now we'll settle things new style.

(*They repeat the scene with the* EDITOR, *the beating, the collapse, the kick.*)

YOUNG MAN. That'll learn ya.

(*The* COWBOY *appears again.*)

COWBOY. Well, boys, have you finished beating up the father figure?

(*Both men turn, ready to shoot. Again the* COWBOY *outdraws them and they fall, holding their sides. The* COWBOY *walks over to them and looks down.*)

COWBOY. Over-compensation for a strong Oedipal drive. It would never have happened if I had got that social club organized.

(*The* BOY *again sees danger coming.*)

BOY. Look out, cowboy.

(*Again the bullet, the broken window, the whirl around by the* COWBOY – *gun in hand. He faces the* VILLAIN.)

COWBOY. Hold your fire, mister. Can't you see that this town has had a significant change in power structure? You're out, mister, and the people will be running things for themselves. We all know why you did what you did, and if you were to pack up and leave quietly, maybe the people could forget a little of what is really coming to you.

VILLAIN. I can't let go that easy. I can't let go.

(*Again the classic confrontation. Only this time when the* VILLAIN *falls the* COWBOY *comes, kneels down by him, and holds his head against his knee.*)

VILLAIN. I did it all for my boy, Cowboy, all for my boy, and, you know, he never loved me.

(*The* VILLAIN *dies, in close-up. The* COWBOY *stands up, faces the camera directly, and speaks to the audience.*)

COWBOY. You've got to earn love; you can't buy it.

(*The* LADY *runs up through the silent crowd and stands beside the* COWBOY. *He kisses her passionately.*)

LADY. It must get kind of lonesome out there in the desert.

COWBOY. It does, ma'am, it does. (*He turns to the* BOY.) Well that is that. Now get me out of this rig. (*While he is getting rid of his fancy clothes, he walks back to the* BOY.) So you

14. Oedipal drive: this is the psychoanalyst's term for a male child's emotional fixation on the mother. In Sophocles' terrible and beautiful play *Oedipus Rex,* Oedipus, unable to escape his fate, fulfils the prophecy of the Delphic Oracle by killing his father and marrying his mother.

see the difference, son.

BOY. Sure do, mister. In the old-fashioned Western straight-shooters always win, law-breakers always lose, and there's lots of shooting.

COWBOY. And in the new version?

BOY. Straight-shooters always win, law-breakers always lose, and there's lots of shooting.

(*The* COWBOY *shrugs. A* SECOND BOY *comes by.*)

SECOND BOY. Come on, let's play cowboy.

(*He runs off, firing. The* BOY *follows him, firing his pistol. The* SECOND BOY *clutches himself, falls, rolls, and lies still, just like the* VILLAIN.)

BOY. Count a hundred and then you're alive again.

(*The* SECOND BOY *rises*).

SECOND BOY. 98 – 99 – 100. I'm a-comin' after you.

(*The* COWBOY *is watching them smiling.*)

BOY. Wait, let's play cowboy, new style.

(*The boys sit down on some steps and lean back looking very serious.*)

SECOND BOY. You see, marshal, I have this recurrent dream....

(*We turn away from them and see the* COWBOY *again as we first saw him perched on the railing, alone.*)

COWBOY. There it is. Folks still like to have the hero come moseyin' in from the hills, but nowadays they get him mixed up with a bunch of modern myths. The cowboy as a social worker. Marshal Dillon as Mary Worth. I kinda miss the good old days when there was shootin' and no talkin'.

(*The* COWBOY *strolls off slowly down the street, reading a paperback on abnormal psychology and shaking his head. The opening song is heard again, slow and sad. Finally, he is only a silhouette against the sky. He turns a corner and disappears.*)

PRODUCING THE PLAY

by Vincent Tovell

When *The Western Hero* was produced in 1960, CBC shows of this type were usually done "live"; that is, they were played through from beginning to end without a stop, as a stage play is done. But they were done in a television studio without an audience. Three or, in this case, four electronic television cameras would "shoot" the action as it went along according to an exact and carefully rehearsed plan, which had been worked out in great detail by the producer with the cast and the cameramen.

Today a script like this would not have to be done "live" with all the risks of mistakes that we ran in doing a continuous performance. It could be shot in sections (either in a studio or out of doors "on location") with electronic television cameras, and later on, the scenes, which would have been recorded on electronic videotape, could be edited together in their most effective order. Or it could even be shot entirely on film with film cameras. As a matter of fact, a great deal of television drama *is* done on film nowadays. Both techniques – electronic tape and film – are used by the CBC, and as a result we have smoother and more varied productions than we were able to manage a few years ago.

The Western Hero was originally performed under great difficulties. Ted Pope, one of the CBC's most imaginative producers, had planned this first of three plays by Gerald Weales and rehearsed it for a week with the cast. Three days before the show was to be done, however, he was killed in an accident. The cast had been booked for only four more hours of rehearsal, and there were still a number of scenes to be polished – the fights, for instance. There were other problems too: details of the studio set, camera positions, light cues, and costume decisions. Together with the designer and a skilled technical crew, the production staff worked around the clock so that I, as substitute producer, could direct the cameras and finish the production on time. We had a fine cast, and we were all carried along by the remarkable performance of Don Francks as the Cowboy. Like Corinne Conley, who played the Girl, he had quick costume changes to make and a number of different moods to create, as he illustrated the various kinds of cowboys you find in Westerns. He managed them all, and the show was done with a will to overcome our own shock and sense of loss and to capture the script's spirit of good-natured satire and cock-eyed fun.

PERFORMING THE PLAY

Film and television techniques are so much alike that the suggestions for presenting *Nobody Waved Good-bye* will be useful in reading and staging *The Western Hero*. But *The Western Hero* lends itself more to performance; in fact it practically cries out for performance! It has fewer scenes and only three settings: the street area and store veranda (which can be the central and "apron" areas on a stage, or any designated areas in the classroom), the saloon, and the editor's office. The latter two can be up right and up left stage, or in the two front corners of the classroom. In an auditorium the long street might be suggested by the use of the aisles, so that the action and shooting "surround" the spectators. The classic confrontation might be arranged with the hero on stage and the villain approaching him up the centre aisle.

Use your favourite Western song during the opening sequence in which the Boy shoots at the Second Boy (who falls) and then walks up to the Cowboy. The success of the reading or production will depend on the talents of the two chief characters; you should be able to find a lanky boy who can speak with a Western drawl (and later with the voice of the cultured Cowboy) and a bright, eager, smaller boy. They should play well together as a team, enjoying themselves and their "high jinks". The minor characters should also be played in a lively fashion, entering into the fun: the sneering chief Villain and his two helpers; the Intellectual Man with his horn-rimmed glasses and scholarly manner, who later becomes the Editor; the Podner; and the Editor's spunky daughter. Western costumes and guns can easily be procured. The crowd should be dressed as tourists, with cameras, and as actors in Western costumes.

Actors will enjoy playing the several "plays" within the play. Perhaps you can find honky-tonk music for the "ay-dult" Western saloon scene where the Lady becomes the Dance-hall Girl. The play should close with the Cowboy strolling off into the distance, reading his paperback on abnormal psychology, while the Western ballad is played once more.

THINKING ABOUT THE PLAY

1. In what way might the satirical comment on the "new" Western in the play be regarded as an antidote to the ideas and characterization in *Nobody Waved Good-bye*?
2. One of the producer's favourite lines was: "I never draw my gun until analysis fails." Select your favourite line or lines and state why they appeal to you.
3. Find examples in which repetition is used effectively (a) for comic value, and (b) to underline the theme of the play. Show in each case how it is effective.
4. State the Western Hero's arguments for and against marrying the girl.

THE ODYSSEY OF RUNYON JONES

NORMAN CORWIN

RADIO DRAMA

Our next two plays are splendid examples of another kind of twentieth-century theatre – radio drama. In his preface to *Thirteen by Corwin,* Carl Van Doren refers to Norman Corwin as "an accomplished, acknowledged master. He is to American radio what Marlowe was to the Elizabethan stage. To Corwin belongs the credit for not only seeing what might be done with the radio script as an art form but also for doing it in a whole series of plays, poetic or humorous, which exhibit the full range of the art at present." *The Odyssey of Runyon Jones* is a classic: a perfect and complete thing. It is a play conceived and written for radio, by an author who directed his own plays and knew the effects he wanted to get.

What are the characteristics of this significant dramatic form which Corwin helped to create? The basic condition that determines the form is that it must make its impression entirely through the ear. This imposes certain limitations on the radio writer. It is difficult to identify the voices of speakers when there are more than two or three in a scene. If you examine *The Odyssey of Runyon Jones,* you will see that it consists chiefly of a series of duologues (two speakers). In these duologues the youthful voice of Runyon is easily recognized, as are the voices of the female characters, Mother Nature, Miss Chrono, and Blossom; the firm business-like voices of the Clerks, Superintendent, and Directors contrast sharply with Runyon's smaller voice; the contrast between his voice and the voices of Father Time and the Giant is even greater. As for the Harpy, there is no difficulty in recognizing her speech!

Radio drama is non-visual entertainment. But there is always a mysterious provision in the scheme of things for balancing weakness with compensating strength. It is true that we are deprived of *seeing* in a radio performance, but our *hearing* is marvellously clarified, and the range of responses that we receive through the ear is greatly increased beyond those we receive when we both hear and *see* a play. In other words, although we lose direct visual contact with the actor, we hear his words and the sounds and music that accompany them with redoubled vividness. Just as our vision is enlarged in the film, so that we are touched by the sight of a tear streaming down the face of an actress amplified to a dozen times its natural size on the screen, so with radio plays a mere sigh fetches a lump to our throats and can affect us more than a shout on the stage.

The first advantage that this enlargement of our hearing sense produces is that we become intimate with the actor. He is close. He can take us into his confidence. As in many novels, we follow clearly the stream of his consciousness. He reveals his innermost thoughts. Runyon Jones is intensely real, and very near to us. He could not be more real if we were watching him.

Another advantage is that the radio author, freed from the restrictions of the stage setting, has a universe over which he can range freely. Radio drama is therefore peculiarly suited to fantasy. There are no limitations, no bounds to the writer's imagination. *The Odyssey of Runyon Jones* shows this in striking fashion. How fantastically easy it is to take the Golden Escalator to the stars, or to ride the Nebula Express!

In this unusual dramatic form all our impressions are received through sound, music, and words. These therefore assume a special importance. Radio writers and producers try to say what they have to say on as many sound levels as possible. Both our radio plays were written with sound and music of almost equal importance to the words that are spoken. The authors had sounds and music in their ears as they wrote.

Sound in particular has a significance it cannot have in a stage play. In *The Odyssey of Runyon Jones* we have the flipping of cards in a file case, the sound of the stamping of papers, footsteps on stone, and the turning of a doorknob – all clear and meaningful in the telling of the story. Then what a range and variety of bigger sounds! Stellar bells, chimes, a Chinese gong, bird noises, the smashing of glass, a wolf cry, and Runyon's small voice set against the Giant's mighty accents. The final proof of the importance of sound is that Corwin has one of his characters speak as a harp, without words!

Music is also extremely important. Musical transitions, or bridges, are the only device the author can use to link his scenes together – unless he employs a narrator. And most radio writers, as pointed out, "think" background music as they write lyrical and emotional passages.

Musical bridges or transitions usually last from twelve to fifteen seconds. They often begin with the mood of the scene that has just been completed, and end with a suggestion of the mood of the scene to follow. Corwin is a master at devising these bridges. All of them in our play deserve careful study. One of the best examples occurs after the quarrel between Runyon and the Second Clerk, leading to the scene with the Superintendent:

> MUSIC: *Transitional cue – an argumentative piece scored for distinct voices at high and low instrumentation. An emphatic statement concludes the piece.*

Thus as the voices cease, the quarrel goes on in the musical bridge between the high instrumentation (Runyon) and the low (the Second Clerk); the "emphatic statement" prepares us for the words of the Superintendent, who will settle the quarrel.

The dialogue of the play is essentially humorous and realistic. Hence background music is not used to any great extent, except "under" the Father Time and Mother Nature sequences.

The engaging notes by Norman Corwin that follow tell you how the play came to be written, and suggest how the parts should be cast and played.

NOTES

by Norman Corwin

The impulse to write this dog story came from my association with an English setter named Nick, who lived down the hill. Apparently he had a falling out with his owners, because he wouldn't speak to them unless they were prepared to back up any statement they made with genuine hamburger. He was a faker and a show-off, and a furious barker after anything which couldn't bark back. Once he refused to enter my house when I was giving shelter to a neighbour's kittens. He hated them and wouldn't go near them, and looked at me with such baleful accusation that I had to drop everything and have a long talk with him. Nick was erratic and irregular, a Grand Hotel of fleas, and all the things a well-bred dog shouldn't be, but his personality was so winning that, had he been Pootzy, an odyssey such as Jones's would seem well worth the effort.

CASTING: Without a sensitive and versatile Runyon, you might as well all go home. He should be between nine and twelve and sound earnest, purposeful, persistent. Don't, under any circumstances, employ a Runyon who sounds fresh or over-smart or whining. Larry Robinson, who performed the role of Runyon the night it was done for the first time, had the right quality.

Father Time must of course be old to be credible. Roy Fant achieved a toothless quality which conveyed the idea that he had been on the job for a long while. The character of Time should justify the "crackpot" comment which is made later by the Chairman of the Board of Curgatory.

Mother Nature is a busy but not overbearing executive type: the efficient controller of all things natural, the kindly helper, the disciplinarian. M.N.'s assistant, Blossom, is a silly child. Those who know Florence Robinson's strange pixie quality will understand what is needed in that role.

The Giant is a stock giant. Arthur Vinton played him with humour and vitality, deepening an already deep voice, and rolling his speech in a wondrous way.

ACTING: Everybody whom Runyon meets in his travels treats him as an adult, never as a child. Nobody wastes sympathy, except perhaps the Superintendent, who is aware of the boy's unusual attachment to his dog. Father Time is too daft to care much; Mother Nature is accustomed to all kinds of strange petitions; the Giant has worries of his own; the personnel of Curgatory is polite but firm, always addressing the boy as Jones. None of the characters should be travestied.

CHARACTERS

RUNYON JONES
CLERK
SECOND CLERK
OFFICER
SUPERINTENDENT
FATHER TIME
VOICE
MISS CHRONO
MOTHER NATURE
BLOSSOM
THE GIANT
CHAIRMAN
DIRECTOR
SECOND DIRECTOR

First broadcast on June 8, 1941, as the sixth of the radio series "Twenty-six by Corwin", under the direction of the author, with the following cast:

RUNYON JONES	Larry Robinson
FATHER TIME	Roy Fant
MOTHER NATURE	Hester Sondergaard
THE GIANT	Arthur Vinton
BLOSSOM	Florence Robinson

The music was composed and conducted by Alexander Semmler.

THE ODYSSEY OF RUNYON JONES

MUSIC: *Introductory cue; plenty of harp and strings for glitter.*

RUNYON (*timidly*). Is this the department of lost dogs?

CLERK. Yes.

RUNYON. I'm looking for my dog.

CLERK (*perfunctorily*). Your name?

RUNYON. Runyon Jones.

CLERK. Runyon?

RUNYON. Yes, sir. It's a terrible name, but Mother says I will like it when I grow up because it's distinguished, she says. The other boys call me Onion.

CLERK. What is the name of your dog?

RUNYON. Pootzy.

CLERK. Pootzy?

RUNYON. Yes, sir. He's very smart, sir.

CLERK. When did you lose him?

RUNYON. Yesterday morning.

CLERK. Where?

RUNYON. Right outside my house. He was chasing an automobile.

CLERK. Why?

RUNYON. He wanted to bite the tires, I think.

CLERK. Front or rear?

RUNYON. All of them.

CLERK. What happened?

RUNYON. The car ran over him.

CLERK. And then?

RUNYON. He was killed, sir.

CLERK. Then you're on the wrong floor. This is the Department of *Lost* Dogs. What you want is the Department of *Deceased* Dogs.

RUNYON. Where is that, sir?

CLERK. Two flights up. Here, take this slip and hand it to the man at the desk.

RUNYON. Thank you, sir.

(MUSIC: *Transitional cue. It should combine the elements of timidity and hope.*)

Is this the Department of Diseased Dogs?

SECOND CLERK. Deceased, not diseased. Let me see that slip.

RUNYON. Yes, sir.

SECOND CLERK. Mr. Pootzy. Are you Runyon Jones?

RUNYON. Yes, sir.

SECOND CLERK. Just a minute; let me look at the file.

(*Sound of file case opening, cards flipped.*)

(*To himself; scarcely audible, mumbling.*) Pootzy Jones . . . one and a half years old . . . inveterate auto-chaser . . . leash . . . attitude . . . mm. (*To* RUNYON.) Young man, I don't think there's anything we can do for you.

RUNYON (*terribly downhearted*). You can't find Pootzy?

SECOND CLERK. Ordinarily, in a good many cases when a boy's dog dies from old age or natural causes, or is merely run over while chasing a cat in line of duty, or is fatally wounded in a fight with other dogs, we can make arrangements with

St. Bernard, the head of Dog Heaven, for the return of the 1
animal on a limited basis.

RUNYON. What's a limited basis?

SECOND CLERK. *But* – in the case of Pootzy, he is down in the files as an inveterate auto-chaser and tire-nipper, Class 4. Also, it is known that he has resisted leashes, that he bit a dog-catcher on August eleventh last, and that he stayed out all night on three separate occasions. I'm sorry to say he's *not* in Dog Heaven.

RUNYON (*freshly disappointed*). No? Gosh! (*Almost at point of tears.*) Are you sure, Mister? Couldn't he have snuck in when nobody was looking?

SECOND CLERK (*firmly*). He is not in Dog Heaven, and that settles that.

RUNYON. Well, where is he, then?

SECOND CLERK. In the place where all ill-behaved curs are
punished, Curgatory. 2

RUNYON. Where's that? I'll go there.

SECOND CLERK. Oh, no. Impossible.

RUNYON. But he won't chase any more automobiles – *I swear it!* Look – honest. I'll spit on my hand and touch my forehead three times. (*Spitting.*) Pft–foo.

SECOND CLERK. What's that mean?

RUNYON. That's the secret oath of the Elmwood Street A.C., which means pledge of honor.

SECOND CLERK. Nevertheless it will be impossible.

RUNYON. But Pootzy will be lonely without me. I *have* to find him.

SECOND CLERK. Please go now. I am busy.

1. It is fitting that St. Bernard should be the head of Dog Heaven. The monks in the Hospice which he founded in 962 at the summit of Great St. Bernard Pass near Mont Blanc used their celebrated dogs to help save the lives of many travellers lost in the snow.
2. Comment on the word "Curgatory". Why is it amusing and appropriate?

RUNYON. But, gee whiz – I came all the way here . . .

SECOND CLERK. Now go quietly, Mr. Jones, or I shall have to call an officer.

RUNYON (*making a scene*). I *won't* go! I won't go without Pootzy! You've got him somewhere, and you're hiding him on me!

SECOND CLERK. Now listen here.

RUNYON. I *won't* listen! You give my dog back or I'll kick you in the shins! (*Calling.*) Pootzy! *Pootzy*! . . . You locked him up, and you won't let me have him because you want to keep him for yourself. I know!

SECOND CLERK. Here! Here! Stop kicking me! Stop that! (*Projecting.*) Officer! Officer! Come here!

RUNYON. (*Continues to protest, ad lib, as the* OFFICER *hurries on.*)

OFFICER (*approaching*). What *is* this? What's going on here?

RUNYON and CLERK. (*Both begin to explain, talking at the same time. Finally the* OFFICER *shushes them.*)

OFFICER. I think you'd both better explain the matter to the Superintendent of the Division.

SECOND CLERK (*indignantly*). I certainly will! I'm not going to stand for being kicked in the shins by any young brat who happens to come along. No wonder his dog's in Curgatory – I can see where the animal learned its bad manners.

RUNYON (*beside himself; almost crying*). You take that back! I did not teach Pootzy his bad manners. He taught himself!

OFFICER. Quiet, both of you, and follow me. We'll explain it all to the Super.

(MUSIC: *Transitional cue – an argumentative piece scored for distinct voices at high and low instru-*

3. Ad lib: from *ad libitum,* at one's pleasure. In the theatre it means improvising suitable words where none are provided by the author.

mentation. An emphatic statement concludes the piece.)

SUPER. (*a kindly sort – the right man for the position*). I see. Well, there are things to be said for both sides. Now, first of all, I suggest that you two shake hands and apologize to each other.

RUNYON. Well, all right. I'm sorry I kicked you in the shins, Mister.

SECOND CLERK. That's all right. (*Clears his throat.*) I may possibly have lost my temper a bit, too.

SUPER. Yes. And now, Mr. Jones, let me explain what the clerk was trying to tell you. We do not keep any dogs here on the premises. The most we can do is to refer applications to the right parties. It so happens we have connections with Dog Heaven through our good friend St. Bernard. But unfortunately there is no contact whatsoever – none at all – with Curgatory.

RUNYON. Well, isn't there any way of getting to Curgatory, sir? Because I'll go myself if you'll only tell me how to get there, sir. I got *here* by myself.

SUPER. (*to* CLERK). Clerk, there's obviously quite an attachment to the dog in this case, and . . .

RUNYON. He was attached to a leash, but he kept breaking 4
away on account of he liked to run fast.

SUPER. Yes. Mm. Now, Mr. Jones, I think you're a likely lad, and so I'm going to tell you frankly that the chances of your ever getting Pootzy back are (*gravely*) very, very slim.

RUNYON (*again disappointed*). They are? Why is that, sir?

SUPER. Because Curgatory is a great, great distance away and extremely hard to get to. In fact, nobody *we* know seems to know just how one does get there. But if you're determined to try to get Pootzy back, and you're willing to take risks and chances . . .

4. Explain why the repetition of the word "attach" in its two forms is amusing. What does the pun reveal about Runyon?

RUNYON (*eagerly*). Yes, sir, I'll do anything. Gee whizzickers, if you only knew Pootzy . . .

SUPER. Then I'll tell you how to get to somebody who *may* know somebody who knows somebody else who can send you to the right place so that you *might* be able to find out how to *set out* for Curgatory.

RUNYON. Gosh, would you, sir?

SUPER. Glad to. Clerk, get me Form 5 – the blue slip – and also applications for the interdivisional visa and interdepartmental passport. Then clip on the transfer coupons and the pink manifest.

CLERK. Yes, sir.

SUPER. Now, Mr. Jones, this is what you do. There is only one person I know who can possibly set you on the right track, and that's the head of the Division of Time. We call him Father Time. His place is quite far, and you'll have to make several changes before you get there. That's what all the tickets are for.

RUNYON. Shall I say you sent me?

SUPER. Oh, that won't do much good! He's very busy and won't have much time to talk to you. Tell him quickly what you are after, and if he can assist you, he'll tell you quickly. He hates to waste time.

CLERK. The papers, sir.

(*Sound of papers.*)

SUPER. Very good. Mr. Jones, will you fill out this blank, and sign these two, while I stamp these documents?

RUNYON. Yes, sir.

(*While they are busy at their respective tasks – sound of stamping – the* SUPERINTENDENT *speaks in a very low, casual manner to the* CLERK.)

SUPER. Er – Clerk – see that he gets put safely on the Golden Escalator with instructions to change at the Inter-

5. What is the author satirizing in this speech?

Heaven Junction for the Nebula Express. 6

CLERK. Wouldn't it be better for him to take the Westbound
Taurus Special? That crosses the Meridian two light-hours 7
ahead of the Neb.

SUPER. Yes, but then he'd have to wait at Asterion for the 8
Ecliptic Local. It's better the other way. 9

CLERK. Maybe you're right.

SUPER. Have you finished, Mr. Jones?

RUNYON. Yes, sir. I got an inkspot all over this sheet here. Will that make any difference?

SUPER. No, no. Well, Mr. Jones, I guess that does it!

RUNYON (*optimistic*). Thank you, Mr. Superintendent. Gosh, Pootzy's sure gonna be glad to see me.

SUPER. (*cautioning*). Ah – don't be too sure you'll find him, because you're liable to be disappointed, you know. But good luck anyway.

RUNYON (*not knowing what to say*). Well – thank you.

CLERK (*with professional cheer, markedly in contrast to his earlier manner*). Now, young man, if you come with me, I'll see that you get on to the Golden Escalator.

6. Nebula: a cloudlike cluster of distant stars, or a luminous patch of gaseous or stellar matter. The idea of having Runyon travel by these heavenly trains is a brilliant and imaginative one.
7. Taurus: the bull; the second of the constellations of the zodiac, or the second sign of the zodiac.
   Meridian: an imaginary circle that is drawn on the earth's surface and passes through the North and the South Pole and any given place. Here the reference is to some heavenly meridian, which, like the Greenwich Meridian, establishes celestial time in "light-hours".
8. Asterion: Corwin's word for one of the asteroids, small planetary bodies that travel about the sun.
9. The Ecliptic Local: as an adjective, ecliptic means of or pertaining to an eclipse. The author may have had in mind the meaning of the noun: the great circle of the celestial sphere, which is the apparent orbit of the sun, so called because eclipses can happen only when the moon is on or near this line.

RUNYON. All right, I'm coming.

(MUSIC: *Cue descriptive of Runyon's celestial journey. Score for separate celeste mike, supported by strings; give tempo of perpetuum mobile; at length retard into rhythm of: assorted tick-tocks, including bells and chimes which keep striking under the following scene at various perspectives in the studio, some quite far off. After this is established:*)

TIME. And you mean to say you come all the way here to ask if I know anybody who can help you find a dog named Pootzy?

RUNYON. Yes, Father Time.

TIME. Don't you realize I'm very busy?

RUNYON. Yes, Father Time, but it won't take you long to tell me whether –

TIME. Quiet! I've got to listen for time signals.

(*A bong.*)

TIME. Aha! That means that the eclipse of three moons on Jupiter was right on time.

RUNYON (*progressively timid*). He was a little dog, about so big . . .

VOICE (*booming out – use P.A.*). When you hear the time signal it will be exactly half past one-sixty-two on Uranus.

TIME. Fah! That was thirty-seven thousandths of a second late! Miss Chrono, make a note of that. We'll have to make it up in the year seven billion, three hundred two.

10. Celeste mike: a microphone especially placed to pick up the heavenly sounds of the celesta, a keyboard instrument with a range of four octaves upward from Middle C.
11. Perpetuum mobile: perpetual motion.
12. Jupiter: the largest of the planets in the solar system.
13. P.A.: the accepted abbreviation for a public address system.
14. Uranus: a remote planet, situated between Saturn and Neptune.
15. Miss Chrono: Why did the playwright give the secretary this name?

CHRONO. Yes, sir.

TIME. Now what was it you wanted, little man?

RUNYON. Well, sir, could you tell me how I could get to Curgatory, because my dog Pootzy . . .

TIME. Oh, yes. Was he a delinquent dog?

RUNYON. No, sir, a mongrel.

VOICE (*P.A.*). When you hear the musical note it will be the hundred seventy-second millionth anniversary of the birth of the first dinosaur.

(*Great booming note of the Chinese gong; reverberation on the board.*)

TIME. Miss Chrono, remind me to send an anniversary message of felicitations to M.N. 16

CHRONO. Yes, sir. Can I have time to go to lunch?

TIME. Later, later. (*To* RUNYON.) Where did you say the dog was?

RUNYON. In Curgatory. I just want to know how to get there.

TIME. Aha! Well, now, the only way . . .

(*Loud buzzer close on mike. Receiver off.*)

TIME. Now who's that?

CHRONO. Main office. Chrono speaking.

TIME. My, my! Look at that green clock. It's getting toward morning on Neptune already. 17

CHRONO. Yes. I'll tell him. Keep your shirt on, he's right here.

TIME (*testily*). Who's that? Who's that on the phone?

CHRONO. Our agent on Alcyone. He says they need a shipment of sand very badly. 18

TIME. Why?

CHRONO. The sands of time are running low all through

16. Who is M.N.?
17. Neptune: the most remote planet of the solar system, except for Pluto.
18. Alcyone: the brightest star of the Pleiades.

the Archipelago of the Pleiades.

TIME. Tell him we're digging some new pits on Mercury and that he'll have his order in two shakes of a comet's tail.

CHRONO. (*Still off, relays* TIME'S *message and hangs up while:*)

TIME. Finest platinum sand in the system. Uh . . . (*With surprise.*) What are *you* doing here?

RUNYON. Don't you remember, Father Time? I'm the one who is looking for my dog. I came . . .

TIME. Oh, yes, yes! Mr. Bones!

RUNYON. Jones.

TIME. You're from Earth, aren't you?

RUNYON. Yes, sir.

TIME (*sharply*). Well, then I want you to know that I am heartily ashamed of the kind of time they have down there in Greenwich.

RUNYON. Yes, sir.

TIME. And I want you to understand why.

RUNYON. Yes, sir.

TIME. Because it's so *mean*! It's *pretty mean* time!

RUNYON. Yes, sir.

TIME. And now about you and your dog. I don't know

19. Pleiades: a group of small stars in the constellation Taurus. How did the expression "the sands of time" originate?
20. Mercury: the planet nearest the sun.
    Corwin is having fun with folk sayings. Can you complete the one that begins "two shakes . . ."?
21. Greenwich: a metropolitan borough on the south bank of the Thames River, east of London. It is famous for its astronomical observatory.
22. The joke about Greenwich and its "mean" time is one that, Corwin ruefully admits, did not work. Hence the repetition: "it's *pretty mean* time". Father Time is ashamed of the time they have "down there in Greenwich" because it's "mean". Greenwich time is the mean or average time for the meridian of Greenwich; it is standard time for English astronomers.

where Curgatory is at all. It used to be on Sirius, the Dog Star, 23
but the neighbours on Furud and Murzim and Adhara complained about the piteous howling and whining that came from there; so they had to move.

RUNYON (*fearing the worst*). Er – why was there howling and whining?

TIME. Because all the dogs in Curgatory are tortured, of course.

RUNYON. Does – does it hurt them bad?

TIME (*laughs*). Well, naturally! What a question! Why, I've heard there are fleas in Curgatory as big as a lion! That's only one of the attractions.

RUNYON (*very tentatively*). Uh – well – is there some way I could find out how to get there?

TIME. Well, the only one I know who could possibly help you is M.N.

RUNYON. M.N.?

TIME. Don't you know anything, lad? Mother Nature!

RUNYON. Oh.

(*Celeste chord, amplified to a startling degree.*)

TIME. Well, well, there goes the vernal equinox on 24
Aldebaran. Now, Mr. Pootzy . . .

RUNYON. No, that's my dog.

TIME. Quiet, Pootzy! . . . Now here's how you get to M.N.'s place . . .

VOICE (*P.A.*). When you hear the note of the bass bautant, that will be time for all visitors – (*significantly*) who weren't invited – to get ready to leave.

23. Sirius: the chief star of the Great Dog constellation; the Dog Star is the brightest star in the sky.
24. Vernal equinox: the vernal (or spring) equinox is one of the two periods in the year when day and night are of equal length, because the sun is then "crossing" the equator.

(MUSIC: *Bass bautant, followed by variations on previous interstellar movement cue. This sustains briefly under the following scene. Establish background of bird noises.*)

MOTHER NATURE (*laughing*). Pootzy? What a funny name!

RUNYON. Yes, ma'am.

MOTHER NATURE. And you came here to ask me . . .

RUNYON. Well, Father Time said you might know where it is.

MOTHER NATURE. Well, I don't, little boy, but let me think. (*Pause.*) I'll tell you who might. Just off the main skyway between Castor and Pollux, before you get to the red light of Mekbuda, there's a harpy who . . .

BLOSSOM. Excuse me, Mrs. Nature, but these papers have to be signed right away if you want to get them on the Solar Limited.

MOTHER NATURE. Yes. Excuse me, Runyon.

RUNYON. Yes, ma'am.

25. Bass bautant: Corwin's note is interesting. "There's no such thing. Chatterton, the poet, coined the instrument in one of his poems, and I have appropriated it to confound musicians. Alex Semmler settled for a bassoon, which is what I meant in the first place. I placed the bassoon in the dead booth, on a public-address microphone whose amplifier fed into the wide space of the studio proper; it made quite a frightful sound, which was what I wanted."
26. Castor and Pollux: two stars in the constellation Gemini, or The Twins. In mythology they were the twin sons of Leda by Tyndarus or by Zeus.
27. Harpy: Corwin obviously chose the word because he wanted a creature that would talk in harp language and would suggest strange and grotesque images to us. In Homer's time, a harpy was a wind-spirit that carried people away. In later Greek and Roman mythology, it was a creature with the body of a woman and the wings and claws of a bird.

MOTHER NATURE (*low, to herself*). Formal complaint about an earthquake in California . . .

BLOSSOM (*idle talk*). Hello.

RUNYON. Hello.

BLOSSOM. You from Betelguese?

RUNYON. No ma'am, I'm from Des Moines.

BLOSSOM. Looking for a job?

RUNYON. No, ma'am. I want to find my dog.

BLOSSOM. Oh. Curgatory?

RUNYON. Yes'm.

BLOSSOM. Too bad. No chance.

test specimen of a new metal
for the mountains of East
Orion . . . new species of ant 28
for the Antilles . . . replace 29
two worn rings on Saturn . . . 30
a petition of twenty-six butterflies of the order Rhopalocera demanding less time in chrysalis and more on the wing . . . requisition for
ersatz beans to take the place 31
of butter-beans . . . rain
wanted in the Panhandle . . . 32

There! That's finished. (*To the girl.*) Here, Blossom, take these and see that they – Wait a minute. What's that you have in your hand?

BLOSSOM. A vacuum bottle, ma'am. Some warm nectar in case I get hungry on the way, and . . .

MOTHER NATURE (*furious*). Don't you know I *abhor* a vacuum? Give me that!

(*Smashing of glass.*)

Now, Blossom, don't let me lose my patience with you again. If you get hungry, there's plenty to drink in the Milky Way.

28. Orion: a large constellation resembling a hunter with belt and sword.
29. Antilles: another name for the West Indies.
30. Saturn: a remote planet, but one of the best known.
    Betelguese: a star of the first magnitude in Orion.
31. Ersatz: substitute or imitation.
32. Panhandle: a geographical term for a long and generally narrow strip of land, resembling the handle of a pan, which projects from the main area of a state or territory.

BLOSSOM. Yes, Mrs. Nature.

MOTHER NATURE (*immediately calm again*). Now, Runyon – as I was saying, this harpy is a very strange spirit, full of lots of esoteric knowledge and . . .

RUNYON. Does he know where I can find Pootzy?

MOTHER NATURE. That I can't tell you. But there's no harm asking. Incidentally, it's a she, not a he. In fact, she's more commonly known as an *it*.

RUNYON. Does it bite?

MOTHER NATURE. Oh, no! But you may have difficulty understanding it, because of the way this harpy talks. You'll have to hold this little charm – oh, now where did I put it – yes, here it is – you'll have to hold this in your left hand while the harpy talks, in order to make out anything at all.

RUNYON. Gee, isn't it pretty? It's like an aggie in marbles.

MOTHER NATURE. Yes. It's the most charming charm I have. Don't lose it, now, because it has the power of translating the harpy's language into your own.

RUNYON. No, ma'am, I won't lose it. I'll take care of it like as if it was Pootzy.

(MUSIC: *Transitional cue, segueing to harp solo. Throughout this scene the harp holds a conversation with Runyon, and its phrases should be as much like conversation as possible – monosyllabic, but at times questioning and expository, as the speech of Runyon indicates.*)

HARPY. (*After a cadenza, a questioning phrase.*)

RUNYON. Yes, sir. I mean yes, ma'am. I mean yes, It.

HARPY. (*Phrase.*)

RUNYON. Pootzy.

HARPY. (*Phrase in which strings are plucked six times, as though spelling out something.*)

RUNYON. No. P-o-o-t-z-y.

HARPY. (*Phrase.*)

33. Segueing: followed by, or leading into.

RUNYON. Chasing an automobile.

HARPY. (*Phrase.*)

RUNYON. Yes'm – sir, I mean . . .

HARPY. (*Phrase broadening into sostenuto tones in lower register.*) 34

RUNYON (*fearfully*). A *giant*?

HARPY. (*Phrase* – "Yes.")

RUNYON. But does he bite?

HARPY. (*Reassuring phrases.*)

RUNYON (*still not too certain this is safe*). Does he know where Pootzy is?

HARPY. (*Phrase* – "Maybe.")

RUNYON. You don't know where he is? Gosh, nobody seems to know where Curgatory is. I hope the giant does. How do I get there, Miss Harpy? I mean, Mr. – I mean The Harpy?

HARPY. (*Cadenza of a most expository nature, broadening into:*)

> (MUSIC: *Full orchestra in transitional cue. The music here should convey a sense of bigness and grotesqueness.*)

RUNYON (*sounding very little*). And so he ran under the automobile before I could get him, Mr. Giant. And that's how he got killed.

GIANT (*a great voice tremendously built up by amplification – laughing*). So you've come here expecting me to tell you where Curgatory is!

RUNYON. Yes, sir. If you know, I mean.

GIANT. Of course I know!

RUNYON (*in a transport of delight*). You *do*? Oh, gee, will you tell me, please! Oh, gee gosh jiminy heck! Then you know where Pootzy is!

GIANT (*laughs*). Do you think I'm gonna tell a little squirt where Curgatory is? Why, I haven't told anybody anything for

34. Sostenuto: sustained.

sixty-seven million years, and I don't see why I should start in now!

RUNYON (*who can't understand how anybody, even a Giant, could be mean enough to withhold information leading to the whereabouts of Pootzy*). But it's Pootzy, don't you understand – Pootzy! Pootzy's there. If you tell me, I can go *get* him.

GIANT (*derisively*). Pootzy! Pshaw! I don't care if *Tootzy's* there. Now beat it, small fry; I got worries of my own – me with my two heads to feed and four sets of teeth, two uppers and two lowers, to clean every night! G'wan, beat it.

RUNYON. Please, Mr. Giant, *please*!

GIANT. What did you ever do for *me*!

RUNYON. Nothing, but I'll do anything you want me to, if I get Pootzy back.

GIANT. Haw, haw! As if you *could* do something for me! G'wan now, scram before I squash you with my little finger.

RUNYON. But listen to me . . .

GIANT. Don't take up my valuable time. Who sent you here in the first place, anyway?

RUNYON. The harpy.

GIANT (*bellowing*). The *harpy*?

RUNYON. Yes, sir.

GIANT. You don't say! Mmmmm. Step on my thumbnail here, and don't slip – I want to talk to you very confidentially. Come up here near my ear. Now – what do you know about the harpy?

RUNYON (*fade in, advancing on mike rapidly*). Well, it told me how to get here. It gave me full directions.

GIANT (*angry*). It? What are you talking about?

RUNYON. The harpy, sir.

GIANT. *Miss* Harpy to you, bunny!

RUNYON. Yes, sir. (*Gulps.*)

GIANT (*low again*). Well, how the Hecuba could you understand her?

35. How the Hecuba: a mild oath. Hecuba was the second wife of Priam, King of Troy.

RUNYON. Why, that was easy.

GIANT. Easy! I've been trying to get next to that creature for the last four million years, and every time I ask her for a date, she gives me queer talk. I can't make her out. I think she's stringing me along.

RUNYON. You mean she talks like this?

(MUSIC: *A shot of harp talk.*)

GIANT (*astounded*). Yeah! Say! How'd you do that?

RUNYON. Well, I'll tell you how if you tell me how to reach Curgatory.

GIANT. Oh, businessman, eh?

RUNYON. No, I just want to swap you, that's all.

GIANT. Well, all right; tell me how.

RUNYON. Oh, no. First you tell me how to get to Curgatory.

GIANT. Hm. (*Growls.*) Well, that's fair enough. Mind you, you're not fooling me now. What you tell me better work!

RUNYON. Sure. It works like a charm, no foolin'.

GIANT. All right, then. Now (*fading*) get this, kid: first you go up through that cloud of meteor dust there on the
trimtram, and then you change at San Sunspot for the Sidereal 36
Ferry . . .

(*Crossing under:*)

(MUSIC: *Transitional cue, similar to the first in combining a feeling of timidity and hope. A long-drawn wolf cry.*)

RUNYON (*frightened*). What was that?

OFFICER. That was merely the soul of a wolf passing by the Curgatorium.

RUNYON. Does – does it bite?

OFFICER. Don't be alarmed, Mr. Jones. You see, the near-
by wolves who occupy what is known as Lupine Limbo resent 37

36. Trimtram: a name for a heavenly train. A tram is a streetcar. Sidereal Ferry: sidereal means of or pertaining to the stars.

37. Lupine Limbo: Limbo is a region close to Hell. Here it means an unpleasant place or prison. Lupine: of a wolf or wolves.

certain of the policies in practice here in Curgatory, to say nothing of the smell.

RUNYON. They do?

(*Bell.*)

OFFICER. Ah, that means the board of directors has reached a decision on your application. We can go in now.

(*Creaking of heavy door.*)

CHAIRMAN. Mr. Jones, will you sit here?

RUNYON. Thank you.

CHAIRMAN. Gentlemen of the board, this is Mr. Runyon Jones of Earth, whose request to be reunited with his dog Pootzy – number seventeen billion, six million twelve – we have just discussed.

BOARD. (*Ad-lib greetings.*)

CHAIRMAN. Jones, we have gone into this matter most carefully.

RUNYON. That's good.

CHAIRMAN. We fully appreciate the pains to which you have gone, and the trouble . . .

RUNYON. Oh, it was nothin'.

CHAIRMAN. . . . you have taken. We are also aware of the unusual devotion you have shown the said Pootzy, and all these factors have entered into our decision.

RUNYON. Yes, sir. Then can I see Pootzy and have him back?

CHAIRMAN. The unanimous decision of the board of directors is that you may not.

RUNYON. What? You mean I can't see . . .

CHAIRMAN. Sorry, but it is entirely contrary to the established rules and regulations of the institution. If we made an exception for you, it might lead to all kinds of complications.

RUNYON (*trying hard to fight back his tears*). Jiminy, can't I see Pootzy for just a minute?

CHAIRMAN. Sorry, Jones.

RUNYON. Not even for a teeny-weeny *second*? Just to peek

at him through the bars and whistle once? Just like this? (*He tries to whistle, but cries instead.*)

CHAIRMAN. We are all very sorry, Jones, but nothing can be done for you. Incidentally, it may be of some consolation to you to know that there are no bars in Curgatory.

RUNYON (*coming up for air*). That's good. (*He sniffles.*) Do you torture Pootzy bad? He's got a lame foot, you know. I hope you don't hurt him awful.

CHAIRMAN. Just a moment, Jones. I am proud to say we do not torture any dogs in Curgatory. Where did you get that terrible idea?

RUNYON. Father Time told me.

(*General indignation mixed with amusement.*)

CHAIRMAN. Father Time? Why, don't take stock in anything he says, Jones. (*Confidentially.*) I shouldn't like this to get back to Father Time, but between you and us – strictly *entre nous* – that job of his seems to have got the better of him. He's more or less known as a – a crackpot.

DIRECTOR. That torture talk is nonsense.

SECOND DIRECTOR. Yes, indeed. . . . Well, we've got a big docket to clear. Hadn't we better show Jones how to get back to the Sidereal Ferry?

CHAIRMAN. Yes, Jones. I'm afraid that closes the case. Sorry.

RUNYON. Can I say just one more thing, gentlemen?

CHAIRMAN. Well, you'll have to make it fast.

RUNYON (*pleading in desperation*). Pootzy is a good dog. He didn't mean to bite no tires. He just wanted to race the cars to show me how fast he could run. And he could of run faster if he wasn't lame in the leg. And the time he bit the dog-catcher, the big bum . . .

CHAIRMAN. Jones! That's no kind of language.

RUNYON (*mad and miserable*). Well, he *was* a big bum! He hurt Pootzy, and Pootzy wasn't doin' no harm to nobody; he was just chasing a cat. And about his staying out all night, that was because he saw me talking to Eddie Mazer's bulldog, and he got jealous. You can't blame a dog for that, can you? Honest, Pootzy is the best dog in the world, or else would I have come all this way for him?

FIRST DIRECTOR. What about the day the auto ran over him and killed him? Didn't he break away from your leash?

RUNYON. No, sir, the leash broke.

CHAIRMAN (*severely*). Are you sure of that, Jones? (*For a moment there is no answer.*) Jones . . . ?

RUNYON (*defeated*). No, sir.

FIRST DIRECTOR. Then the said Pootzy did break away?

RUNYON (*now crying*). Yes, sir.

CHAIRMAN. Well, there you are. Again, please understand that we are sorry, but there is nothing we can do.

(*Gavel.*)

Next item, gentlemen.

OFFICER. This way out, Mr. Jones.

RUNYON. Good-bye. And tell Pootzy I – I . . . (*He can't finish.*)

CHAIRMAN. Yes. I'll tell him.

RUNYON (*going off*). Good-bye. (*Shouting.*) Good-bye, Pootzy! Can you hear me?

CHAIRMAN (*gravely*). No, he cannot. I will tell him good-bye for you.

RUNYON. Thank you, sir.

FIRST DIRECTOR. Wait a minute, Jones. Where did you get that mark over your right eye?

RUNYON. Oh, this? Oh, that's nothing. I got that in the accident.

CHAIRMAN. What accident?

RUNYON. When I tried to prevent Pootzy from being run over.

FIRST DIRECTOR. And?

RUNYON. And nothing.

CHAIRMAN. Well, didn't you reach Pootzy in time?

RUNYON. No, sir. Almost – but, you see, the car ran over me first.

THE BOARD (*shocked*). It did?

RUNYON. Yes, sir. That's how *I* got killed.

CHAIRMAN. Well, now . . . (*He clears his throat uncomfortably.*) Ahem – just a moment, Jones.

BOARD. (*An indistinguishable ad-lib conference. At length:*)

CHAIRMAN. Jones, the status of the case is changed by the fact that you gave your life to save your dog. That comes under the Priorities Ruling affecting the Seventh Clause of the Constitution of Curgatory.

RUNYON (*not getting it*). I see. Well, good-bye, gentlemen.

BOARD. (*Ad-libs under:*)

CHAIRMAN. No, no – you don't understand! You can have the said Pootzy back!

RUNYON (*incredulously*). I can see Pootzy?

CHAIRMAN. Yes, sir! We'll release the said Pootzy from Curgatory in your custody.

RUNYON. You mean – now?

CHAIRMAN (*pleased as Punch – no, more so*). Yes. The officer will take you.

OFFICER. Come, Mr. Jones.

RUNYON. Yes, right away. Gee!

(*Door closes. Footsteps on stone for ten seconds.*)

OFFICER. He's down at the end of the long corridor.

(*More footsteps. At length:*)

Well, here we are. He's right inside that door.

RUNYON (*hardly able to control his voice*). Is he? Right inside there?

OFFICER. Yes. Just open the door and walk right in.

RUNYON. Er – wait a minute.

OFFICER. What's the matter?

RUNYON. Do I look all right?

OFFICER (*chuckling*). Oh, yes, Mr. Jones.

(*Clear, clean sound of doorknob and the beginning of the door opening, whereat there is an immediate dissolve into:*)

(MUSIC: *Conclusion.*)

PRODUCTION NOTES

by Norman Corwin

SOUND: The only problem is that of the background for the Father Time sequence. I found that the best effect was achieved by slowing down a recording of a cuckoo clock. At normal speed this effect was a pleasant *ding,* followed by a cheerful *cuckoo,* but I reduced it to a speed so low that the *ding* became a tremendous and deep-chested BONG, and the optimistic chirrup of the cuckoo became a lugubrious two-note wail of the melancholy whistling buoy. This succeeded somehow in creating an effect of great space, of mysterious gyrations, of the weird inner workings of the solar system.

REHEARSAL ROUTINE: The chief production worries are the blending of sound, music, and speech in the Time sequence and the interview between the Giant and Runyon. The former can best be accomplished by using a separate microphone for each element, being careful not to allow the background of sound to override speech. This scene will be soupy unless one works hard to maintain clear perspectives.

In the Giant scene, complete isolation is necessary if Runyon is to sound small and the Giant big. I placed Runyon in a dead booth and reduced the level of his microphone on the control board, while the Giant had the whole studio to himself, and an echo chamber to boot.

PERFORMING THE PLAY

Many schools where this book will be used will have a public address system in the auditorium, and will be able to "stage" our radio plays. If three microphones are available, one should be used for sound effects, and the other two for the actors. The actors should sit in a semicircle on the stage, coming to the microphone when they speak. The school will have specialists who can instruct the cast in the proper use of the microphones. The student in charge of sound effects should be one who makes a hobby of working with "hi-fi" and other sound equipment; there are usually several in every school. Many of Corwin's "effects" in *The Odyssey of Runyon Jones* are too elaborate to be imitated by the amateur, but a resourceful student can do wonders in approximating them.

What should be done about the audience? If the production is given in a small hall or classroom, and the program can be "piped" to other classrooms, the audience will hear the production under normal radio conditions. But if the performance is given in the auditorium, it seems foolish to close the curtains when the spectators could be a studio audience and have the additional pleasure of watching the actors (and perhaps the sound-effects man) at work.

If no sound-amplifying equipment is available, two courses are open – apart from a straight classroom reading of the play. The first is to improvise one or two "dummy" microphones and place them in front of the class, with the actors performing as they would in a live studio presentation. A tape-recorder or phonograph playing sound effects and suitable music can be provided at a separate "microphone".

Another method is to forget the microphone and all attempts to imitate a studio production, and to translate the play into terms of the stage. The Clerks could be at desks with their papers. The Second Clerk and Runyon could go to the Superintendent's table in another corner of the room. Mother Nature and Blossom might be in still another corner. When Runyon comes to the Giant, he might find him on a table or desk top, towering above him. The play could close with Runyon attending an actual board meeting and then passing down an aisle to meet his faithful friend Pootzy.

Two expressions used in Norman Corwin's "Production Notes" should be explained. A "dead booth" is a booth whose walls are made of sound-absorbing materials. It is set up within the studio. The voice of an actor in a dead booth can be heard clearly, apart from the sound or dialogue coming from the main studio. An "echo chamber" is an empty room in which sound reverberates from wall to wall and is picked up by a microphone and sent back to the control board.

Another possibility is to record the play on a tape recorder. The recording can then be played back to the group or class that prepared the production. If it is considered worthy of presentation to a larger audience, it can be piped to other classrooms on the P.A. system.

THINKING ABOUT THE PLAY

1. Why is the word "Odyssey" used in the title?
2. Where is the climax of the play? Is it the moment when we learn that Runyon is dead, or is it just at the end of the play

when he is at last about to see Pootzy? Give reasons to support the choice you make.

3. Is the conclusion a good one? We do not hear Runyon greet his friend Pootzy. Instead, we hear the door open, and the scene dissolves into a passage of music. Why did the author end the play this way?

THE LAND OF EPHRANOR

JOSEPH SCHULL

A CANADIAN RADIO CLASSIC

The great age of American radio drama, the leader of which was Norman Corwin, had its Canadian counterpart. Among the brilliant young writers contributing to the *Stage* series, the national showcase for the best of the new talent, was Joseph Schull, whose *The Land of Ephranor* was presented in 1945, four years after *The Odyssey of Runyon Jones* was broadcast. *The Land of Ephranor* was directed by Andrew Allan, producer of the series; Fletcher Markle and John Drainie, well-known Canadian broadcasting personalities, were in the cast.

The Land of Ephranor was so highly regarded that it was revived for a CBC *Stage* presentation on March 20, 1966. It has been included in our volume as an example of Canadian radio writing at its best. Its author, now firmly established as one of Canada's outstanding writers, has contributed an introductory note which will help you to enter into the spirit and meaning of the play and enjoy it to the full.

The Land of Ephranor is a classic because in its form and in its content it is both timeless and contemporary. It has beauty and meaning for us today, as it had when it was written and as it will have tomorrow. As you read the play, you will be aware of its shape: how inevitably and powerfully it moves onward, stronger as it goes, until it reaches its climax, and then draws to its serene conclusion. You will be caught up in the spell of its legendary atmosphere, ironic mood, and hauntingly lovely language. And you will learn much from its gentle wisdom, humour, and humanity. You will be encouraged, perhaps with the humility that Othran learned, to face with a good heart the folly and evil of man, and to do what you know in your heart you must do toward a better ordering of the world.

INTRODUCTORY NOTE

by Joseph Schull

There is, of course, no such land as Ephranor; and the play is a fairy tale which more or less grew by itself. It was fun in the writing, and I should like to think that some sense of gaiety will communicate itself through the lines to young actors.

The lighter the touch and the simpler the staging, the better. The teller of the tale and the people of the story are exaggerating a moral and they know it. They share their secret with the audience, inviting them to use their imagination and to laugh with Othran and Naina and the others over the faded follies they are recalling. Yet it would not be all laughter; people do walk in their own lives, as Othran did, the rocky road to disillusion. Yet, if the trip is made in good heart, they find it worth while, and perhaps in the long run what they find at the end is better than they expected.

CHARACTERS

STORY-TELLER
NAINA
OTHRAN
HALGOR
BEGGARS
COBBLERS
TANNERS
LORD
KING
OTHERS

Produced on CBC *Stage* Sunday, March 20, 1966, with the following cast:

STORY-TELLER	John Scott
NAINA	Jane Casson
OTHRAN	Frank Perry
HALGOR	Tommy Tweed
FIRST BEGGAR	Joe Austin
LORD	Gillie Fenwick
KING	Sandy Webster
OTHERS	Douglas Master, Claude Rae, Neil LeRoy, Fred Diehle, Drew Thompson, Jim Barron

Produced by Esse W. Ljungh

THE LAND OF EPHRANOR

ANNOUNCER. The Land of Ephranor.

(MUSIC: *Theme – light, pastoral, ironic.*)

NAINA. I am Naina. 1

OTHRAN. I am Othran.

HALGOR (*cracking a walnut with his teeth*). I am Halgor the Hermit, whom men call wise because I have pointed out that they are fools.

NARRATOR. And I am the teller of the tale.

NAINA (*crisply*). A foolish tale and best forgotten, for years have passed and we are wiser –

NARRATOR (*gently*). But –

NAINA. But if it please you to hear of faded follies, then –

NARRATOR. – the tale is thus: Once upon a time a foolish man had a wise son, to whom learning was better than laughter
and a syllogism more shapely than a fair maid. From the time 2
of puberty his thoughts walked much among the heavens, brooding from on high upon the strange spectacle of earth and man. His words were weighty on the ear and troubling to the mind and his foolish father marvelled, saying:

1. Naina: pronounced Nah-eé-nah.
2. Look up the word syllogism in your dictionary. In what sense is a syllogism "shapely"?

FATHER. Truly, what unimagined seed of wisdom lay in the bosom of my good wife now deceased; for this jungle of great thought springs from no roots of mine.

NARRATOR. And he looked upon his son and shook his woolly head. In the nineteenth year of the son, Messer Death came lightly to the side of his father and the good man spoke within himself again, saying:

FATHER. If it be now for me to die then die I must; and I am sorry to go for I know no better. And though I am a great fool I shall leave the lands and property of my son close-guarded in the parchment-coloured hands of men of law. For this at least I have the wit to know: that a fool and his money dwell longer together than a father's wealth in the hands of a son who knows no word shorter than "dialectical".

NARRATOR. And so he did and died. And the youth, grieving, yet comforted himself with the thought that his foolish father was now as great and wise as the Great King, who was also dust. And finding the cares of funeral and fortune made light for him by the men of law (who were honest men, for this was a strange land) he set himself to a matter which had long been of concern to him. For there were many things not well ordered in the ways of man; and he was of a mind to alter them before the years should take him to lie down beside his father.

HALGOR. And so he came to me. (*Short, sarcastic cackle.*)

NARRATOR. Yes. And so he came to Halgor, the Hermit of the Hill That Looks to Heaven. For he was a humble young man as well as a grave and comely; and sought enrichment from the wisdom of the wisest man on earth. Upon a great highway he set forth, winding into strange horizons and beyond the boundaries of distant lands. Through the forest –

3. What is implied after the phrase "for I know no better"?
4. Why are the hands of the men of law "parchment-coloured"?
5. Can you quote the common proverb that begins "a fool and his money . . ."?
6. What does "dialectical" mean? Why is it a fitting word to use about the vocabulary of the young man?

(SOUND: *Tinkle of cowbells; birds; waterfall; establish sounds in BG throughout following speech where appropriate in narration.*) 7

– of Gal he came, and the valleys of Ar and Vem; rich with deep meadows where the bells of grazing kine were pleasant on the ear. Under the gloom of lonely crags he passed, and dared the fordings of harsh waters and out again upon remoter heaths where the grass lay uncropped nor scarred with the paths of men and not even a whistling herdsman sat upon a slope to wave him good journey. . . . At last, remote and venerable, the mountain of his seeking came to view; and his weary steps were lighter as he neared its slope. The way wound steeply upward by a tortuous and wooded path; and high above him, carved in the blue sky, was a ledge whereon he saw a figure standing.

NAINA (*calling, off, with outdoor echo*). Halo-o-o!

OTHRAN (*on, trifle breathless*). Halo-o-o! I seek the Hermit of the Hill.

NARRATOR. It was a boy or maiden that hailed him and vanished as he called. But, toiling upward, as he came around a turning of the path he spied the figure hurrying toward him and perceived that it was a maid. Dark she was, clad in a brief and tattered smock; and would have been the better for a washing.

NAINA (*approaching, trifle breathless*). What do you come for here?

OTHRAN. I come to take counsel of the wise hermit.

NAINA (*short, sarcastic laugh*). Another! And what is *your* resolve? To sell the stars for lemons?

OTHRAN. That is idle talk, I am come upon a mission of weight.

NAINA. So are all of you. Follow me.

NARRATOR. The maiden turned upon her dusty toes and moved before him up the winding path. At last they stood

7. BG: This refers to the sound or music that provides a background to the spoken dialogue.

beyond the trees upon the sunswept brow, and many lands lay spread beneath them. The maiden pointed to the thatch of the sacred hovel and to the ancient standing by its threshold.

NAINA. There he is. (*Calling.*) Hey! . . . another.

NARRATOR. The young man raised his eyes to behold the radiance of the head that held man's greatest store of wisdom. And a cloud of gentle puzzlement entered into his eyes to remain there for long. For the head was bald and wrinkled and there was a matting of leaves upon it, roofing from the sun a petulant visage and a mouth busied at the moment in the mastication of a walnut.

OTHRAN (*approaching*). Great Master –

HALGOR (*crunch of nut between teeth*). Well, what do *you* want?

OTHRAN. I am Othran, son of Jobar, and I seek to remedy the ills of man.

HALGOR (*crunch of nut*). Well, what d'ye want of me?

OTHRAN. Wisdom, Great Master. I have seen that many things are not well with man –

HALGOR. Uh-huh –

OTHRAN. – that the world is not ordered for his happiness, though it might be – that he who glories in his mastery of earth yet goes about as a child or a quarrelsome, vicious animal bringing only misery upon himself.

HALGOR (*crunch – absently*). Oh – huh. (*Sharply.*) Well?

OTHRAN. Master, are not these things so?

HALGOR. Certainly.

OTHRAN. But they should not be so. They need not be so. The remedies are simple. I have thought long about them. I have –

HALGOR. (*Loud cr-runch. Pause.*)

NARRATOR. The young man paused, though still there was a light upon his face. The hermit munched testily, raised his squinting eyes at last to glower upon the visitor. Then he stooped, took up a clod of earth and held it forth.

HALGOR. There. See that? Earth. Mud. Was man, is man, will be man. You think a man's three score years and ten away from it. You'll see.

OTHRAN. I do not understand. Are not these true – the evils I see? Are not the remedies obvious and reasonable?

NAINA (*scornful laugh*). He's just like all the others.

HALGOR (*to her*). Of course he is. (*To him. Raising his voice in sudden irritation.*) And of course they are! Go away! Go away!

OTHRAN. But Master, I seek your help, your counsel.

HALGOR. You have it. Go away. Go home.

OTHRAN. Master, I would remedy the ills of man.

HALGOR. You're a fool.

OTHRAN. I have come far.

HALGOR. You're a bigger fool.

OTHRAN (*pleading*). Master –

HALGOR (*pause*). All right. So you want to remedy the ills of man? Come over here. Look – (*pause*) see that city down there beyond the hills and the farthest valleys?

OTHRAN. Yes, Master.

HALGOR. That's the Land of Ephranor. You'll find lots of ills there just as you said. Go down and remedy 'em.

OTHRAN (*thrilled*). Master! I have judged truly, then?

HALGOR. Quite truly. Go on down. Naina will take you. (*Calling.*) Naina! Where's that dratted girl?

NAINA. Here, old rogue.

HALGOR. Take him down to Ephranor.

NAINA. This fool?

HALGOR. Yes, this fool. And mind you, none of your tricks.

OTHRAN (*manifesting distaste*). Who is this – person – Master?

HALGOR. How should I know who she is? Slave girl – answers to Naina – lazy, insolent –

OTHRAN. But – has she – wisdom . . . ?

HALGOR (*cackling*). Ho! Ho! Wisdom? . . . of course not . . . think I'm a fool?

OTHRAN (*helplessly*). But –

NAINA (*short laugh*). Come, stranger. It is a long journey and we shall be fortunate to return.

OTHRAN. But –

NAINA (*sardonically*). I will lead you to the Land of Ephranor, where you will see as fine a crop of ills as any in the world. Follow me . . . the path is narrow. . . . Farewell, old rogue . . . (*She begins to whistle.*)

HALGOR (*fading – crunch*). Farewell . . .

NAINA (*whistling*). This way – (*Resumes whistling. Whistling fades to sporadic background for following:*)

NARRATOR. So bravely, though not as he had dreamed, the young man set forth upon his mission, following the whistling slave girl down the path of the mountain. The slopes gave way to murmurous woods, and they to alien moors and silence, and there was at last a dusty highway crawling to the gates of Ephranor. And as they approached the gate he saw a beggar sitting in the dust before it. The beggar's eyes were closed against the sunlight and a gentle snore proceeded from his nostrils. He was most miserable to look upon in his tatters and his filth; his feet were bruised and bare and the young man looked upon him with compassion.

OTHRAN. Is not this a picture of the ills of man?

NAINA. It is a picture of dirt and laziness.

OTHRAN. I shall speak with him.

NAINA. It will cost you a piece of silver. (*Jogging him with her foot.*) Here – Beggar!

BEGGAR (*waking*). Oh-oo . . .! (*Slipping quickly into his whine.*) Alms, fair lord . . . alms in charity . . .

OTHRAN. There –

BEGGAR. Thank ye –

OTHRAN. Do you find life pleasant, good man?

BEGGAR. Nay. I find it sad and filled with evil. There are too few who give me alms.

OTHRAN. But must you beg by the gate?

BEGGAR. Aye, I must. I cannot work in the fields for my feet are bruised. I have no shoes.

OTHRAN. But are there not shoes a-plenty in Ephranor?

BEGGAR. There are many shoes, but the miserly cobbler keeps them upon his shelves and will not give me even the poorest of them.

OTHRAN. But if he has many shoes he needs not and you have none, obviously he should give you some. 8

BEGGAR. Obviously. But he will not.

OTHRAN (*softly, with exaltation*). Here we begin.

NAINA (*with sarcasm*). Yes. Here we begin.

OTHRAN. Come, good man. Come with me. We shall reason with this miserly cobbler. We shall get you shoes.

BEGGAR (*leaping up delighted*). Eh? So! . . .

NARRATOR. And the beggar rose and walked with the young man and the slave girl through the streets of Ephranor –

NAINA. See with what alacrity he trots beside you now, shoeless and all!

NARRATOR. And there were many shoeless in the streets who, seeing the beggar walking by the side of the young lord, came up to him.

CAST. (*Street voices, beginning to grow.*)

SHOELESS 1 (*confidentially*). Where d'ye go?

BEGGAR (*same*). We go to the cobbler. This lord will get me shoes.

SHOELESS 1 (*lifting up a wail*). But I too lack shoes!

OTHRAN. Come you also with us, good man.

VOICES. And I – And I – And I –

OTHRAN. Come you all with us.

CAST. (*Eager voices joining in. Gathering crowd moving along street.*)

NARRATOR. So the young man and the tattered maid come to the cobbler with a multitude of eager shoeless following behind. And the cobbler came out of his shop, amazed and blinking in the sunlight.

COBBLER. What is this riot?

OTHRAN. Be not alarmed, good cobbler. We come to speak to you of shoes.

COBBLER. Ah!

8. Watch for the repetition of the word "obviously" throughout the play. Be prepared to suggest why the dramatist repeats it.

OTHRAN. Here, cobbler, are many shoeless feet. And in your shop are many idle shoes. Is this not obviously wrong?

COBBLER. Obviously.

OTHRAN. Then would it not be well to put these idle shoes upon these shoeless feet that both might serve as they are intended?

COBBLER. True. But having shod the shoeless without gold, where am I to get hides to make more shoes? And how am I to live? Obviously these have nothing to share with me save their poverty and wretchedness.

OTHRAN. Are there not many idle hides in Ephranor?

COBBLER. Many indeed.

OTHRAN. Then let us go to the tanners and get them.

COBBLER. Agreed. But first I will lock my shop lest the shoeless serve themselves before I am served.

NAINA (*scornful laugh*). Truly, we shall be a multitude now, when all the cobblers have joined us!

NARRATOR. And truly they became a large body hastening through the streets of Ephranor as the other cobblers, seeing their brother walking with the young man, spoke to him.

COBBLER 2 (*confidentially*). Where d'ye go?

COBBLER (*same*). I go with the young lord to the tanner. He will get me hides.

COBBLER 2 (*lifting up a wail*). But I too am a cobbler.

OTHRAN. Come you too, good cobbler.

VOICES. And I – And I – And I –

OTHRAN. Come you all with us.

NAINA. (*Laughs sarcastically.*)

CAST. (*Sounds of swelling crowd.*)

NARRATOR. Now they came to the place of the tanner, who emerged, blinking, into the sunlight; and the young man, scorning to hold his kerchief to his nose (for was not the

9. This is the second time this sequence of dialogue from "Where d'ye go?" to "Come you all with us" has been used. Why does the playwright repeat it?
10. Why would it be natural for the young man to hold his kerchief to his nose?

tanner also his brother?) spoke to him –

OTHRAN. Good tanner, we are come here for hides.

TANNER. Good. How many will ye buy?

OTHRAN. It is not gold and silver we deal in. It is justice and reason. Here are cobblers needing hides and shoeless needing shoes; and many hides lie baled in idleness upon your floor. Is this not obviously wrong?

TANNER. Obviously, but if I give away my hides where am I to get more? The rich man who owns the cattle whose skins I tan will not give me them for smiles.

OTHRAN. Let us go to the rich man and demonstrate that he should give the skins of his cattle to you.

TANNER. Agreed! But first I will lock my shop.

CAST. (*Rising commotion of crowd's moving.*)

TANNER 2 (*confidentially*). Where d'ye go with the young lord?

TANNER (*same*). To the rich man. This lord will get me skins.

TANNER 2 (*lifting up a wail*). But I too am a tanner!

OTHRAN. Come you too.

VOICES. And I – And I – And I –

OTHRAN. Come you all.

NAINA (*her whistling has been heard background*). Aye, come you all. Let us have a great march of fools while the sun shines.

CAST. (*Crowd noises swelling.*)

NARRATOR. And so they came as last, the young man and the slave girl, the shoeless and the cobblers and the tanners of Ephranor, to the manor house of the rich farmer. And the farmer turned from the contemplation of his cows and came from his fields, blinking at the multitude that raised a dust in the road.

FARMER. Good day, young lord. Does this stinking rabble follow you?

NAINA (*laughing*). There is one at least will believe his own nose!

OTHRAN. They do, good farmer. And they are no rabble.

They are honest men all, the shoeless and the cobblers and the tanners, and they have come to you for the skins of cattle.

FARMER. So?

OTHRAN. Here are many tanners to tan hides, and many cobblers to make shoes, and many shoeless feet to wear them; yet the hides remain upon the backs of these fat and idle cattle. Is this not obviously wrong?

NARRATOR. "Obviously," said the farmer, for he did not consult his cattle –

FARMER. Obviously. But if I am to give my cattle without return, whence shall I have gold to pay the lord, my Suzerain, who watches over his tithe of my wealth with a jealous eye?

OTHRAN. And has he need of the tithe?

FARMER. How can he have need – he with his great house and many lands and much gold?

OTHRAN. Then let us go to him and ask that he remit the tithe.

FARMER. Willingly, for I am anxious that justice be done in the world. First I will lock the gates of my fields and set men to watch my cattle. Then we will go.

NAINA. (*Commences whistling. Into –*)

CAST. (*Rising commotion of multitude moving off.*)

NARRATOR. So they moved off again, though with some grumbling of impatience among the shoeless who found the road hard. And word went about among the farmers of Ephranor that tithes were to be remitted and they made haste to join the multitude; and the butchers and tallow-makers of the land hearing that the skins of cattle should be henceforth free said, "Why not also the meat and the tallow, for are not these also of the animals?" – and they too made haste to join; until, approaching the castle of the Suzerain, it was a multitude winding like a great snake along the road between the fields. And at the head of all marched the young man and the girl Naina.

11. Suzerain: a feudal overlord, entitled to a tithe, or a tenth part of the wealth of his tenant-farmers.

NAINA (*sarcastic*). Of a truth there has not been such a holiday in Ephranor since the hanging of the Bad King, and that I do not remember.

OTHRAN (*joyfully*). Is it not as I said?

NAINA. *What* did you say, wise one?

OTHRAN. That the ills of man and the remedies therefor are simple and obvious and that men will mend them when they know.

NAINA. Oh, obviously.

OTHRAN. Look back upon the multitudes. See how joyful are their faces.

NAINA. They seem dirty and greedy as ever to me.

OTHRAN. You are an ignorant slave girl.

NAINA. True. And I would not trade brains with you.

(MUSIC: *Pipes or flute distantly playing a gay air. Cued above.*) 12

NAINA. Aha, the minstrels join us. They are never the ones to miss a good rout.

OTHRAN. Let them come. It is well that there should be music this day. (*Calling.*) Play on, minstrels!

(MUSIC: *Pipes come up over the crowd sounds playing a gay air. Background.*)

NARRATOR. And so in a great and joyful train with flutes playing, the multitude came into the courtyard of the Suzerain. The great gate of the castle was thrown wide, heralds raised their trumpets.

(MUSIC: *Flourish of trumpets.*)

NARRATOR. And the lord, with his retinue attending, came graciously to greet them.

CAST. (*Sigh of respectful admiration from the crowd.*)

12. Cued above: This means that the gay air of the pipes or flute was heard, faintly at first, as background music for some of the preceding speeches.

LORD (*slightly off*). Greetings to you, good people. And you, young stranger, why are you come at the head of this multitude?

OTHRAN. My lord, there are many shoeless who seek shoes from many cobblers who seek hides from many tanners who seek skins from many farmers –

BUTCHER (*off*). And we are butchers who seek meat –

TALLOWMAKER (*off*). And we are tallow-makers who seek tallow –

OTHRAN. Yes, and butchers and tallow-makers too, who seek these things from those who have them and cannot give them, because they must pay tithes to you who need them not. Is this not obviously wrong?

LORD. Obviously. But my revenues are sacred to me in that they are a part of the possessions of the Great King, and no jot nor tittle of them may be abated without his high and gracious permission.

OTHRAN. Then let us go to the Great King that the jots and tittles may be abated and the tithes remitted, and so down the long train the shoeless may at last have shoes.

LORD. Willingly, for I have long seen the justice of the abatement. First let me charge my servants that they guard well my castle, and I and my retinue will join you.

(MUSIC: *Montage of heraldic flourishes and music suggesting movement of great throng.*)

NARRATOR. And now the marching multitude was great and wonderful to look upon as other lords and their retinues, hearing that there was to be an abatement of the King's tribute, hastened to join the march. There was a flourishing of trumpets and a neighing of horses; and as the throng wound through the gate and into the courtyard of the Great King,

13. Slightly off: This indicates that the voice of the Lord *appears* to come from a short distance away.
14. Find the sentences that are parallel to this one in the play. What value has the repetition (a) in the style or shape of the drama, and (b) as a continuing comment on the character of men?

the Land of Ephranor behind them lay empty and deserted in the sunlight, for all were come here. And the knights dismounted and the cobblers and the farmers and the tanners took off their hats, and the shoeless tenderly rubbed their aching toes as, led by the young man and the maid, they entered the great hall and a herald announced them.

(SOUND: *Flourish of trumpets.*)

HERALD (*off; loudly, with echo*). Othran, son of Jobar, with many lords and many farmers and many tanners and cobblers and many shoeless ones, to make petition to the Great King.

(SOUND: *Flourish of trumpets. Soft murmur and shuffling of multitude; reverent.*)

NARRATOR. Thereupon the young man, with the girl Naina, as always hard upon his heels, advanced toward the throne of the Great King. And the multitude crowded breathlessly behind him, the shoeless in the fore, as the Great King spake.

KING. Young stranger, lords and people of Ephranor, we welcome you and give you greeting. You have a petition to make of us?

OTHRAN. We have, great Majesty; a simple thing and soon granted.

KING. Speak –

OTHRAN. Is it not good, Majesty, for a man to have shoes that he may walk in comfort and, forgetful of his feet, reflect on higher things?

KING. It is indeed. It has ever been our fondest wish that our people should reflect upon higher things.

CAST. (*Reverent murmur of appreciation.*)

OTHRAN. Then here, Great Majesty, are many loyal shoeless of your realm, whose feet are worn and in pain and whose thoughts are turned much upon their toes because of this. And they lack shoes while the cobblers, having many shoes which they use not, require hides which the tanners hold and use not, because the farmers have cattle which they keep and use not, because they must pay tithes which the lords demand

and need not, because they must pay revenue to you. Is this not obviously wrong?

KING. Obviously.

CAST. (*Great, relieved, sighing cheer.*)

KING. My lords, the revenues I demand of you should be abated –

LORDS. (*Cheers.*)

KING. Good farmers, you should be free of tithes –

FARMERS. (*Cheers.*)

KING. Tanners, you should have skins; butchers, meat; tallow-makers, tallow –

CAST. (*Cheers.*)

KING. Cobblers, hides –

COBBLERS. (*Cheers.*)

KING. And the shoeless, shoes.

CAST. (*Loud cheers.*)

KING. But . . . (*Pause.*)

CAST. (*Deep groan.*)

KING (*sonorously*). The shoeless and the hideless, the tithes and revenues and all that you seek to change have come down to us from of old, yea, even from the hanging of the Bad King in the time of my grandfather; and clearly, therefore, proceed from the eternal arrangement of the One on high –

CAST. (*Uneasy . . . wordless murmur.*)

NARRATOR. There was a murmuring of the multitude and a great and hairy man among the shoeless, moving closer with his fellows crowded about the throne, muttered –

SHOELESS 1. There are no shoes in *these* words!

KING (*continuing above murmur*). – and therefore, good people, since these are obviously the eternal arrangements of the One on high, to whom alone we may go for redress of earthly evils –

SHOELESS 1 (*over commotion*). Then *go* to him!

KING. (*Stir, gasping groan.*)

CAST. (*Great gasp from multitude.*)

NARRATOR. Then there was a great and horror-stricken gasp within the hall for the mighty and hairy man of the shoeless had stepped forth and thrust his knife into the throat of the King, and the King was dead.

CAST. (*Murmur rising.*)

NARRATOR. And there was an awful sighing and murmur of the stricken multitude in the great hall.

CAST and VOICES (*great sighing and murmur rising*). The King is dead – He has killed the King – The King is dead – (*The murmur rises in volume . . . becomes purposeful.*)

TANNER 2 (*loud; well off*). Make the young lord our King!

BEGGAR. He will give us shoes.

TANNER 2. Make him King.

BUTCHER. He will give us meat.

TALLOWMAKER. And tallow.

VOICES (*growing in volume and numbers*). King! Make him King! – King! Make him King – King! Make him King! (*Grows to great volume. Cut abruptly on final* "Make him King!")

NARRATOR. And thus it was that the young man, who had desired so simple and obvious a good, found himself lifted in sweaty arms and thrust suddenly upon the throne of the King whose blood still dripped in small and spreading beads upon the flags beneath.

(SOUND: *steady drip drip-drop – drip-drop.*)

NARRATOR. But in the land of Ephranor there was great rejoicing, for now the good young lord sat upon the throne and all was well. And the shoeless fell upon the cobblers to take the shoes that were their due, and the cobblers upon the tanners, and the tanners and the butchers and the tallowmakers upon the farmers, and the farmers upon the lords, and since none could agree upon his deserts there was such fire and slaughter as had not been seen since the time of the Bad King. And the young King looked from his palace window and wrung his hands –

(SOUND: *Distant tumult.*)

NARRATOR. – and as the night grew bright with flames the slave girl came running to him.

NAINA (*approaching; breathless, but still sarcastic*). Come, fool.

OTHRAN. Come where?

NAINA. To the hills beyond, if you would live. They are coming to burn the palace and kill you, for you are suddenly become a tyrant who gives no man his deserts.

OTHRAN. But these are they whom I sought to help.

NAINA. Assuredly they are. And they will split your throat and burn your palace down about your ears.

OTHRAN. It is obviously unjust.

NAINA. Obviously. Now do you come, or do I go alone?

OTHRAN. You are an ignorant slave.

NAINA. Look from this window.

CAST. (*Distant – approaching tumult; shouts*: Kill the tyrant. Kill the tyrant.)

OTHRAN. They *do* come – with torches and knives and spears.

NAINA. Obviously. Come – they are at the gate –

(SOUND: *Clatter and banging upon iron gate. Crash of stones and missiles.*)

OTHRAN (*fading*). It is not reasonable . . .

(SOUND/CAST: *Tumult and voices and shouts rise to big volume. Crash of doors. Sounds of flame. Whole mélange rises to big volume. Fades into sounds of birds and flowing water.*)

NARRATOR. They fled by night from the multitude up the wooded paths of the hills and flung themselves down at last by a little stream. And with morning they looked far below to see the burning city of Ephranor and the army of great lords gathering to quell the tumult. The face of the young man, looking upon these things, was pale and grave, and there was a bloody gash upon his temple and cheek where one had struck him with a stone as he fled. Naina, the girl, watched too and turned to him at length.

NAINA. So now Master Mend-the-World, who is the wise one of us?

OTHRAN (*wearily*). Peace, girl.

NAINA. Have you sufficiently played the ass, or would you meddle again with the ways of men?

OTHRAN. I will meddle no more.

NAINA. I do not believe it. For the folly is a disease and he who is touched with it dies in it.

OTHRAN (*pathetically*). But I do not understand! It –

NAINA. So! You grow wiser at last. There is something you do not understand.

NARRATOR. He moved his hands mutely under the lash of her tongue and looked again upon the burning city. And suddenly she did a very strange and womanly thing.

NAINA. (*Sobs.*)

NARRATOR. She flung her arms about his neck and kissed his bleeding cheek so that her own lips were red with the trickle of his blood.

NAINA (*sobbing*). Do not look so! Do not look upon them ever again. You are worth ten thousand of them. Nay, the whole Land of Ephranor is not worth the little finger of your hand! . . . (*Sobs fade under.*)

NARRATOR. But he still looked sadly, though not so sadly as before, upon the flames beneath; and he put his arm about her as he looked and comforted her in her weeping.

NAINA. (*Sobbing in a little. Fade out under.*)

NARRATOR. And the lords in council among the ruins of Ephranor, having quelled the tumult, spoke together, saying:

LORD. It is well that the tyrant is fled and many of the shoeless hanged and all shall be again as it was.

LORD 2. True. I grieve that the tyrant was not hanged and flayed and dragged through the streets as an example and terror to all. Yet, notwithstanding, we shall have peace.

LORD 3. But it is a true and obvious thing and one we have always known, and needful to the peace of the realm, that all men should henceforth go with shoes upon their feet. Let it be so. On pain of death.

LORDS (*sonorously together*). Let it be so. On pain of death.

NARRATOR. And it was so. The young man and the girl,

Naina, made their way wearily among the hills, hiding by day from those that pursued and travelling footsore by night, for now their own shoes were worn from their feet. And still the girl was of a sharp tongue, but it had a pleasanter sound.

NAINA. Come now, my great fool. They have given over seeking us. We go home to the hermit.

OTHRAN. Why?

NAINA. That we may be married and beget us some more fine fools, unlike their father, that must be kicked onward in spite of themselves, for whom better men die and are spit upon for dying.

OTHRAN. (*Sighs.*)

NARRATOR. And they came at last by long and devious ways to the hermit. The news of their journey had come to him ahead of them and he looked upon their weary, tattered figures with a mocking squint.

HALGOR (*crunch*). So. You are back.

OTHRAN (*dejected*). Aye, master. And now I understand that which you told me on the first day. All men are but clods of earth.

HALGOR. (*Cru-runch – Pause.*)

NARRATOR. Again as on the first day there was a silence. Then the unreasonable old man bent again and taking up a clod of earth held it closely first to his own ear and then to the ear of the young man.

HALGOR. Listen. D'ye hear anything?

OTHRAN. No, master.

HALGOR. You will. Earth it is and earth is man. Muck of the muck. Slime of the slime. But there is a sound of growing in it: a breaking open of seeds that is like the breaking of hearts; a slow and very quiet sound, and only a lifetime is long enough to hear it in.

NAINA (*gently*). Rest you now.

15. This is an important speech. Discuss the comment that is made in it on the two kinds of men who comprise the human race.

HALGOR (*gentle chuckle*). Aye, rest. Have ye not done well? In all the land of Ephranor there is today but one shoeless 16
man, and that is you.

16. Why is this a good "curtain" line?

MORE LIGHT ON RADIO DRAMA

Reading the play will add to your knowledge and appreciation of the art of radio drama. You will remember that in the introduction to *The Odyssey of Runyon Jones* we spoke of the problem of identifying the characters by their voices alone. In *The Land of Ephranor,* the problem is met head-on at the beginning of the play: the three chief characters and the Narrator tell us who they are. Then the Narrator introduces Othran's father: ". . . his foolish father marvelled, saying". Later he identifies in turn the other minor characters: Beggar, Cobbler, Tanner, Farmer, Lord, and King. As for the remaining characters – beggars, cobblers, and so forth – they are not individualized; we know them only as members of the crowd. The three Lords who proclaim the end of the rebellion and promise shoes for all are stronger for their chorus-like impersonality.

When the telling of the story is complicated with many scenes and characters, most radio writers use a narrator; this is the case in *The Land of Ephranor.* (A narrator is not necessary in *The Odyssey of Runyon Jones,* as we have seen, because it is largely a series of duologues.) The Narrator's voice and mood are easily differentiated from those of the other chief characters. He is a story-teller; they are actors. Moreover the two men are differentiated from him in age – one younger and one older – and the girl is easily recognized. He himself identifies all the other characters, as has been noted above.

Sounds are as important as they are in *The Odyssey of Runyon Jones.* Indeed, the story is almost told in sound: the mountain echo, Halgor's cackling and crunching, the shuffling and murmuring of the crowd building to the great climax with trumpets in the hall, the gasp from the multitude, the shouts for the new King, the tumult, the battering at the gates, Naina's sobs, and Halgor's cackling and crunching again to end the tale.

There is little background music, apart from the opening and closing theme, Naina's whistling, and the music of the minstrels in the "great march of fools". But musical *sounds* are effective under the descriptive passages, especially Othran's journey to the mountain, in which we hear the cries of birds, the sound of waterfalls, and the tinkle of cowbells. The most startling and effective of the transitions, or bridges, is the one in which the sounds of doors crashing and flames crackling fade into those of birds singing and water flowing.

Finally, *The Land of Ephranor*, like *The Odyssey of Runyon Jones*, affords proof that radio drama is an ideal medium for fantasy. It imposes no limits on the imagination of the writer. From the mountain heights many lands are spread out before us; we dare "the fordings of harsh waters"; we almost hear the "breaking open of seeds that is like the breaking of hearts".

PERFORMING THE PLAY

The suggestions made for performing *The Odyssey of Runyon Jones* will be helpful in presenting this play. If it is given a radio production the Narrator should, as far as possible, have one microphone, the actors another, and the crowd the third or sound-effects microphone. Music for the theme and the minstrels can be selected and played on a tape recorder or record player; many of the sound effects (such as trumpet calls and bird songs) are also available on records. Your actors will have to work hard to achieve the crowd sounds: the shuffling, sighing, murmuring, shouting, gasping, and final tumult.

It would be interesting to perform the play as if it were a stage production. The Narrator should remain at a lectern throughout. The dying father can speak from a sick man's chair. Othran can travel around the auditorium or classroom aisles on his way to the mountain, to the accompaniment of bird songs and the sound of cowbells. Halgor and Naina can be on a platform or on a desk or table. Othran and Naina can make the journey to Ephranor by the roundabout route. The Beggar, the Cobbler's shop, the Tanner's place, the manor house, the castle, and the great hall of the King can be stations on their progress – with the big staging effects saved for the King's death and the escape of Othran and Naina. Then would come the journey in reverse back to the mountain.

The important thing, whether presenting the play as a radio or stage performance, is to remember Joseph Schull's admonition that the mood should be one of gaiety: "The lighter the touch and the simpler the staging, the better." The performance should be in the mood of the musical theme: "light, pastoral, ironic".

THINKING ABOUT THE PLAY

1. According to Halgor, what is one way to have men call you a wise man?
2. How do we identify Halgor as he speaks?
3. Why does the author suggest that the Herald's voice, in the hall of the King, should be heard "off" loudly, with echo?
4. Where is the climax of the play? Is it the moment of the King's death, or the escape of Othran and Naina, or the moment when Othran begins to learn wisdom and humility, and Naina is at last kind to him? Or have you another suggestion? Give reasons to support the choice you make.
5. Othran's idea is a sensible one: to find some way (as the economists say) to increase purchasing power. Has the modern welfare state found a way to give shoes to the beggar?
6. In his plea to the King, Othran asks for shoes for the people, so that they could walk in comfort and "reflect on higher things". What is your opinion of this? Once a man has shoes and can walk in comfort does he necessarily "reflect on higher things"? What about the young people in *Nobody Waved Good-bye*? On the other hand, is it possible to reflect on higher things *without shoes*?

A MARRIAGE PROPOSAL

ANTON CHEKHOV

English Version by

BARRETT H. CLARK

and

HILMAR BAUKAGE

COMEDY OF COURTSHIP

A Marriage Proposal is a comedy of courtship in old Russia. It is a happy play, full of hearty laughter. The characters are broadly drawn, as is fitting in a comedy which is almost a farce. Natalia is the most natural of them – a pleasant, robust girl, spirited and proud of her possessions. Lomov, the nervous suitor, who suffers from palpitations of the heart, is well-nigh a caricature (a ridiculous cartoon or drawing of a real person). So also is the temperamental old father. We can imagine both of them in a comic strip.

When playing the roles enter into the spirit of the lines with great zest. Over-play the parts. Remember that the Russians are warm-hearted and easily excited. In the climaxes shout and stamp about in a colossal rage. Enjoy yourself mightily while you do this, but remember to keep a straight face and *appear* to be in deadly earnest. Nothing marks an inexperienced actor so definitely as to see him smile when his audience laughs.

We enjoy Lomov because he is a bashful suitor unable to bring himself to the point of a proposal. The unexpected and comic development in this play is that in the course of two attempts to propose he is drawn into a quarrel with the lady of his choice. Even in the final moment of the play, when they have kissed and the bargain is made, we know that another happy brawl is about to begin.

We are amused at Lomov also because of his heart palpitations and other physical infirmities. Yet although he seems near to collapsing, he is a redoubtable warrior in a quarrel. Natalia, too, is a game fighter, and we enjoy seeing them squabble and storm at one another. Tschubukov blusters and struts about. He is pompous and domineering. Yet he is a likeable character. Indeed, we do not laugh *at* any of them. Although they are little more than types, the author has drawn them with sufficient understanding and sympathy to make us like them.

The simpler the scenery for the play the better. It is interesting and effective to stylize the setting. Have the door up centre. It can be simply a break in your curtains. Down centre, place a couch or a bench. Equally distant from this, down right and down left, put two chairs. Natalia can use the chair down right; her father, the chair down left; Lomov the centre bench. In the quarrel, father and daughter should march up and down, and to the extreme right and left, angrily, returning to threaten Lomov, down centre. This parallel movement, if well executed, is always amusing. When Natalia returns before the second quarrel she should sit on the bench with Lomov.

Lighting should be bright for this comedy, as for all comedies.

The quarrels begin in an atmosphere of elaborate courtesy and friendliness. The two lovers edge into them in gingerly fashion. First they are polite. Then they are firm. Yet still they smile. Then the smiles stop. Anger begins to colour their voices. Then they are moved to righteous indignation and to sharp reproof. Finally the wave of temper sweeps up to the climax of shouting and violent movement. In each of the two quarrels the build-up to the climax should be carefully planned. The actors should hold something back. They should not let themselves go completely until the biggest moment.

When Lomov leaves the room Natalia storms at him, joining with her father to call him all the names under the sun. Then she learns that he has come to propose. Immediately she collapses, and like a child that has lost its temper, cries and kicks her feet against the chair and works herself into a tantrum of rage. Lomov returns. Instantly there is a transformation in her manner. She is gentle and friendly to him. But this does not last long. The second quarrel is soon on its merry way.

An effective closing picture is made by having the father stand on the centre sofa or bench, upstage of and above the two quarrelling lovers, trying to drown them out with his shouting as he calls for champagne.

The play impresses us as being easily written by a sure craftsman of the theatre. There is no straining after effect. It builds cheerfully, even gaily, to its climaxes in the two quarrels and the final amusing curtain.

Take your places for *A Marriage Proposal.* Be good Russians for this half-hour, and enjoy yourselves immensely.

CHARACTERS

STEPAN STEPANOVITCH TSCHUBUKOV, *a country farmer*
NATALIA STEPANOVNA, *his daughter (aged twenty-five)*
IVAN VASSILIYITCH LOMOV, *Tschubukov's neighbour*

A MARRIAGE PROPOSAL

SCENE: *The reception room in* TSCHUBUKOV'*s home.* TSCHUBUKOV *discovered as the curtain rises.*

(*Enter* LOMOV, *wearing a dress-suit.*)

TSCHUB. (*going toward him and greeting him*). Who is this I see? My dear fellow! Ivan Vassiliyitch! I'm so glad to see you! (*Shakes hands.*) But this is a surprise! How are you?

LOMOV. Thank you! And how are you?

TSCHUB. Only so-so, my friend. Please sit down. It isn't right to forget one's neighbour. Now tell me, why all this ceremony? Dress clothes, white gloves, and all? Are you on your way to some engagement, my good fellow?

LOMOV. I have no engagement except with you, Stepan Stepanovitch.

TSCHUB. But why in evening clothes, my friend? This isn't New Year's.

LOMOV. You see, it's simply this, that – (*Composing himself.*) I have come to you, Stepan Stepanovitch, to trouble you with a request. It is not the first time I have had the honour of turning to you for assistance, and you have always, that is – I beg your pardon, I am a bit excited! I'll take a drink of water first, dear Stepan Stepanovitch. (*He drinks.*)

TSCHUB. (*aside*). He's come to borrow money! I won't give him any! (*To* LOMOV.) What is it, then, my dear Lomov?

LOMOV. You see – dear – Stepanovitch, pardon me, Stepan – Stepan – dearvitch – I mean – I am terribly nervous, as you will be so good as to see –. What I mean to say – you are the only one who can help me, though I don't deserve it, and – and I have no right whatever to make this request of you.

TSCHUB. Don't beat about the bush, my dear fellow. Tell me!

LOMOV. Immediately – in a moment. Here it is, then: I have come to ask for the hand of your daughter, Natalia Stepanovna.

TSCHUB. (*joyfully*). Angel Ivan Vassiliyitch! Say that once again! I didn't quite hear it!

LOMOV. I have the honour to beg –

TSCHUB. (*interrupting*). My dear, dear man! I am so happy that everything is so – everything! (*Embraces and kisses him.*) I have wanted this to happen for so long. It has been my dearest wish! (*He represses a tear.*) And I have always loved you, my dear fellow, as my own son! May God give you His blessings and His grace and – I always wanted it to happen. But why am I standing here like a blockhead? I am completely dumbfounded with pleasure, completely dumbfounded. My whole being – I'll call Natalia.

LOMOV. Dear Stepan Stepanovitch, what do you think? May I hope for Natalia Stepanovna's acceptance?

TSCHUB. A fine boy like you – and you think she won't accept you in a flash! Lovesick as a cat and all that! (*He goes out, right.*)

LOMOV. I'm cold. My body is trembling as though I were going to take my examination! But the chief thing is to settle matters! If a person meditates too much, or hesitates, or talks

1. This aside is spoken while Lomov goes to a table or bureau upstage to pour himself a drink of water.
2. It is a custom in some European countries in moments of greeting or affection for men to embrace, and to kiss on both cheeks.

about it, waits for an ideal or for true love, he never gets it. Brrr! It's cold! Natalia is an excellent housekeeper, not bad-looking, well educated – what more could I ask? I am so excited my ears are roaring! (*He drinks water.*) It would be a mistake not to marry, that would never do! In the first place, I'm thirty-five – a critical age, you might say. In the second place, I must live a well-regulated life. I have a weak heart, continual palpitations; I am very sensitive and always getting excited. My lips tremble and the pulse in my right temple throbs terribly. But the worst of all is the problem of sleep! I hardly lie down and begin to doze before something in my left side begins to pull and tug, and something else begins to hammer in my left shoulder – and in my head, too! I jump up like a madman, walk about a little, lie down again, but the moment I fall asleep I have a terrible cramp in the side. And so it goes all night long!

(*Enter* NATALIA STEPANOVNA.)

NATALIA. Ah! It's you. Papa said to go in; there was a dealer in there who'd come to buy something. Good afternoon, Ivan Vassiliyitch.

LOMOV. Good day, my dear Natalia Stepanovna.

NATALIA. You must pardon me for wearing my apron and this old dress; we are working today. Why don't you come oftener to see us? You've not been here for so long! Sit down. (*They sit down.*) Won't you have something to eat?

LOMOV. Thank you, I have just had lunch.

NATALIA. Smoke, do; there are the matches. Today it is beautiful and only yesterday it rained so hard that the workmen couldn't do a stroke of work. How many bricks have you [3] cut? Think of it; I was so anxious that I had the whole field mowed, and now I'm sorry, because I'm afraid the hay will rot. It would have been better if I had waited. But what on earth is this? You are in evening clothes! The latest cut! Are you on your way to a ball? And you seem to be looking better than

3. The clay in some of the meadows was suitable for making bricks.

usual, too – really. Why are you dressed up so gorgeously?

LOMOV (*excitedly*). You see, my dear Natalia Stepanovna – it's simply this: I have decided to ask you to listen to me – of course, it will be a surprise, and indeed you'll be angry, but I – (*aside*). How fearfully cold it is!

NATALIA. What is it? (*A pause.*) Well?

LOMOV. I'll try to be brief. My dear Natalia Stepanovna, as you know, for many years – since my childhood, I have had the honour to know your family. My poor aunt and her husband, from whom, as you know, I inherited the estate, always had the greatest respect for your father and your poor mother. The Lomovs and the Tschubukovs have been for decades on the friendliest, indeed the closest, terms with each other, and furthermore my property, as you know, adjoins your own. If you will be so good as to remember, my meadows touch your birch woods.

NATALIA. Pardon the interruption. You said "my meadows" – but are they yours?

LOMOV. Yes, they belong to me.

NATALIA. What nonsense! The meadows belong to us – not to you.

LOMOV. No, to me! Now, my dear Natalia Stepanovna!

NATALIA. Well, that is certainly news to me. How do they belong to you?

LOMOV. How! I am speaking of the meadows lying between your birch woods and my brick-earth.

NATALIA. Yes, exactly. They belong to us.

LOMOV. No, you are mistaken, my dear Natalia Stepanovna, they belong to me.

NATALIA. Try to remember exactly, Ivan Vassiliyitch. Is it so long ago that you inherited them?

LOMOV. Long ago. As far back as I can remember they have always belonged to us.

NATALIA. But that isn't true! You'll pardon my saying so

LOMOV. It is all a matter of record, my dear Natalia Stepanovna. It is true, at one time the title of the meadows was disputed, but now everyone knows they belong to me. There is no room for discussion. Be so good as to listen: my aunt's grandmother put these meadows at the disposal of your father's grandfather's peasants for a certain time while they were making bricks for my grandmother. These people used the meadows free of cost for about forty years, living there as they would on their property. Later, however, when –

NATALIA. There's not a word of truth in that. My grandfather, and my great-grandfather, too, knew that their estate reached back to the swamp, so that the meadows belong to us. What further discussion can there be? I can't understand; it is really most annoying.

LOMOV. I'll show you the papers, Natalia Stepanovna.

NATALIA. No, either you are joking, or trying to lead me into argument. That's not at all nice! We have owned this property for nearly three hundred years, and now all at once we learn that it doesn't belong to us. Ivan Vassiliyitch, you will pardon me, but I really can't believe my ears. So far as I am concerned, the meadows are worth very little. In all they don't contain more than five acres and they are worth only a few hundred roubles, say three hundred, but the injustice of the thing is what affects me. Say what you will, I can't bear injustice.

LOMOV. Only listen until I have finished, please! The peasants of your respected father's grandfather, as I have already had the honour to tell you, baked bricks for my grandmother. My aunt's grandmother wished to do them a favour –

NATALIA. Grandfather! Grandmother! Aunt! I know nothing about them. All I know is that the meadows belong to us, and that ends the matter.

LOMOV. No, they belong to me!

NATALIA. And if you keep on explaining it for two days, and put on five suits of evening clothes, the meadows are still ours, ours, ours! I don't want to take your property, but I refuse to give up what belongs to us!

LOMOV. Natalia Stepanovna, I don't need the meadows, I am only concerned with the principle. If you are agreeable, I beg of you, accept them as a gift from me!

NATALIA. But I can give them to you, because they belong to me! Until now we have considered you a good neighbour and friend; only last year we lent you our threshing machine so that we couldn't thresh until November, and now you treat us like thieves! You offer to give me my own land. Excuse me, but neighbours don't treat each other that way. In my opinion, it's a very low trick – to speak frankly –

LOMOV. So I'm a usurper, am I? My dear lady, I have never appropriated other people's property, and I shall permit no one to accuse me of such a thing! (*He goes quickly to the bottle and drinks water.*) The meadows are mine!

NATALIA. That's not the truth! They are mine!

LOMOV. Mine!

NATALIA. I'll prove it to you! This afternoon I'll send my reapers into the meadows.

LOMOV. W–h–a–t?

NATALIA. My reapers will be there today!

LOMOV. And I'll chase them off!

NATALIA. If you dare!

LOMOV. The meadows are mine, you understand? Mine!

NATALIA. Really, you needn't scream so! If you want to scream and snort and rage you may do it at home, but here please remain within the limits of common decency.

LOMOV. My dear lady, if it weren't that I were suffering from palpitation of the heart and hammering of the arteries in my temples, I would deal with you very differently! (*In a loud voice.*) The meadows belong to me!

NATALIA. Us!

LOMOV. Me!

(*Enter* TSCHUBUKOV, *right.*)

TSCHUB. What's going on here? What is he yelling about?

NATALIA. Papa, please tell this gentleman to whom the meadows belong, to us or to him?

4. These three words – scream, snort, and rage – indicate the violent action Chekhov expected from his actors.

TSCHUB. (*to* LOMOV). My dear fellow, the meadows are ours.

LOMOV. But merciful heavens, Stepan Stepanovitch, how do you make that out? You at least might be reasonable. My aunt's grandmother allowed the use of the meadows free of cost to your grandfather's peasants; the peasants lived on the land for forty years and used it as their own, but later when –

TSCHUB. Permit me, my dear friend. You forget that your grandmother's peasants never paid, because there had been a lawsuit over the meadows, and everyone knows that the meadows belong to us. You haven't looked at the map.

LOMOV. I'll prove to you that they belong to me!

TSCHUB. Don't try to prove it, my dear fellow.

LOMOV. I will!

TSCHUB. My good fellow, what are you shrieking about? You can't prove anything by yelling, you know. I don't ask for anything that belongs to you, nor do I intend to give up anything of my own. Why should I? If it has gone so far, my dear man, that you really intend to claim the meadows, I'd rather give them to the peasants than to you, and I certainly shall!

LOMOV. I can't believe it! By what right can you give away property that doesn't belong to you?

TSCHUB. You must allow me to decide what I am to do with my own land! I'm not accustomed, young man, to having people address me in that tone of voice. I, young man, am twice your age, and I beg you to address me respectfully.

LOMOV. No! No! You think I am a fool! You're making fun of me! You call my property yours and expect me to stand quietly by and talk to you like a human being. That isn't the way a good neighbour behaves, Stepan Stepanovitch! You are no neighbour, you're no better than a landgrabber. That's what you are!

TSCHUB. Wh–at? What did you say?

NATALIA. Papa, send the reapers into the meadows this minute!

TSCHUB. (*to* LOMOV). What was that you said, sir?

NATALIA. The meadows belong to us and I won't give them

up. I won't give them up! I won't give them up!

LOMOV. We'll see about that! I'll prove in court that they belong to me.

TSCHUB. In court! You may sue in court, sir, if you like! I know you – you are only waiting to find an excuse to go to law. You're an intriguer, that's what you are! Your whole family were always looking for quarrels. The whole lot of them!

LOMOV. Kindly refrain from insulting my family. The entire race of Lomov has always been honourable! And never has one been brought to trial for embezzlement, as your dear uncle was!

TSCHUB. And the whole Lomov family were insane!

NATALIA. Every one of them!

TSCHUB. Your grandmother was a dipsomaniac, and your aunt, Nastasia Michailovna, ran off with an architect.

LOMOV. Your mother limped. (*He puts his hand over his heart.*) Oh, my side pains! My temples are bursting! Lord in Heaven! Water!

TSCHUB. And your dear father was a gambler and a glutton!

NATALIA. And your aunt was a gossip like few others!

LOMOV. And you are an intriguer. Oh, my heart! And it's an open secret that you cheated at the elections – my eyes are blurred! Where is my hat?

NATALIA. Oh, how low! Liar! Disgusting thing!

LOMOV. Where's the hat? My heart! Where shall I go? Where is the door? Oh – I feel – I'm dying! I can't – my legs won't hold me – (*Goes to the door.*)

TSCHUB. (*following him*). May you never darken my door again!

5. Dipsomaniac: a person with an insatiable craving for alcohol.
6. Lomov's hat might be on the table or bureau upstage with the water pitcher, or it might be on a second one, exactly the same in appearance, on the opposite side of the stage, so that the setting like much of the movement, might be balanced, as suggested in the introduction.

NATALIA. Bring suit! We'll see!

(LOMOV *staggers out, centre.*)

TSCHUB. (*angrily*). Huh!

NATALIA. Good-for-nothing! What he says about being good neighbours!

TSCHUB. Loafer! Monster!

NATALIA. A swindler like that takes over a piece of property that doesn't belong to him and then dares argue about it!

TSCHUB. And to think that this fool dares to make a proposal of marriage.

NATALIA. A proposal of marriage?

TSCHUB. He came here to make you a proposal of marriage.

NATALIA. Why didn't you tell me?

TSCHUB. That's why he had on his evening clothes! The poor fool!

NATALIA. Proposal for me? Oh! (*Falls into an armchair and groans.*) Bring him back! Bring him back!

TSCHUB. Bring who back?

NATALIA. Faster, faster, I'm sinking! Bring him back! (*She becomes hysterical.*)

TSCHUB. What's wrong with you? (*His hands to his head.*) I'm cursed with bad luck! I'll shoot myself! I'll hang myself!

NATALIA. Bring him back!

TSCHUB. In a minute! Don't bawl! (*He rushes out, centre.*)

NATALIA (*groaning*). What have they done to me? Bring him back! Bring him back!

TSCHUB. (*comes running in*). He's coming at once, devil take him! Talk to him yourself, I can't.

NATALIA (*groaning*). Bring him back!

TSCHUB. He's coming, I tell you. Oh Lord! I'll cut my throat. I really will cut my throat. We've argued with the fellow, insulted him and now, we've thrown him out – and you did it all, you!

NATALIA. No, you! You have no manners, you are brutal. If it weren't for you, he wouldn't have gone!

TSCHUB. Oh yes, I'm to blame! If I shoot or hang myself,

remember *you'll* be to blame. You forced me to. (LOMOV *appears in the doorway.*) There, talk to him yourself! (*He goes out.*)

LOMOV. Terrible palpitation! My leg is lamed! My side hurts me!

NATALIA. Pardon us, we were angry, Ivan Vassiliyitch. I remember now – the meadows really belong to you.

LOMOV. My heart is beating terribly! My meadows – my eyelids tremble – (*They sit down.*) We were wrong. It was only the principle of the thing – the property isn't worth much to me, but the principle is worth a great deal.

NATALIA. Exactly, but let us talk about something else.

LOMOV. Because I have proofs that my aunt's grandmother had, with the peasants of your good father –

NATALIA. Enough, enough. Are you going hunting soon?

LOMOV. Yes, respected Natalia Stepanovna. I expect to begin after the harvest. Oh, did you hear? My dog, Ugadi, you know him – well, he limps!

NATALIA. What a shame! How did that happen?

LOMOV. I don't know. Perhaps it's a dislocation, or maybe he was bitten by another dog. (*He sighs.*) The best dog I ever had – to say nothing of his price! I paid Mironov a hundred and twenty-five roubles for him.

NATALIA. That was too much, Ivan Vassiliyitch.

LOMOV. In my opinion it was very cheap. A wonderful dog!

NATALIA. Papa paid eighty-five for his Otkatai, and Otkatai is much better than your Ugadi.

LOMOV. Really? What an idea! Otkatai better than Ugadi!

NATALIA. Of course he is better. True, Otkatai is still young, he isn't full-grown yet, but in the pack or on the leash with two or three, there is no better than he, even –

LOMOV. I really beg your pardon, Natalia Stepanovna, but you quite overlook the fact that he has a short lower jaw, and a dog with a short lower jaw can't snap.

NATALIA. Short lower jaw? That's the first I ever heard of that!

LOMOV. I assure you, his lower jaw is shorter than the upper.

NATALIA. Have you measured it?

LOMOV. I have measured it. He is good at running, though.

NATALIA. In the first place our Otkatai is pure-bred, a full-blooded son of Sapragavas and Stameskis, and as for your mongrel, nobody could ever figure out his pedigree; he's old and ugly, and as skinny as an old hag.

LOMOV. Old, certainly! I wouldn't take five of your Otkatais for him! Ugadi is a dog and Otkatai is – it is laughable to argue about it! Dogs like your Otkatai can be found by the dozens at any dog dealer's, a whole pound-full!

NATALIA. Ivan Vassiliyitch, you are very contrary today. First our meadows belong to you and then Ugadi is better than Otkatai. I don't like it when a person doesn't say what he really thinks. You know perfectly well that Otkatai is a hundred times better than your silly Ugadi. What makes you keep on saying he isn't?

LOMOV. I can see, Natalia Stepanovna, that you consider me either a blind man or a fool. But at least you must admit that Otkatai has a short lower jaw!

NATALIA. It isn't so.

LOMOV. Yes, a short lower jaw!

NATALIA. It's not so!

LOMOV. What makes you scream, my dear lady?

NATALIA. What makes you talk such nonsense? It is high time that Ugadi was shot, and yet you presume to compare him with Otkatai!

LOMOV. Pardon me, but I can't carry on this argument any longer. I have palpitation of the heart!

NATALIA. I have always noticed that the hunters who do the most talking know the least about hunting.

LOMOV. My dear lady, I beg of you to be still. My heart is bursting! (*He shouts.*) Be still!

NATALIA. I won't be still until you admit that Otkatai is the better dog!

(*Enter* TSCHUBUKOV.)

TSCHUB. Has it begun all over again?

NATALIA. Papa, say frankly, on your honour, which dog is better: Otkatai or Ugadi?

LOMOV. Stepan Stepanovitch, I beg of you, just answer this: has your dog a short lower jaw or not? Yes or no?

TSCHUB. And what if he has? Is it of such importance? There is no better dog in the whole country.

LOMOV. Except my Ugadi. Tell the truth, now!

TSCHUB. Don't get so excited, my dear fellow. Permit me. Your Ugadi certainly has his good points. He is from a good breed, has a good stride, strong haunches, and so forth. But the dog, if you really want to know it, has two faults; he is old and he has a short lower jaw.

LOMOV. Pardon me. I have palpitation of the heart! Let us keep to facts – just remember in Maruskin's meadows, my Ugadi kept ear to ear with the Count Rasvachai and your dog –

TSCHUB. He was behind, because the Count struck him with his whip.

LOMOV. Quite right. All the other dogs were on the fox's scent, but Otkatai found it necessary to bite a sheep.

TSCHUB. That isn't so! I'm sensitive about that and beg you to stop this argument. He struck him because everybody looks on a strange dog of good blood with envy. Even you, sir, aren't free from that sin. No sooner do you find a dog better than Ugadi than you begin to – this, that – his, mine – and so forth! I remember distinctly.

LOMOV. I remember something, too.

TSCHUB. (*mimicking him*). I remember something, too! What do you remember?

LOMOV. Palpitation! My leg is lame – I can't –

NATALIA. Palpitation! What kind of hunter are you? You ought to stay in the kitchen by the stove and wrestle with the potato peelings, and not go fox-hunting! Palpitation!

TSCHUB. And what kind of hunter are you? A man with your diseases ought to stay at home and not jolt around in the saddle. If you were a hunter – ! But you only ride round in order to find out about other people's dogs and make trouble for everyone. I am sensitive! Let's drop the subject. Besides, you're no hunter.

LOMOV. And are you? You only ride around to flatter the Count! My heart! You intriguer! Swindler!

TSCHUB. And what of it? (*Shouting.*) Be still!

LOMOV. Intriguer!

TSCHUB. Baby! Puppy! Walking drug-store!

LOMOV. Old rat!

TSCHUB. Be still or I'll shoot you – with my worst gun, like a partridge! Fool! Loafer!

LOMOV. Everyone knows that – oh, my heart! – that your poor late wife beat you. My leg – my temples – Heavens – I'm dying – I –

TSCHUB. And your housekeeper wears the trousers in your house!

LOMOV. Here – here – there – there – my heart has burst! My shoulder is torn apart. Where is my shoulder? I'm dying! (*He falls into a chair.*) The doctor! (*Faints.*)

TSCHUB. Baby! Half-baked clam! Fool!

NATALIA. Nice sort of hunter you are! You can't even sit on a horse. (*To* TSCHUB.) Papa, what's the matter with him? (*She screams.*) Ivan Vassiliyitch! He is dead!

LOMOV. I'm ill! I can't breathe! Air!

NATALIA. He is dead! (*She shakes* LOMOV *in the chair.*) Ivan Vassiliyitch! What have we done! He is dead! (*She sinks into a chair.*) The doctor – doctor! (*She goes into hysterics.*)

TSCHUB. What is it? What's the matter with you?

NATALIA (*groaning*). He's dead!

TSCHUB. Who is dead? Who? (*Looking at* LOMOV.) Yes, he is dead! Good Heavens! Water! The doctor! (*Holding the glass to* LOMOV*'s lips.*) Drink! He won't drink! He's dead! What a terrible situation! Why didn't I shoot myself? Why have I never cut my throat? What am I waiting for now? Only give me a knife! Give me a pistol! (LOMOV *moves.*) He's coming to! Drink some water – there!

LOMOV. Sparks! Mists! Where am I?

TSCHUB. Get married! Quick, and then go to the devil!

She's willing. (*He joins the hands of* LOMOV *and* NATALIA.) She's agreed! Only leave me in peace!

LOMOV. Wh–what? (*Getting up.*) Whom?

TSCHUB. She's willing! Kiss each other and devil take you both!

NATALIA (*groans*). He lives! Yes, yes, I'm willing!

TSCHUB. Kiss each other!

LOMOV. Whom? (NATALIA *and* LOMOV *kiss.*) Very nice! Pardon me, but what is this for? Oh, yes, I understand! My heart – sparks – I am happy, Natalia Stepanovna. (*He kisses her hand.*)

NATALIA. I'm happy, too!

TSCHUB. A load off my shoulders!

NATALIA. And now at least you'll admit that Ugadi is worse than Otkatai!

LOMOV. Better!

NATALIA. Worse!

TSCHUB. Now the domestic joys have begun – Champagne!

LOMOV. Better!

NATALIA. Worse, worse, worse!

TSCHUB. (*trying to drown them out*). Champagne, champagne!

CURTAIN

OTHER PLAYS BY CHEKHOV

A Marriage Proposal is one of Chekhov's lighter plays. Of a similar nature are *The Wedding, The Boor,* and *The Anniversary.* Different entirely are his longer plays, *The Seagull, Uncle Vanya, The Three Sisters,* and *The Cherry Orchard,* which were first produced by the famous Moscow Art Theatre. They are remarkable for an absence of "well-made" plot – an apparent aimlessness. The characters appear, talk (often about themselves), and drift off the stage, to reappear later, all with no seeming plan or purpose. But they are drawn with fine psychological truth and subtle insight. They are educated people, and they talk well. As we listen to them they cast a spell over us. They become intensely real. For the most part they are unhappy. As they talk they mirror the lightless soul of Russia in the days before the revolution. They do not wail; they struggle where there is no hope. They recognize clearly the beauty and worth of life; they love and dream and aspire. But their visions and hopes come to nothing. Yet, because they have struggled and believed to the last, they have a nobility and greatness which sets them apart from the ordinary characters in the majority of realistic plays.

Here is the poignant passage that closes *The Three Sisters.* It will give you some idea of the spiritual significance of these plays.

"The bands are playing so gaily, so bravely, and one does so want to live. O, my God! Time will pass and we shall depart for ever, we shall be forgotten: they will forget our faces, voices, and even how many there were of us, but our sufferings will turn into joy for those who will live after us, happiness and peace will reign on earth, and people will remember with kindly words, and bless those who are living now. . . . It seems that in a little while we shall know why we are living, why we are suffering. If we could only know, if we could only know!"

THINKING ABOUT THE PLAY

1. Near the opening of the play Tschubukov says, in an *aside,* "He has come to borrow money! I won't give him any." What is an *aside,* and with what movement or gestures should the line be read on the stage?
2. Look up the word "soliloquy". Find an example of a soliloquy in the play.

3. Why does Chekhov tell us that Natalia's age is twenty-five? Why not eighteen? Why not forty?
4. You may find it interesting to draw a chart that will show how the excitement mounts to climaxes in the two quarrels and at the final curtain. This can be done on the board or in your notebooks.

   Draw a horizontal line and divide it into a number of equal spaces corresponding to the number of pages of dialogue. Interest is aroused on the first page by Tschubukov's strange mannerisms, Lomov's palpitations, and the colourful Russian costumes both men wear. Your graph line will climb sharply, and then ease off. When Tschubukov discovers that Lomov is going to ask for his daughter's hand there is a new wave of excitement, with a corresponding wave on your graph. He rushes out to get Natalia.

   You may feel that Lomov's long speech when he is alone lets down the tension a little, but if the part is well acted, this need not be so. With Natalia's entrance there is a quickening of interest that accompanies the appearance of a new character, especially when this one is the lady whose hand Lomov seeks in marriage. For a while the interest may drop a little as they talk pleasantly and naturally. Then as the quarrel begins, the line of your graph will climb steadily to the first high point or climax when Lomov staggers out.

   There is a brief let-down until Natalia hears that Lomov has come to propose to her. Then, as she becomes hysterical, with Tschubukov rushing back and forth threatening to cut his own throat, there is a new wave of interest.

   The lover appears and again the play tension relaxes, the line of the graph curving downward to a median low position. Then the second quarrel begins and this time your line of interest shoots up at an even steeper incline to the point where, in the second and highest climax, Lomov faints and they think he is dead. There is a slight drop then as Lomov revives. Father and daughter are happy once again. The lovers kiss and we have apparently arrived at the happy ending. But no! As the play draws to an end the quarrelling begins anew, to the lusty cheers of Tschubukov. The curtains close with your graph line moving upward toward a third climax.

CAMPBELL OF KILMOHR

J. A. FERGUSON

ONE OF THE FINEST ONE-ACT TRAGEDIES

In *Campbell of Kilmohr* we have an outstanding example of tragedy, which has been called the noblest form of drama. Although it is only a one-act play, it has something of the power of the great tragedies of Sophocles and Shakespeare; it submits us to what Aristotle called "catharsis" – the purging or cleansing of the spirit by terror and pity.

The action takes place in the Highlands of Scotland during the winter of 1746, following the battle of Culloden, at which the army of the Young Pretender was overwhelmed by the forces of the Duke of Cumberland. The events and characters are fictitious, but many such incidents are known to have occurred. The leaders of the rebellion, including Bonnie Prince Charlie himself, are in hiding, hoping to escape from the country. A young Scottish lad, Dugald Stewart, has brought food to them. He now returns to his home to secure more necessities for their survival. On the way he travels by night, crossing mountains and swimming rivers to avoid the redcoats who are watching every road and bridge.

When the play opens, his old mother, Mary Stewart, is expecting him. With her is Morag Cameron, a young, sensitive girl, who lacks the courage and strength of purpose that Mary Stewart has. Dugald arrives and tells his mother (the young girl overhearing him) where the leaders *were*. The mother doesn't trust Morag, however, and sends her on an errand. It is then that Dugald tells her where the leaders *will be*, for they have already moved to a new hiding-place.

Archibald Campbell – Campbell of Kilmohr – then arrives with his secretary, James Mackenzie, and the officer in charge of the soldiers in the area, Captain Sandeman. The character of Campbell of Kilmohr is based on that of a real person, Campbell of Glenfalloch, who behaved in much the same unscrupulous and cruel manner. Campbell's task is the pacification of the Highlands following the rebellion; his chief desire is to seize the leaders, whose whereabouts Dugald and his mother know. He tries to secure this information from each of them in turn, and is unsuccessful. When Dugald is about to be shot, Morag tells him where they are. His promise to give Dugald back to her, unhanged, in return for what she has told him, proves a cruel mockery when a shot rings out. He leaves, thinking he has been successful, but there is some satisfaction for us in knowing that his triumph is not real and that Morag's information will not help him. The mother returns and the play closes with her lament – a paean in which she praises the courage of her dead son.

These final words of Mary Stewart are the most important in the play. They are like a song at the end of a tragic story – a song that thrills us and gives us a strange pride and content that are almost happiness. We breathe more deeply as we listen to it; triumph swells up in us, as in Mary Stewart's heart. The words give meaning to the story.

The author has suggested that the first part of the speech, to "fine tales", should be intoned or chanted. The words should have a full, brave, singing quality. Then when Mary tells of how the great men came in their pride, her words rush along as in a flood. This part finished, the three sentences beginning "Let the heart of you rejoice" bring us back to the haunting, eloquent mood of the first part of the speech. The last sentence is spoken quietly, tenderly, as if the old mother has come down from the heights, where she had been dwelling in her thoughts, and returns to the earthly task that remains to be done.

Since this is the most significant speech in the drama, teacher and class should try to find the best player for the part of Mary Stewart by having each girl in the class read one of the sentences. Choose three or four who have rich, low, musical voices and who read the lines well; then let these read the entire speech. From among them choose the girl who is to play the role.

Campbell of Kilmohr is almost equally important. Indeed, the play is really a conflict between him and Mary Stewart. He is a materialist; she is an idealist. He believes that material things are all-important; he thinks that men and women can be bought with bribes and broken with threats. She and her son prove that with some, at least, this is not true.

He is a politician and has the gift of speech. His sense of humour is lively; he is shrewd and calculating. In attempting to gain the information from son and mother he assumes many moods like an actor, changing from one to another with lightning speed. One moment he is friendly; the next dangerous. He quotes the Psalmist with effect. Perhaps his most effective moment is when he tries to stir the mother by recalling the childhood of her son, and then threatens him with the rope.

Campbell has had a "lairge experience o' life". For years he has been a politician in the parliament at Edinburgh, with thin hands at the bottom of empty pockets, and he has learned to shed the "fine notions" of his youth. He has never yet seen a sensible man "insensible to the touch of yellow metal". But this night, as Dugald says, he adds to his experience.

In choosing Campbell select two or three speeches characteristic of his various moods, and by elimination find the student actor who is most convincingly powerful and eloquent.

Next in importance is Morag Cameron. Like Sniggers in *A Night at an Inn*, a later play in this volume, she must set the mood of the play in the opening scene and intensify it with her restless, frightened acting. She should give the appearance of great youth, in contrast to Mary Stewart, who must seem an old woman.

Dugald Stewart is young and capable; he is fearless and obstinate in his refusal to give Campbell the information.

Sandeman is a blunt, honest soldier. He is an honourable man and, in his own way, as much opposed to Campbell of Kilmohr and the things he stands for as Dugald Stewart and his mother. He won't listen behind doors and he doesn't approve of Campbell's methods. He has a cool, quiet contempt for the wily politician. Although young, he has the rank of captain and is in charge of a regiment of soldiers. His part must be played with authority.

Mackenzie, Campbell's clerk, is the only one who yields to Campbell. He is a "yes" man, a nobody, impressed by the great man's brain and tongue. After Campbell has been challenged by the son, the mother, and finally Captain Sandeman, he is left alone with his clerk. In the scene that follows, Mackenzie acts as a kind of second self, echoing Campbell's thoughts. Campbell is free to speak out, as if to himself, the things that are in his mind. This is most valuable, because the playwright can have Campbell admit that he has been beaten. In this scene we have the core of the play's philosophy: that there are intangible and illogical ideals that can defeat the material and rational forces of life. "A dream can be stronger than a strong man armed. . . . And so I am powerless before the visions and dreams of an old woman and a half-grown lad." We are kept interested during this discussion because we know that the paper that Campbell is about to sign will bring the death of Dugald Stewart.

Your production of the play will be improved if parts are memorized and it is given in a sombre setting, with lighting in low key. This helps to set the mood of fear and tragedy. The faces should seem to be lit always by the gleam of the peat fire. The moment when Morag covers the fire and places the candle in the window as Dugald is about to enter is most effective if properly handled.

From the author's stage directions it will be clear to you that from the moment Morag is brought in by the soldiers, to the last scene of the play, she is hardly noticed by the audience. She is turned away from us, with a shawl over her head, and is little more than a shadow in the gloomy background. Thus when she does speak, just as Campbell is about to leave, her words have a startling effect and we realize what a struggle has been going on inside her to decide whether or not to tell what she knows.

This is a play worthy of your earnest study. Some of us, when confronted with a challenging work, evade the issue by saying we don't like it. It is only too easy to take this attitude toward anything which is unusual or difficult to follow. It is not so easy to be properly receptive and humble, and to withhold judgment until we understand fully. Read and act this play with all the sympathy and intelligence you can command. If it still doesn't seem important, read it again. If you approach it in this spirit you will find it, in the end, one of the most satisfying of our plays for the theatre.

CHARACTERS

MARY STEWART
MORAG CAMERON
DUGALD STEWART
CAPTAIN SANDEMAN
ARCHIBALD CAMPBELL
JAMES MACKENZIE

Produced by the Scottish Repertory Theatre Company at the Royalty Theatre, Glasgow, on Monday, March 23, 1914, with the following cast:

JAMES MACKENZIE	C. Stewart Robertson
MARY STEWART	Agnes Lowson
MORAG CAMERON	Rita Thom
DUGALD STEWART	Nicholas Hanven
CAPTAIN SANDEMAN	N. N. Wimbush
ARCHIBALD CAMPBELL	W. S. Hartford

Directed by Lewis Casson

CAMPBELL OF KILMOHR

SCENE: *Interior of a lonely cottage on the road from Struan to Rannoch in North Perthshire.*
TIME: *After the Rising of '45.*

MORAG *is restlessly moving backwards and forwards. The old woman is seated on a low stool beside the peat fire in the centre of the floor.*

The room is scantily furnished and the women are poorly clad. MORAG *is barefooted. At the back is the door that leads to the outside. On the left of the door is a small window. On the right side of the room, there is a door that opens into a barn.* MORAG *stands for a moment at the window, looking out.*

MORAG. It is the wild night outside.

MARY STEWART. Is the snow still coming down?

MORAG. It is that then – dancing and swirling with the wind too, and never stopping at all. Aye, and so black I cannot see the other side of the road.

MARY STEWART. That is good.

(MORAG *moves across the floor and stops irresolutely. She is restless, expectant.*)

MORAG. Will I be putting the light in the window?

MARY STEWART. Why should you be doing that! You have not heard his call – (*turns eagerly*) have you?

MORAG (*with sign of head*). No, but the light in the window would show him all is well.

MARY STEWART. It would not then! The light was to be put there *after* we had heard the signal.

MORAG. But on a night like this he may have been calling for long and we never hear him.

MARY STEWART. Do not be so anxious, Morag. Keep to what he says. Put more peat on the fire now and sit down.

MORAG (*with increasing excitement*). I canna, I canna! There is that in me that tells me something is going to befall us this night. Oh, that wind, hear to it, sobbing round the house as if it brought some poor lost soul up to the door, and we refusing it shelter.

MARY STEWART. Do not be fretting yourself like that. Do as I bid you. Put more peat to the fire.

MORAG (*at the wicker peat-basket*). Never since I . . . What was that?

(*Both listen for a moment.*)

MARY STEWART. It was just the wind; it is rising more. A sore night for them that are out in the heather.

(MORAG *puts peat on the fire without speaking.*)

MARY STEWART. Did you notice were there many people going by today?

MORAG. No. After daybreak the redcoats came by from Struan; and there was no more till nine, when an old man like the Catechist from Killichonan passed. At four o'clock, just when the dark was falling, a horseman with a

1. Struan: a village a short distance from Pitlochry, on the road which goes in a northerly direction from Edinburgh to Inverness.
2. Catechist: a teacher who gives oral instruction, using the question and answer method. Killichonan is on Loch (Lake) Rannoch, on the road that runs west from Pitlochry.

lad holding to the stirrup, and running fast, went by towards Rannoch.

MARY STEWART. But no more redcoats?

MORAG (*shaking her head*). The road has been as quiet as the hills, and they as quiet as the grave. Do you think he will come?

MARY STEWART. Is it you think I have the gift, girl, that 3
you ask me that? All I know is that it is five days since he was here for meat and drink for himself and for the others – five days and five nights, mind you; and little enough he took away; and those in hiding no' used to sore lying I'll be thinking. He must try to get through tonight. But that quietness, with no one to be seen from daylight till dark, I do not like it, Morag. They must know something. They must be watching.

(*A sound is heard by both women. They stand listening.*)

MARY STEWART. Haste you with the light, Morag.

MORAG. But it came from the back of the house – from the hillside.

MARY STEWART. Do as I tell you. The other side may be watched.

(*A candle is lit and placed in the window.* MORAG *goes hurrying to the door.*)

MARY STEWART. Stop, stop! Would you be opening the door with a light like that shining from the house? A man would be seen against it in the doorway for a mile. And who knows what eyes may be watching? Put out the light now and cover the fire.

(*Room is reduced to semi-darkness, and the door unbarred. Someone enters.*)

MORAG. You are cold, Dugald!

(STEWART, *very exhausted, signs assent.*)

3. The gift: the ability to see things that are far away or to foretell events that are to take place in the future.

MORAG. And wet, oh, wet through and through.

STEWART. Ericht Brig was guarded, well guarded. I had to win across the water.

(*The old woman has now relit candle and taken away plaid from fire.*)

MARY STEWART. Ericht Brig – then –

STEWART (*nods*). Yes – in a corrie, on the far side of Dearig, half-way up.

MARY STEWART. Himself is there then?

STEWART. Aye, and Keppoch as well, and another and a greater is with them.

MARY STEWART. Wheest! (*Glances at* MORAG.)

STEWART. Mother, is it that you can . . .

MARY STEWART. Yes, yes, Morag will bring out the food for ye to carry back. It is under the hay in the barn, well hid. Morag will bring it. Go, Morag, and bring it.

(MORAG *enters other room or barn which opens on right.*)

STEWART. Mother, I wonder at ye; Morag would never tell – never.

MARY STEWART. Morag is only a lass yet. She has never been tried. And who knows what she might be made to tell.

STEWART. Well, well, it is no matter, for I was telling you where I left them, but not where I am to *find* them.

MARY STEWART. They are not where you said now?

STEWART. No; they left the corrie last night, and I am to find them (*whispers*) in a quiet part on Rannoch Moor.

MARY STEWART. It is well for a young lass not to be know-

4. Ericht Brig: the bridge over the Ericht River.
5. Corrie: a hollow on the mountainside where deer often lie. Dearig is a mountain to the north of Struan; it is over 3,300 ft. high.
6. Keppoch: a Scottish chieftain, who was one of the leaders in the Uprising. Can you guess who "another and a greater" was?
7. Rannoch Moor: a tract of open land south and west of Loch Rannoch; it is some forty miles from Dearig mountain.

ing. Do not tell her.

STEWART. Well, well, I will not tell her. Then she cannot tell where they are even if she wanted to.

(*He sits down at table; the old woman ministers to his wants.*)

STEWART. A fire is a merry thing on a night like this; and a roof over the head is a great comfort.

MARY STEWART. Ye'll no' can stop the night?

STEWART. No. I must be many a mile from here before the
day breaks on Ben Dearig. 8

(MORAG *re-enters.*)

MORAG. It was hard to get through, Dugald?

STEWART. You may say that. I came Ericht for three miles, and then when I reached low country I had to take to walking
in the burns because of the snow that shows a man's steps and 9
tells who he is to them that can read; and there's plenty can do that abroad, God knows.

MORAG. But none spied ye?

STEWART. Who can tell? Before dark came, from far up on the slopes of Dearig I saw soldiers down below; and away towards Rannoch Moor they were scattered all over the country like black flies on a white sheet. A wild-cat or anything that couldna fly could never have got through. And men at every brig and ford and pass! I had to strike away up across the slopes again; and even so as I turned round the bend beyond Kilrain I ran straight into a sentry sheltering behind a great rock. But after that it was easy going.

MORAG. How could that be?

STEWART. Well, you see, I took the boots off him, and then I had no need to mind who might see my steps in the snow.

MORAG. You took the boots off him!

STEWART (*laughing*). I did that same. Does that puzzle your bonny head? How does a lad take the boots off a redcoat?

8. The sun catches the mountain top early.
9. Burn: the Scottish word for stream.

Find out the answer, my lass, while I will be finishing my meat.

MORAG. Maybe he was asleep?

STEWART. Asleep! Asleep! Well, well, he sleeps sound enough now, with the ten toes of him pointed to the sky.

(*The old woman has taken up dirk from table. She puts it down again.* MORAG *sees the action, and pushes dirk away so that it rolls off the table and drops to the floor. She hides her face in her hands.*)

MARY STEWART. Morag, bring in the kebbuck o' cheese. Now that all is well and safe it is we that will look after his comfort tonight. (MORAG *goes into barn.*) I mind well her mother saying to me – it was one day in the black winter that she died, when the frost took the land in its grip and the birds fell stiff from the trees, and the deer came down and put their noses to the door – I mind well her saying just before she died –

(*Loud knocking at the door.*)

A VOICE. In the King's name!

MARY STEWART (*recovering first*). The hay in the barn – quick, my son.

(*Knocking continues.*)

A VOICE. Open in the King's name!

(STEWART *snatches up such articles as would reveal his presence and hurries into barn. He overlooks dirk on floor. The old woman goes towards door, slowly, to gain time.*)

MARY STEWART. Who is there? What do you want?

A VOICE. Open, open.

10. Dirk: a dagger. Why does Morag push it away and hide her face in her hands?
11. Kebbuck o' cheese: a cheese made of ewe-milk and cow's milk.

(MARY STEWART *opens door,* and CAMPBELL OF KILMOHR *follows* CAPTAIN SANDEMAN *into the house. Behind* KILMOHR *comes a man carrying a leather wallet,* JAMES MACKENZIE, *his clerk. The rear is brought up by* SOLDIERS *carrying arms.*)

SANDEMAN. Ha, the bird has flown.

CAMPBELL (*who has struck dirk with his foot and picked it up*). But the nest is warm; look at this.

SANDEMAN. It seems as if we had disturbed him at supper. Search the house, men.

MARY STEWART. I'm just a lonely old woman. You have been misguided. I was getting through my supper.

CAMPBELL (*holding up dirk*). And this was your toothpick, eh? Na! na! We ken whaur we are, and wha we want, and, by Cruachan, I think we've got him. 12

(*Sounds are heard from barn, and soldiers return with* MORAG. *She had stayed in hiding from fear, and she still holds the cheese in her hands.*)

SANDEMAN. What have we here!

CAMPBELL. A lass!

MARY STEWART. It's just my dead brother's daughter. She was getting me the cheese, as you can see.

CAMPBELL. On men, again; the other turtle-doo will no' be far away. (*Bantering, to the old woman.*) Tut, tut, Mistress Stewart, and do ye have her wait upon ye while your leddyship dines alane! A grand way to treat your dead brother's daughter; fie, fie, upon ye!

(SOLDIERS *reappear with* STEWART, *whose arms are pinioned.*)

CAMPBELL. Did I no' tell ye! And this, Mrs. Stewart, will be your dead sister's son, I'm thinking; or aiblins your 13

12. Cruachan: a mountain almost 3,700 ft. high, some forty-five miles south-west of Loch Rannoch.
13. Aiblins: perhaps.

leddyship's butler! Weel, woman, I'll tell ye this: Pharaoh spared ae butler, but Erchie Campbell will no spare anither. Na! na! Pharaoh's case is no' to be taken as forming ony preceedent. And so if he doesna answer certain questions we have to speir at him, before morning he'll hang as high as Haman.

(STEWART *is placed before the table at which* CAMPBELL *has seated himself.* TWO SOLDIERS *guard* STEWART. *Another is behind* CAMPBELL*'s chair and another is by the door. The clerk,* MACKENZIE, *is seated up at corner of table.* SANDEMAN *stands by the fire.*)

CAMPBELL (*to* STEWART). Weel, sir, it is within the cognizance of the law that you have knowledge and information of the place of harbour and concealment used by certain persons who are in a state of proscription. Furthermore, it is known that four days ago certain other proscribed persons did join with these, and that they are banded together in an endeavour to secure the escape from these dominions of His Majesty, King George, of certain persons who by their crimes and treasons lie open to the capital charge. What say ye?

(STEWART *makes no reply.*)

CAMPBELL. Ye admit this then?

(STEWART *as before.*)

CAMPBELL. Come, come, my lad. Ye stand in great jeopardy. Great affairs of state lie behind this which are beyond your simple understanding. Speak up, and it will be the better for ye.

(STEWART *silent as before.*)

14. For the story of Pharaoh and the butler, see Genesis 40.
15. Speir: ask.
16. Haman: See Esther 7.
17. State of proscription: state of being proscribed or outlawed.
18. Capital charge: one punishable by death.

CAMPBELL. Look you. I'll be frank with you. No harm will befall you this night (and I wish all in this house to note my words) – no harm will befall you this night if you supply the information required.

(STEWART *silent as before.*)

CAMPBELL (*with sudden passion*). Sandeman, put your sword to the carcass o' this muckle ass and see will it louse 19
his tongue.

(SANDEMAN *does not move.*)

STEWART. It may be as well then, Mr. Campbell, that I should say a word to save your breath. It is this: Till you talk
Rannoch Loch to the top of Schiehallion ye'll no' talk me into 20
a yea or nay.

CAMPBELL (*quietly*). Say ye so? Noo, I wadna be so very sure if I were you. I've had a lairge experience o' life, and speaking out of it I would say that only fools and the dead never change their minds.

STEWART (*quietly too*). Then you'll be adding to your experience tonight, Mr. Campbell, and you'll have something to put on to the other side of it.

CAMPBELL (*tapping his snuff-box*). Very possibly, young sir, but what I would present for your consideration is this: While ye may be prepared to keep your mouth shut under the condition of a fool, are ye equally prepared to do so in the condition of a dead man?

(CAMPBELL *waits expectantly.* STEWART *silent as before.*)

CAMPBELL. Tut, tut, now if it's afraid ye are, my lad, with my hand on my heart and on my word as a gentleman. . . .

STEWART. Afraid!

(*He spits in contempt towards* CAMPBELL.)

19. Muckle: great.
20. Schiehallion: a mountain to the south of Loch Rannoch, higher than Ben Dearig.

CAMPBELL (*enraged*). Ye damned stubborn Hieland stot... (*To* SANDEMAN.) Have him taken out. We'll get it another way.

(CAMPBELL *rises.* STEWART *is moved into barn by* SOLDIERS, *who remain with him.*)

CAMPBELL (*walking*). Some puling eediots, Sandeman, would applaud this contumacy and call it constancy. Constancy! Now, I've had a lairge experience o' life, and I never saw yet a sensible man insensible to the touch of yellow metal. If there may be such a man, it is demonstrable that he is no sensible man. Fideelity! quotha, it's sheer obstinacy. They just see that ye want something oot o' them, and they're so damned selfish and thrawn they winna pairt. And with the natural inabeelity o' their brains to hold mair than one idea at a time, they canna see that in return you could put something into their palms far more profitable. (*Sits again at table.*) Aweel, bring Mistress Stewart up.

(*Old woman is placed before him where son had been.*)

CAMPBELL (*more ingratiatingly*). Weel noo, Mistress Stewart, good woman, this is a sair predeecament for ye to be in. I would jist counsel ye to be candid. Doubtless yer mind is a' in a swirl. Ye kenna what way to turn. Maybe ye are like the Psalmist and say: "I lookit this way and that, and there was no man to peety me, or to have compassion upon my fatherless children." But, see now, ye would be wrong; and, if ye tell me a' ye ken, I'll stand freends wi' ye. Put your trust in Erchie Campbell.

MARY STEWART. I trust no Campbell.

CAMPBELL. Weel, weel, noo, I'm no' jist that set up wi' them myself. There's but ae Campbell that I care muckle aboot,

21. Stot: bullock.
22. So . . . thrawn . . . pairt: so perverse they will not give you what you want.
23. Kenna: know not.
24. There's but ae Campbell: There is only one Campbell.

after a'. But, good wife, it's no' the Campbells we're trying the
noo; so, as time presses, we'll jist *birze yont,* as they say them- 25
selves. Noo then, speak up.

(MARY STEWART *is silent.*)

(CAMPBELL, *begins grimly, and passes through astonishment, expostulation, and a feigned contempt for mother and pity for son, to a pretence of sadness which, except at the end, makes his words come haltingly.*)

Ah! ye also. I suppose ye understand, woman, how it will go wi'
your son? (*To his clerk.*) Here's a fine mother for ye, James!
Would you believe it? She kens what would save her son – 26
the very babe she nursed at her breast; but will she save him?
Na! na! Sir, he may look after himself! A mother, a mother!
Ha! ha!

(CAMPBELL *laughs,* MACKENZIE *titters foolishly.* CAMPBELL *pauses to watch effect of his words.*)

Aye, you would think, James, that she would remember the time when he was but little and afraid of all the terrors that walk in darkness, and how he looked up to her as to a tower of safety, and would run to her with outstretched hands, hiding his face from his fear, in her gown. The darkness! It is the dark night and a long journey before him now.

(*He pauses again.*)

You would think, James, that she would mind how she happit 27
him from the cold of winter and sheltered him from the summer heats, and, when he began to find his footing, how she had
an eye on a' the beasts of the field, and on the water and the
fire that were become her enemies. And to what purpose all this
care? – tell me that, my man, to what good, if she is to leave

25. Birze yont: press forward.
26. Kens: knows.
27. Happit: covered.

him at the last to dangle from a tree at the end of a hempen rope – to see his flesh to be meat for the fowls of the air – her son, her little son!

MARY STEWART (*softly*). My son – my little son! . . . Oh – (*more loudly*) – but my son he has done no crime.

CAMPBELL. Has he no'? Weel, mistress, as ye'll no' take my word for it, maybe ye'll list to Mr. Mackenzie here. What say ye, James?

MACKENZIE. He is guilty of aiding and abetting in the concealment of proscribed persons; likewise with being found in the possession of arms, contrary to statute, both very heinous crimes.

CAMPBELL. Very well said, James! Forby, between ourselves, Mrs. Stewart, the young man in my opeenion is guilty of another crime – (*snuffs*) – he is guilty of the heinous crime of not knowing on which side his bread is buttered. Come now . . .

MARY STEWART. Ye durst not lay a finger on the lad, ye durst not hang him.

MACKENZIE. And why should the gentleman not hang him if it pleesure him?

(CAMPBELL *taps snuff-box and takes a pinch.*)

MARY STEWART (*with intensity*). Campbell of Kilmohr, lay but one finger on Dugald Stewart and the weight of Ben Cruachan will be light to the weight that will be laid on your soul. I will lay the curse of the seven rings upon your life. I will call up the fires of Ephron, the blue and the green and the grey fires, for the destruction of your soul. I will curse you in your homestead and in the wife it shelters, and in the children that will never bear your name. Yea and ye shall be cursed.

CAMPBELL (*startled, betrays agitation – the snuff is spilt from his trembling hand*). Hoot, toot, woman, ye're, ye're . . . (*Angrily.*) Ye auld beldame, to say such things to me! I'll have

28. Forby: besides.
29. Beldame: an old woman, a witch.

ye first whippet and syne droont for a witch. Damn thae stub- 30
born and superstеetious cattle! (*To* SANDEMAN.) We should have come in here before him and listened in the barn, Sandeman!

SANDEMAN (*in quick staccato, always cool*). Ah, listen behind the door you mean! Now I never thought of that!

CAMPBELL. Did ye not! Humph! Well, no doubt there are a good many things in the universe that yet wait for your thought upon them. What would be your objections, now?

SANDEMAN. There are two objections, Kilmohr, that you would understand.

CAMPBELL. Name them.

SANDEMAN. Well, in the first place, we have not wings like crows to fly . . . and the footsteps on the snow . . . . Second point: the woman would have told him we were there.

CAMPBELL. Not if I told her I had the power to clap her in Inverness jail.

MARY STEWART (*in contempt*). Yes, even if ye had told me ye had power to clap me in hell, Mr. Campbell.

CAMPBELL. Lift me that screeching Jezebel oot o' here; 31
Sandeman, we'll mak' a quick finish o' this. (SOLDIERS *take
her towards barn.*) No, not there, pitch the old girzie into the 32
snow.

MARY STEWART (*as she is led outside*). Ye'll never find him, Campbell, never, never!

CAMPBELL (*enraged*). Find him, aye, by God I'll find him, if I have to keek under every stone on the mountains from the
Boar of Badenoch to the Sow of Athole. 33

(*Old woman and* SOLDIERS *go outside, leaving only* CAMPBELL, MACKENZIE, SANDEMAN, *and* MORAG *in the room;* MORAG *huddled up on stool.*)

30. Syne droont: soon drowned.
31. Jezebel: the wicked wife of Ahab, King of Israel. (I Kings 16:31) The name is freely applied to any wicked woman.
32. Girzie: a noisy woman.
33. Badenoch and Athole: districts north of Pitlochry.

And now, Captain Sandeman, you an' me must have a word or two. I noted your objection to listening ahint doors and so on. Now, I make a' necessary allowances for youth and the grand and magneeficent ideas commonly held, for a little while, in that period. I had them myself. But, man, gin ye had trod the floor of the Parliament Hoose in Edinburry as long as I did, wi' a pair o' thin hands at the bottom o' toom pockets ye'd ha'e shed your fine notions, as I did. Noo, fine pernickety noansense will no' do in this business –

SANDEMAN. Sir!

CAMPBELL. Softly, softly, Captain Sandeman, and hear til what I have to say. I have noticed with regret several things in your remarks and bearing which are displeasing to me. I would say just one word in your ear; it is this: These things, Sandeman, are not conducive to advancement in His Majesty's service.

SANDEMAN (*after a brief pause in which the two eye each other*). Kilmohr, I am a soldier, and if I speak out my mind you must pardon me if my words are blunt: I do not like this work, but I *loathe* your methods.

CAMPBELL. Mislike the methods you may, but the work ye must do! Methods are my business. Let me tell you the true position. In ae word it is no more and no less than this. You and me are baith here to carry out the proveesions of the Act for the Pacification of the Highlands. That means the cleaning up of a very big mess, Sandeman, a very big mess. Now, what is your special office in this work? I'll tell ye, man; you and your men are just beesoms in the hands of the law-officers of the Crown. In this district, I order and ye soop. (*He indicates door of barn.*) Now soop, Captain Sandeman.

SANDEMAN. What are you after? I would give something to see into your mind.

34. Gin: if.
35. Toom: empty.
36. Beesoms: brooms.
37. Soop: sweep.

CAMPBELL. Ne'er fash aboot my mind: what has a soldier 38
to do with ony mental operations? It's His Grace's order that 39
concern you. Oot wi' your man and set him up against the wa'.

SANDEMAN. Kilmohr, it is murder – murder, Kilmohr!

CAMPBELL. Hoots awa', man, it's a thing o' nae special 40
signeeficence.

SANDEMAN. I must ask you for a warrant.

CAMPBELL. Quick, then; Mackenzie will bring it out to you.

(CLERK *begins writing as* SANDEMAN *goes and orders the soldiers to lead* STEWART *outside.* CAMPBELL *sits very still and thoughtful.* CLERK *finishes writing and places warrant before* CAMPBELL *for his signature.*)

MACKENZIE. At this place, sir.

CAMPBELL (*again alert*). Hoots, I was forgetting.

MACKENZIE. It is a great power ye have in your hands, Kilmohr, to be able to send a man to death on the nod, as ye might say.

CAMPBELL (*sitting back, pen in hand*). Power! Power, say ye? Man, do ye no' see I've been beaten? Do ye no' see that? Archibald Campbell and a' his men and his money are less to them than the wind blowing in their faces.

MACKENZIE. Well, it's a strange thing that.

CAMPBELL (*throwing down the pen and rising*). Aye, it's a strange thing that. It's a thing fit to sicken a man against the notion that there are probabilities on this earth . . . Ye see, James, beforehand I would have said nothing could be easier.

MACKENZIE. Than to get them to tell?

CAMPBELL. Aye, just that. But you heard what he said: "You'll be adding to your experience this night, Mr. Campbell, and you'll have something to put to the other side of it," says

38. Fash: worry.
39. Ony: any.
40. Hoots awa': an exclamation of disagreement or disgust.

he. (*Paces away, hands behind back.*) Aye, and I have added something to it, a thing I like but little. (*Turning to face* MACKENZIE *with raised hand.*) Do you see what it is, James? A dream can be stronger than a strong man armed! Just a whispered word, a pointed finger even, would ha'e tell'd us a'. But no! no! And so I am powerless before the visions and dreams of an old woman and a half-grown lad.

MACKENZIE (*who now stands waiting for the warrant*). No' exactly powerless, Kilmohr, for if ye canna open his mouth ye can shut it; and there's some satisfaction in that.

CAMPBELL (*sitting down to sign warrant*). No' to me, man, no' to me. (*He hands the paper to* MACKENZIE, *who goes out.*) For I've been beaten. Aye, the pair o' them have beat me, though it's only a matter o' seconds till one o' them be dead.

MORAG (*her voice coming quickly, in sharp whisper, like an echo of* CAMPBELL*'s last words as she sits up to stare at him*). Dead!

CAMPBELL (*startled*). What is that?

MORAG (*slowly*). Is he dead?

CAMPBELL (*aloud*). Oh, it's you. I'd forgotten you were there.

MORAG (*in same tone*). Is he dead?

CAMPBELL (*grimly*). Not yet. But if ye'll look through this window preesently ye'll see him gotten ready for death.

(*He picks up hat, gloves, cloak, and is about to go out.*)

MORAG (*after a pause, very slowly and brokenly*). I – will – tell – you.

CAMPBELL (*astounded*). What!

MORAG. I will tell you all you are seeking to know.

CAMPBELL (*in a whisper, thunderstruck*). God, and to think, to think I was on the very act . . . on the very act of . . . (*Recovering.*) Tell me – tell me at once.

MORAG. You will promise that he will not be hanged?

CAMPBELL. He will not. I swear it.

MORAG. You will give him back to me?

CAMPBELL. I will give him back – unhung.

MORAG. Then (CAMPBELL *comes near.*) in a corrie half-way up the far side of Dearig – God save me!

CAMPBELL (*in exultation*). Dished after a'. I've clean dished them! Loard, Loard! (*With intense solemnity, clasping hands and looking upwards.*) Once more I can believe in the rationality of Thy world. (*Gathers up again his cloak, hat, etc.*) And to think . . . to think . . . I was on the very act of going away like a beaten dog!

MORAG. He is safe from hanging now?

CAMPBELL (*chuckles and looks out at window before replying, and is at door when he speaks*). Very near it, very near it. Listen!

(*He holds up his hand – a volley of musketry is heard.* KILMOHR *goes out, leaving door wide open. After a short interval of silence, the old woman enters and advances a few steps towards the girl, who has sunk on her knees at the volley.*)

MARY STEWART. Did you hear, Morag Cameron, did you hear?

(*The girl is sobbing, her face covered by her hands.*)

MARY STEWART. Och! be quiet now. I would be listening till the last sound of it passes into the great hills and over all the wide world. . . . It is fitting for you to be crying, a child that cannot understand, but water shall never wet eye of mine for Dugald Stewart. Last night I was but the mother of a lad that herded sheep on the Athole hills; this morn it is I that am the mother of a man who is among the great ones of the earth. All over the land they will be telling of Dugald Stewart. Mothers will teach their children to be men by him. High will his name be with the teller of fine tales. . . . The great men came, they came in their pride, terrible like the storm they were, and cunning with the words of guile were they. Death was with them. . . . He was but a lad, a young lad, with great length of days before him, and the grandeur of the world. But he put it all from him. "Speak," said they, "speak, and life and great riches will be for yourself." But he said no word at all! Loud was the swelling of their wrath! Let the heart of you rejoice, Morag Cameron, for the snow is red with his blood. There are things greater than death. Let them that are children shed the tears. . . . (*She comes forward and lays her hand on the girl's shoulder.*) Let us go and lift him into the house, and not be leaving him lie out there alone.

CURTAIN

IN DEFENCE OF TRAGEDY

If you like *Campbell of Kilmohr,* you may be interested in reading the plays of two famous dramatists, one English and one American. The Englishman is John Masefield, author of *The Tragedy of Nan, The Faithful,* and *Good Friday*. Of these, *The Tragedy of Nan* is close in spirit to *Campbell of Kilmohr.* It is a sombre story, illumined by the poetry of a half-mad old fiddler and the lonely exultation of Nan's death. In a foreword to the play Masefield writes: "Commonplace people dislike tragedy, because they dare not suffer and cannot exult." He defines the scope and purpose of tragedy: "Tragedy at its best is a vision of the heart of life. The heart of life can only be laid bare in the agony and exultation of dreadful acts. The vision of agony, or spiritual contest, pushed beyond the limits of the dying personality, is exalting and cleansing. It is only by such vision that a multitude can be brought to the passionate knowledge of things exulting and eternal."

The American is Eugene O'Neill, perhaps the greatest American playwright. You will undoubtedly enjoy reading his plays, such as *The Emperor Jones, Beyond the Horizon, The Hairy Ape*, and *Marco Millions.* O'Neill, like Masefield, has stated his conception of tragedy. In defending his plays from the charge that they are sordid, depressing, and pessimistic, he insists that tragedy has the meaning the Greeks gave it. "To them it brought exaltation, an urge toward life and ever more life. It roused them to deeper spiritual understanding and released them from the petty greeds of every-day existence. . . . The point is that life itself is nothing. It is the dream that keeps us fighting – willing – living! Achievement in the narrow sense of possession is a stale finale. The dreams that can be completely realized are not worth dreaming. The higher the dream, the more impossible it is to realize it fully. But you would not say, since this is true, that we should dream only of easily attained ideals. A man wills his own defeat when he pursues the unattainable. But his struggle is his success. He is an example of the spiritual significance which life attains when it aims high enough, when the individual fights all the hostile forces within and without himself to achieve a future of nobler values."

CHARACTERIZATION IN TRAGIC PLAYS

How important is characterization in *Campbell of Kilmohr*?

It is true that Campbell himself is clearly drawn, but can the same be said for Morag Cameron, for Mary and Dugald Stewart? Is it possible to characterize a tragic figure?

In his essay *The Tragic Theatre,* W. B. Yeats says: "When we go back a few centuries and enter the great periods of drama, character grows less and sometimes disappears, and there is much lyric feeling. . . . Suddenly it strikes us that there is much tragedy . . . where its place is taken by passions and motives . . . ." And again, "When we look at the faces of the old tragic paintings, whether it is in Titian or in some painter of medieval China, we find there sadness and gravity, a certain emptiness even, as of a mind that waited the supreme crisis." Quoting these two passages in his valuable book *A Study of the Modern Drama,* Barrett Clark writes: "The tragic poet, it seems, has little to do with what we ordinarily term character, which is usually idiosyncratic, accidental, realistic; it is his business to idealize character through poetry, divesting it of these personal details which differentiate one person from the other. We may say that comedy is the presentation of men, that tragedy is the presentation of man."

This raises an interesting issue. Is Hamlet only an embodiment of "passions and motives", the symbol of an idea or attitude toward life? Is he less real than Falstaff? The supremely tragic protagonists of Greek and Elizabethan drama do transcend ordinary character as we understand it, in their greater than human struggle against the forces that oppose them. But have the characters in the serious plays of modern drama less vitality and actuality than comic characters in plays of the same period? What of Masha in Chekhov's play *The Three Sisters*, of St. John Ervine's *John Ferguson*, of Nora in *A Doll's House*? Surely these are three-dimensional figures, completely alive.

In the problem play and the drama of ideas, character is obviously in danger of being subordinated to social purpose or to the ideas that are being advanced by the dramatist. Shaw's characters, for example, are, in the main, mouthpieces for his ideas. Only rarely, as in *Candida* and *Saint Joan*, does the portrait come to life. We have already noted that in farce there is a definite unnaturalism that militates against genuine characterization. The same may be said of melodrama, where emotion and movement are predominant, and where characters are largely types.

It is impossible to exhaust the subject in a brief discussion, but we shall probably be near the truth when we suggest that while genuine character is to be found in serious drama and (in a heightened and idealized way) in tragedy, the greatest opportunities for characterization are in comedy. The writer of comedy excels in so far as he is able to create living character.

THINKING ABOUT THE PLAY

1. After reading "In Defence of Tragedy", comment on the suggestion that *Campbell of Kilmohr* is a sad play.
2. C. E. Montague, a distinguished British writer, pointed out that sufferings of our own provide a new range of experience, but that they are apt to numb us and shock us so that we cannot profit from them. He suggests that when we read a tragic play we are able to widen our experience without the actual suffering that occurs when we endure some personal loss. Show how *Campbell of Kilmohr* may serve this purpose in your own case.
3. Which sentence in Mary Stewart's final speech states the theme or central idea of the play?

THE GRAND CHAM'S DIAMOND

ALLAN MONKHOUSE

EXPERT AND HILARIOUS COMEDY

Father, mother, and daughter are spending a quiet evening at home. Too quiet for mother, who is bored with her humdrum existence. She protests that nothing ever happens to her.

Suddenly something *does* happen to her. A diamond belonging to the Grand Cham (really the Grand Khan, an Eastern Emperor) is flung through the window. For a while, things happen fast and furiously. When they calm down at last, father and daughter are ashamed of the way mother has behaved, but she doesn't care. She has had her bit of fun and romance. She has had her fling.

Ma should be played in a spunky, vigorous way, by a girl with great spirit and energy and a lively sense of humour. All her life, she exclaims, she has been too safe. She dreams of "livin' at ease, motors an' champagne". When fate suddenly brings within her grasp the things she has dreamed of, she fights her family, the villain, and her prospective son-in-law doggedly and resourcefully to hold them. Her family find her "wantin' in the el'ments of morality", but we in the audience like her and enjoy the things she says and does.

Father is an old stick. Before his family he puts on a knowing front. He is a man of the world. He can tell his wife what thieves do with diamonds. But as Ma says, he really has "no 'magernation".

Polly, the daughter, is better educated than her parents and reproves them for their language and manners on occasion. She is more self-conscious socially than they are, more prim and proper. But she is composed of much weaker stuff than her mother, and weeps when the dangerous diamond is thrown through the window.

The villain is an absurd portrait, an amusing mixture of all the villains of literature. He is so darkly villainous that we feel like hissing and booing him, as did the audiences for the melodramas of the last century. We are delighted to see him foiled. He should be played in straightforward fashion, with dreadful earnestness.

You will have no trouble casting Albert, Polly's lover. He is an up-and-coming detective – already a successful member of Scotland Yard.

Except for the villain, these are all ordinary people in a London suburb. You must try to enter into their lives. You must feel the deadly monotony of their days. The play provides you with splendid opportunities for good comedy and character acting.

The plot falls into two parts: the family comedy scenes, in which quiet boredom is punctuated by spats and amusing dialogue; and the scenes with the villain and Albert. There is a return in the last moment of the play to the first mood of dullness and monotony. In acting the play the first section is taken at a yawning pace, but after the diamond is thrown in, the tempo quickens and the speeches follow one another at a headlong rate. In this second section the characters move about a great deal. The action needs to be carefully rehearsed so that everything will go smoothly, despite the impression of turmoil and excitement.

The Grand Cham's Diamond is an expertly written and hilarious play. It is one of the best of farce comedies, with an added happy dash of mystery hokum thrown in for good measure. Like mother, you are in for a good time. You are in for your "bit of fun".

CHARACTERS

MRS. PERKINS
MR. PERKINS
MISS PERKINS
STRANGER IN BLACK
ALBERT WATKINS

First produced at the Birmingham Repertory Theatre by Mr. John Drinkwater, with the following cast:

MRS. PERKINS	Cathleen Orford
MR. PERKINS	Reginald Gatty
MISS PERKINS	Sidney Leon
STRANGER	Noel Shammon
ALBERT	J. Adrian Byrne

THE GRAND CHAM'S DIAMOND

SCENE: *A sitting-room in a small house in a London suburb. The window is in the wall to the left of the spectator and the door in the right half of the back wall. The furniture is ordinary. On the chimneypiece, to the right of the spectator, is a clock. The room is lit by electric light. It is some time after the evening meal.* MR. PERKINS *is reading a newspaper.* MRS. PERKINS *is darning a sock, and* MISS PERKINS *is engaged upon a jigsaw puzzle.*

MRS. PERKINS. What I mean t' say is that it's not much fun for us.

MR. PERKINS. All right, Ma.

MISS PERKINS (*engaged on her puzzle*). Bother!

MRS. PERKINS. It makes a long evenin' of it. Same every
night. We 'ave our tea and then we just set down till it's time 1
to go to bed. It's not fair.

MR. PERKINS. Same for all of us.

1. It is a custom in many English homes to have a substantial tea, rather than supper or dinner, as an evening meal.

MRS. PERKINS. That it's not.

MR. PERKINS. Why isn't it?

MRS. PERKINS. Do y' or do y' not get out o' this 'ouse every mornin' and spend the day out?

MR. PERKINS. It'd be a poor job for you if I didn't.

MRS. PERKINS. I don't say anythin' about that. I don't interfere.

MR. PERKINS. 'Ow could y' interfere?

MISS PERKINS. Bother!

MRS. PERKINS. Don't interrup' like that when me and your pa's talkin', Polly.

MISS PERKINS. My name isn't Polly.

MR. PERKINS. What is it?

MISS PERKINS. It's Marie.

MR. PERKINS. Well, I'm blowed!

MRS. PERKINS. An' why shouldn't she 'ave a bit of a change? She's tired of bein' Polly.

MISS PERKINS. I do think we might have a little more change.

MR. PERKINS. Don't you start.

MISS PERKINS. We might have gone out to the pictures to-night, as Mother said.

MR. PERKINS. Your young man might 'ave come and found you out.

MISS PERKINS. You know he's engaged in the evenings.

MR. PERKINS. Yes, and what at?

MISS PERKINS. Never mind!

MRS. PERKINS. I do think, Polly, that he ought to be a bit more open with you. What *does* he do?

MR. PERKINS. Ay, what does Albert Watkins do?

MISS PERKINS. Never you mind!

MRS. PERKINS. 'E's never told 'er.

MR. PERKINS. I 'ope it's nothin' to be ashamed of.

MISS PERKINS. P'raps I know more than you think.

MRS. PERKINS. 'As 'e said?

MISS PERKINS. It's confidential.

MR. PERKINS. Oh! I know that tale.

MRS. PERKINS. Well, Polly's got 'er young man and you've got your business an' out all day seein' people. What 'ave I got?

MR. PERKINS. Well, what should y' 'ave? What does any woman 'ave? I dunno what you're botherin' about. Y' 'ad a week at Margate this year. 2

MRS. PERKINS (*derisively*). 'Ome from 'ome!

MR. PERKINS. A good woman ought to like 'er 'ome.

MRS. PERKINS. I never said I didn't like it.

MR. PERKINS. Well –

MRS. PERKINS. 'Ome's a place to come back to.

MISS PERKINS. Mother's romantic. That's what she is.

MRS. PERKINS. What *is* that, Polly? It's a word I never rightly –

MR. PERKINS. Romantic! At 'er age!

MRS. PERKINS. You know what it is, do y'?

MR. PERKINS. It's penny dreadfuls and the pictures and 3 gassin' about love and the deep blue sea.

MRS. PERKINS. Well, y' might do worse.

MR. PERKINS. Whatever's come over 'er?

MRS. PERKINS. I've always thought I should like to travel.

MISS PERKINS (*at her puzzle*). I think there's a bit missing.

MRS. PERKINS. Eh! A bit missin'? That's the way with me; there's always bin a bit missin'.

MR. PERKINS. I dunno why y're startin' like this now. Y've 'ad all these years to settle down in. What's come over yer?

MRS. PERKINS. Eh! Don't ask me. I think 'er Albert's comin' about 'as unsettled me.

MISS PERKINS. Albert!

2. You can find Margate on your map of England. It is a seaside resort where families like the Perkinses go for their week's holiday each year. Mrs. Perkins is tired of it. They have probably gone to the same boarding house for years, so that it is just like being at home away from home.
3. Penny dreadfuls are cheap magazines and books dealing with love and crime. What do you think of Mr. Perkins's definition of romance?

MRS. PERKINS. Well, I see 'im an' you and I think what might 'a been.

MR. PERKINS. What's that?

MRS. PERKINS. Well, I was young onct.

MR. PERKINS. But y're not now.

MRS. PERKINS. You've no call to throw it in m'teeth.

MR. PERKINS. Teeth indeed!

MRS. PERKINS. Don't be insultin', Mr. Perkins.

MR. PERKINS. I wasn't bein'.

MRS. PERKINS. Yes, y' was.

MISS PERKINS. I don't see why Albert should unsettle you.

MRS. PERKINS. If I was you I'd want to know 'ow 'e spends 'is evenings.

MISS PERKINS. It's no business of yours, Ma.

MR. PERKINS. It'll be some bus'ness of mine. I think it's about time Albert spoke to me.

MISS PERKINS. Spoke to you?

MR. PERKINS. Placed 'is position an' prospects before me.

MISS PERKINS. Well, I believe he's a confidential agent.

MRS. PERKINS. A what!

MR. PERKINS. What sort of a' agent?

MISS PERKINS. It's confidential – or financial p'raps.

MR. PERKINS. He's kiddin' yer.

MRS. PERKINS. Do they work at night?

MISS PERKINS. I've always understood that Rothschilds and people like that did their business at parties – on the quiet.

MR. PERKINS. Bosh!

MISS PERKINS. Oh, very well, Pa. (MISS PERKINS *settles to her puzzle.*)

(MRS. PERKINS *darns stolidly.* MR. PERKINS *returns to the paper. A short pause.*)

4. What does Mr. Perkins mean?
5. The Rothschilds are the famous and wealthy European banking family whose financial empire was established in the latter part of the eighteenth century by Anselm Rothschild in Frankfurt, Germany.

MRS. PERKINS. Well, it's too late for the movies now.

MISS PERKINS. Ah! That's it. (*She finds the missing bit.*)

MRS. PERKINS. What's in the paper, Pa?

MR. PERKINS. There's a Cabinet crisis.

MRS. PERKINS. Isn't there anythin' interestin'? 6

MR. PERKINS. 'Ere's a child stole a shillin' an' swallowed it t' escape detection.

MRS. PERKINS. Poor thing!

MR. PERKINS. 'Ere! Is this more in your line? Great Jewel Robbery! The Grand Cham's Diamond Missing.

MRS. PERKINS. Eh! What's that?

MISS PERKINS. Who is the Grand Cham?

MR. PERKINS. 'E's – one o' them Eastern potentates. 'E's 7
been stayin' at the Majestic Hotel. The dimond was taken out
of the settin' and a walnut substituted.

MRS. PERKINS. A walnut! It must be a whopper.

MISS PERKINS. Why did they substitute a walnut?

MR. PERKINS. You must substitute somethin'.

MISS PERKINS. Why?

MR. PERKINS. I don't know. They always do. The brightest
treasure of the East. Not the slightest trace. Supposed Asiatic
gang. Sherlock Holmes and Father Brown have been sum- 8
moned and a telegram despatched to Mossier Lecock.

MRS. PERKINS (*with satisfaction*). Well, that's somethin' like.

6. Do you find this question and the two speeches that precede it amusing or revealing? If so, why? What do they tell us about Mrs. Perkins?
7. Potentate: a prince or ruler.
8. In this sentence Mr. Perkins names three of the most famous detectives of fiction. Sherlock Holmes is, of course, the celebrated creation of Sir Arthur Conan Doyle. Father Brown is G. K. Chesterton's humble priest, more interested in saving the souls of the criminals he arrests than in their conviction. Monsieur Lecoq – Mr. Perkins pronounces this name as Mossier Lecock – was one of the two detective creations of Emile Gaboriau, the Parisian writer who invented the long detective story.

MISS PERKINS. What's it worth?

MR. PERKINS. Eh! I dunno. Thousands, thousands. They say it makes the Koh-i-noor take a back seat.

MRS. PERKINS. Reelly?

MR. PERKINS. What 'ud you do, old lady, if I brought it 'ome for y'r birthday?

MRS. PERKINS. Well, I'd wear it, I s'pose.

MISS PERKINS. You'd never dare, Ma.

MRS. PERKINS. I would that.

MISS PERKINS. But thieves'd always be after it.

MRS. PERKINS. What d' these thieves do with it when they've got it?

MR. PERKINS. I s'pose they chop it up and sell it in bits.

MRS. PERKINS. What a shame!

MR. PERKINS. I dessay they're off to South America.

MRS. PERKINS. Why?

MR. PERKINS. No extrydition.

MRS. PERKINS. What's that? D' y' mean last 'dition extra?

MISS PERKINS. No, Ma. It means that thieves can't be turned out.

MRS. PERKINS. Why not?

MR. PERKINS. It's like it used to be with slaves here. Once the South American flag's waved over 'em, they're all right.

MISS PERKINS. It isn't all one country there, Pa.

MR. PERKINS. Well, I reckon they're much of a muchness.

MRS. PERKINS. An' could you sell it there?

MR. PERKINS. Yes, they're great people for jew'lry.

MRS. PERKINS. Polly, you're doin' nothin'. Y' might as well be mendin' that blind.

MISS PERKINS. Oh, bother!

MRS. PERKINS. It looks bad hangin' down like that.

MISS PERKINS (*going towards the window*). People'll see in.

9. The Kohinoor is a famous Indian diamond, which became one of the British Crown jewels in the reign of Queen Victoria.
10. Extradition: the surrender of a fugitive foreign criminal to the proper authorities.

MRS. PERKINS. There's not many passin' at this time o' night.

MISS PERKINS. It makes it so public. (*She takes the blind from the lower part of the window and begins to mend it.*) Where's the white thread, Ma?

MRS. PERKINS. Here y' are. Now, make a job of it.

(MR. PERKINS *has returned to his paper, his daughter is more or less intent on her work,* MRS. PERKINS *darns and yawns.* MR. PERKINS *snores gently.*)

Might as well all be asleep.

MISS PERKINS. Listen, Ma!

MRS. PERKINS. Somebody runnin'. Seem in an 'urry.

(*Something crashes through the window and falls with broken glass upon the floor.*)

MISS PERKINS. Good gracious!

MRS. PERKINS. Mercy on us!

MR. PERKINS (*waking up*). Fire! Where is it?

MRS. PERKINS. Nonsense, Pa! It's them boys. Out arter 'em. 11

MR. PERKINS. What! Where?

MISS PERKINS. No. Don't go. Don't leave us. It can't be boys.

MR. PERKINS (*seeing the broken window*). This is very careless, Polly.

MISS PERKINS. It wasn't me. It's a stone, I think.

MRS. PERKINS. They're far enough now. Where is it?

MISS PERKINS. I'm all of a tremble.

MRS. PERKINS. You ought to 'ave run right out, Pa, and you might 'ave caught 'em. I never did see such a thing.

MR. PERKINS. It's an outrage, this is. Did y' see anybody?

MRS. PERKINS. We 'eard somebody runnin'.

MISS PERKINS. I thought I 'eard somebody passing after that. Quietly like. Runnin' very light.

MR. PERKINS. Nonsense, Polly. Better put that blind up now.

11. Out arter 'em: Out after them.

MISS PERKINS. You put it up.

MR. PERKINS. Do as I tell you.

MISS PERKINS. I don't like.

MRS. PERKINS. 'Ere, 'ere. Give it me. (*She puts it up and peers out into the street.*)

MISS PERKINS. Come away, Ma.

MR. PERKINS. Where's the stone?

(*They all look about the floor.*)

MISS PERKINS. Here it is. Here's something. (*She picks it up.*) Why! It's a lump of glass.

MR. PERKINS. Let's look!

MRS. PERKINS. Let me see.

(*They crowd round.*)

MR. PERKINS. I say!

MISS PERKINS. What is it? What is it?

MRS. PERKINS. Give it me, Polly. (*She grabs it.*)

MR. PERKINS. Hold it up to the light.

MISS PERKINS. Why! What can it be?

MRS. PERKINS (*relinquishing it to her husband*). Nonsense! Nonsense! (*She goes back to her chair and begins to fumble with her darning. She is greatly agitated.*)

MR. PERKINS. It's a rum thing, this is.

MISS PERKINS. Eh! Isn't it beautiful?

MR. PERKINS. It might be a –

MISS PERKINS. Diamond?

MR. PERKINS. Nonsense!

MRS. PERKINS (*rushing forward*). Hide it! (*She seizes the diamond and looks about the room.*)

MISS PERKINS. Why! What d' y' mean, Ma?

MRS. PERKINS. It's it.

MR. PERKINS (*feebly*). What's it?

MRS. PERKINS. You know.

MR. PERKINS. What – what rubbish! The idea!

MRS. PERKINS (*looking at it in her palm*). It's the Grand Cham's dimond.

MR. PERKINS. Then it's dangerous.

MRS. PERKINS. Never mind that.

MISS PERKINS. What shall we do? (*She begins to whimper.*)

MRS. PERKINS. Stop that, Polly.

MR. PERKINS. P'raps we'd better look out for a policeman.

MRS. PERKINS. No.

MR. PERKINS. If it is it, we're not safe.

MRS. PERKINS. I don't care.

MR. PERKINS. But what d' y' want to do?

MRS. PERKINS. Here! Let's put it inside the clock. (*She opens the back of the clock and crams it in.*) Now!

MR. PERKINS. What are y' up to, Ma?

MISS PERKINS. I wish you'd throw it out in the street again.

MRS. PERKINS. No, no.

MR. PERKINS. But what *are* y' up to?

MRS. PERKINS. It's come to us, this 'as. We'll stick to it if we can.

MR. PERKINS. But –

MISS PERKINS. Oh, Ma!

MRS. PERKINS. They may not find the 'ouse again. They're all alike in this street.

MR. PERKINS. There's the broken window.

MRS. PERKINS. Let's 'ave the bits of glass out. Then it won't be noticed. (*She peers out into the street. Then she begins to pluck the fragments of broken glass from the window. She winces and licks her fingers.*)

MR. PERKINS. You've cut yourself now.

MRS. PERKINS. Never mind that. Polly, pick all the bits off the floor. Don't leave a trace. (*She licks her finger.* MISS PERKINS *obeys.*)

MR. PERKINS. Now, what's all this about?

MISS PERKINS (*on the floor*). I dunno what's come over 'er.

MRS. PERKINS. 'Ere, Polly, look alive. 'Ave y' got 'em all?

MISS PERKINS. All I can find.

MRS. PERKINS. Drat it! A bit's fallen outside. Go out and pick it up, Pa. No; p'raps better not.

MR. PERKINS. Look here! What's y'r game?

MRS. PERKINS. Give here! (*She takes all the fragments together and puts them under the sofa cushion. She looks round the room, listens at the window and returns to her darning.*) If anyone comes, mind we know nothin' about it.

MR. PERKINS. It depends 'oo comes, doesn't it?

MRS. PERKINS. No.

MR. PERKINS. It might be the police.

MRS. PERKINS. Never mind the police.

MR. PERKINS. Why! What d' y' mean? What *do* y' mean?

MRS. PERKINS. It's the chanct of a lifetime. We'll take it.

MISS PERKINS. Oh, Ma!

MR. PERKINS. Look 'ere –

MRS. PERKINS. It's come to us. It might 'a' bin the answer to a prayer.

MR. PERKINS. Was it?

MRS. PERKINS. Not exactly, but I've been thinkin' a lot.

MR. PERKINS. More likely the devil.

MRS. PERKINS. There's no such thing. Y're talkin' nonsense.

MR. PERKINS. No devil. Then is there God?

MRS. PERKINS. There may be. 'E may 'ave sent it.

MR. PERKINS. It's awful talk, this.

MISS PERKINS. Why! What could you do with it?

MRS. PERKINS. Chop it up and sell it.

MR. PERKINS. Where?

MRS. PERKINS. In South America.

MR. PERKINS. Good 'eavens!

MISS PERKINS. Ma, how can you?

MR. PERKINS. 'Ave y' took leave of y'r senses?

MRS. PERKINS. Yes, if y' like.

MR. PERKINS. Well, I've 'eard tell as women aren't honest like men and now I know it.

MRS. PERKINS. 'Ow do I know you're honest?

MR. PERKINS. I've never took a thing in my life. I've a record, 'aven't I?

MRS. PERKINS. I dessay. I dunno. I won't give it up. I won't. I won't. So there!

MR. PERKINS. 'Ow can y' 'elp it?

MRS. PERKINS. I've sat there darnin' and mendin', waitin' and dozin' till I'm tired. I've never 'ad a go at anythin'. The chanct 'as come.

MISS PERKINS. I did think you were honest, Ma.

MRS. PERKINS. Honest. It's ours.

MR. PERKINS. 'Ow can it be?

MRS. PERKINS. 'Oo's is it?

MR. PERKINS. Why! That Grand Cham's.

MRS. PERKINS. An' 'ow did 'e get it? 'E's a tyrant. 'E stole it off some native. Now it's come to me. It's mine. It's mine as much as anyone's. It's come like a miracle.

MISS PERKINS. But you can't keep it.

MR. PERKINS. Y'r ma amazes me.

MRS. PERKINS. First thing in the mornin' y'll get a list o' them ships sailin' for South America.

MISS PERKINS. Oh, Ma! Ma!

MR. PERKINS. She's off 'er chump. 12

MRS. PERKINS. I'll go alone if y' like.

MR. PERKINS. It's dangerous. It's dangerous. There may be a revolver levelled at y' now.

MRS. PERKINS. I don't care.

MR. PERKINS. I never knew she was like this.

MISS PERKINS. South America? Where?

MRS. PERKINS. Y' shall 'ave jewels and dresses no end, Polly.

MISS PERKINS. Don't, Ma.

MR. PERKINS. South America! Like that chap Jabez Balfour. 13

12. She's off 'er chump: She's acting foolishly.
13. Jabez Balfour (1843-1912) was an English businessman, whose real estate companies, called the Balfour Group, went bankrupt in 1892, ruining some twenty-five thousand small householders of whom Balfour, a Liberal Member of Parliament, was supposed to be the political champion. He escaped to Argentina, where he eluded extradition for three years. In 1895 he was brought back to England, found guilty of fraud, and sentenced to fourteen years in prison.

MISS PERKINS. He was brought back, wasn't he?

MR. PERKINS. I object to be put along of 'im, any'ow.

MRS. PERKINS. We'd manage better than that. Riches! Livin' at ease. Motors an' champagne. We've never 'ad a chanct!

MR. PERKINS. It can't be done. It's all nonsense. An' it's 'orrible to think of.

MRS. PERKINS. Oh! It's a beautiful thing. I couldn't bear to break it up. We'll keep it. We'll look at it now and then. Every Sunday.

MR. PERKINS. Sunday!

MRS. PERKINS. I could go on settin' 'ere if I knew it was there all the time. I think I could be 'appy.

MISS PERKINS. You'd never be safe.

MRS. PERKINS. Safe! I've bin too safe.

MR. PERKINS. Oh, missis! Oh, missis!

MISS PERKINS. It's strange nobody's come.

MRS. PERKINS. Nobody's comin'. It's a gift.

MR. PERKINS. It may not be – what y' think.

MRS. PERKINS (*fiercely*). It is.

MR. PERKINS. Then they'll be after us. Police – or worse.

MRS. PERKINS. Let 'em come.

(*There is a ring at the doorbell. They all stand tense.*)

MR. PERKINS. Now, there.

MISS PERKINS. Oh, dear!

MRS. PERKINS. You'll not say a word. You'll do as I tell you. Mind that. We know nothing.

MISS PERKINS. There's the window.

MRS. PERKINS. Leave that to me.

MR. PERKINS. Oh! But I say –

MRS. PERKINS. Thomas Perkins, you'll rue it to your dyin' day if –

(*The ring again.*)

MR. PERKINS. Who's goin'?

MRS. PERKINS. I am. Remember! (*She goes out.*)

MISS PERKINS. What are we to do, Pa?

MR. PERKINS. Eh! I'm beat.

MISS PERKINS. Shall we throw it out of the window?

MR. PERKINS. No, no. Best not. Humour her a bit. It may be nothin'.

MRS. PERKINS (*outside*). No, you don't. 'Ere. I tell yer –

STRANGER. Excuse me.

MRS. PERKINS. Pa, 'ere's a man forcin' 'is way –

MISS PERKINS. Oh, dear!

MR. PERKINS. Dash it all! I say!

(MRS. PERKINS *and a dark* STRANGER, *dressed in black, enter together. She is resisting his advance, but he presses on ruthlessly. As he enters she gives way and changes her tactics.*)

MRS. PERKINS. Well, I must say! Pushin' a lady about like that! What bis'ness 'ave y' 'ere?

STRANGER. I've told you, madam.

MRS. PERKINS. A fine tale! Y'r boy an' 'is glass marble! Where is 'e? I tell yer we know nothin' about it. Do we, Pa? (*Behind the* STRANGER, *with a terrific frown, she shakes her fist at him.*)

MR. PERKINS (*feebly blustering*). Now what's all this?

MISS PERKINS. Oh, Ma!

MRS. PERKINS. Shut up!

STRANGER. I'm sorry to intrude, sir, but I've lost something in your room.

MRS. PERKINS. What nonsense! 'Ow could yer?

STRANGER. As I have told this lady, my little boy –

MRS. PERKINS. Where is 'e?

STRANGER (*to* MR. PERKINS). His favourite glass marble. He pretended to throw it. It slipped from his hand and, I am sorry to say, went through your window. I apologize and shall be glad to pay. Please give me the – marble at once. Where is it? I've no time to lose.

MRS. PERKINS. Where's the boy?

STRANGER. He's just round the corner.

MRS. PERKINS. D' y' expect us to believe that tale?

STRANGER (*with a flash of menace*). You'd better. (*To* MR. PERKINS.) Now, sir!

MR. PERKINS. It's a bit thick, y' know; I mean, thin.

STRANGER. It will have to do. No trifling. Come!

(*He is looking about the room, having cursorily glanced at the floor. He strides to the window and pulls down the blind.*)

MRS. PERKINS. None o' y'r liberties here. Get out!

MR. PERKINS. 'Ere, y' know! (*Aside to* MRS. PERKINS.) Ma, I don't like it.

STRANGER. The devil! Where's the glass?

MRS. PERKINS. What glass?

STRANGER. The pane's gone. You see! I knew this was the house.

MRS. PERKINS. That's easy explained.

MISS PERKINS. Oh, Ma! Tell him and –

MRS. PERKINS. Of course I'll tell 'im. (*She menaces* MISS PERKINS *surreptitiously.*) It's my daughter's new-fangled ideas of ventilation. She would 'ave it so. It's been that way a fortnight. No – let's see – today's Tuesday. Nigh on a month.

STRANGER. Damnation! Where is it? Where's the diamond?

MRS. PERKINS (*with a shriek of exultation*). The dimond!

STRANGER. Yes. Let me tell you then. Your lives are in danger. You've got the Grand Cham's diamond.

MR. PERKINS. 'Ow did it get 'ere?

STRANGER. The thief was pursued. He threw it in.

MR. PERKINS (*querulously*). Why did 'e throw it in 'ere?

STRANGER. Don't be a fool.

MRS. PERKINS. An' oo' are you?

STRANGER. I am – the Grand Cham's representative.

MRS. PERKINS. Prove it.

STRANGER. Enough of this. (*He draws a revolver.*)

14. It's a bit thick . . . thin: It's a bit much to expect us to believe; I mean, it's a thin excuse. The wordplay is between "thick" and "thin".

(MISS PERKINS *shrieks.* MR. PERKINS *recoils and edges away.* MRS. PERKINS *stands firm.*)

MR. PERKINS. Ma! Ma!

STRANGER (*rapping the butt of the revolver on the table*). Where is it?

MRS. PERKINS. I'll tell yer.

STRANGER. At once.

MRS. PERKINS. I've swallered it.

STRANGER (*greatly discomposed*). What?

MRS. PERKINS. It went down as easy as a oyster.

STRANGER. Swallowed it! You're joking!

MRS. PERKINS. No. I got the idea out of the evenin' paper. Where is it, Pa? 'Ere. "Child Swallows Shillin'. Curious Case."

STRANGER (*to the others*). Is this true?

MISS PERKINS. Oh, I don't know.

MR. PERKINS. Y' see, I was asleep.

STRANGER. Asleep!

MR. PERKINS. Wasn't I, Mother?

MRS. PERKINS. 'E'd sleep through anythin'.

STRANGER. D' you mean to say – ? Where is it?

MRS. PERKINS. I've just told yer.

STRANGER. On your oath –

MRS. PERKINS. Oath! D' y' doubt the word of a lady?

STRANGER. Then – d' you feel it – I mean – whereabouts is it now?

MRS. PERKINS. I don't think that's a question a gentleman 'd ask.

STRANGER. Kites of hell. You'll have to be cut open.

MRS. PERKINS. Nay, I won't.

STRANGER (*to himself*). Cremation? Would it melt the diamond?

MRS. PERKINS. I won't be cremated. There! Y've to get the deceased's consent. I'm goin' to be buried when my time comes.

15. Kites of hell: A strong exclamation or oath. A kite is a bird of prey.

STRANGER (*pacing about in agitation while* MRS. PERKINS *controls the others by nods and winks*). What's to be done? An emetic?

MRS. PERKINS. You'd better go 'ome an' say it's lost.

STRANGER. Unhappy woman! Do you understand that your life is a trifle, a pawn in the game?

MRS. PERKINS. Pawn! Yes, an' y' can't get it out without the ticket.

STRANGER. It's impossible. It can't be. (*He turns on the others.*) The truth! Did she swallow it? If she did, she dies.

MISS PERKINS. Oh, no, no. She didn't.

MRS. PERKINS. You silly!

MISS PERKINS. Oh, Ma!

MR. PERKINS. Ma, Ma, what can we do?

MRS. PERKINS. Y' can 'old y'r tongues. Y're no 'elp at all.

STRANGER. What folly this is! What can you do with it? That diamond means death to you. Death! Destruction! You haven't a chance of keeping it. You're mad. Your lives now are not worth a minute's purchase.

MISS PERKINS. Give it up, Ma. I'll tell you where it is. It's –

MRS. PERKINS (*in a terrible voice*). Stop!

MR. PERKINS. What can you do, Ma? Chuck it! Chuck it!

MRS. PERKINS. 'E don't bluff me. 'E's in a great 'urry. I believe 'e's the thief.

STRANGER. Thousand devils! We're wasting time. (*He looks at the clock and then plucks out his watch.*) Your clock's slow. It's stopped. It was that time when I came in.

MISS PERKINS. Tell him. Tell him.

MR. PERKINS. Oh, chuck it!

STRANGER (*perceiving that he is getting "warm"*). What stopped the clock?

MISS PERKINS (*hysterically*). Give it 'im.

MRS. PERKINS. Polly, I'm ashamed of yer.

(*A face appears at the window, but they do not see it.*)

STRANGER. Is it there? (*He makes for the clock, and* MRS. PERKINS *throws herself in front.*)

MRS. PERKINS. No, it's not; and y' shan't meddle with my furniture.

STRANGER (*pointing the revolver at her*). Move aside!

MRS. PERKINS. Move aside yerself.

STRANGER (*he hesitates, then turns the revolver on* MISS PERKINS). Is it there? Quick!

(MISS PERKINS *shrieks, a hand with a revolver in it is thrust through the empty pane, the revolver is fired, the* STRANGER *drops his, stamps, curses, and wrings his hands. A man opens the window-sash and springs into the room.*)

MISS PERKINS. Albert!

MRS. PERKINS. What! It's Albert.

(*The* STRANGER *rushes to the switch and turns off the light. Darkness, shouting, and confusion. The light is turned on. The furniture is disarranged, the* STRANGER *and the clock have gone, the others are distributed about the room,* MRS. PERKINS *sitting in the chair she first occupied.*)

ALBERT. Who's got it?

MR. PERKINS. He's gone.

MISS PERKINS. Oh! Albert!

ALBERT. Where's the diamond?

MR. PERKINS. It was in the clock.

ALBERT. The clock? Where is it?

MISS PERKINS. Oh! Albert!

MR. PERKINS. 'E's taken it. 'E's got the clock.

MRS. PERKINS. Nay, 'e 'asn't. (*She produces the clock from under her petticoats.*)

MR. PERKINS. Well, I'm blowed!

MISS PERKINS. Oh, Ma!

ALBERT. What is it? Have you got it?

MRS. PERKINS. I've got it right enough. (*She carries the clock to the chimneypiece, opens it, and takes out the diamond.*) Will that gentleman come back?

ALBERT. No, he won't.

MRS. PERKINS. How d' y' know?

ALBERT. I know.

MRS. PERKINS. Polly, just put that blind back, will yer? I don't like bein' too public.

MISS PERKINS. Oh! I daren't.

ALBERT. Now, ma'am, give it to me.

MRS. PERKINS. Eh?

ALBERT. Let's have it. Quick.

MRS. PERKINS. Where d' you come in, Albert?

ALBERT. Come on. This'll be the making o' me.

MRS. PERKINS. O' me too, I 'ope. But 'adn't we all better be movin'?

MISS PERKINS. Where to, Ma?

MRS. PERKINS. Out at the back door. Pack a few things in a bag.

ALBERT. What are y' up to? What y' mean?

MRS. PERKINS. Now, Albert, there's no time to make explanations. We're all in at this, aren't we?

ALBERT. Well – in a way. But look here –

MRS. PERKINS. South America's the place, isn't it? D' y' know anythin' o' the sailin's? Or 'ad we better cross to France? Better take the midnight train somewhere.

ALBERT. Has she gone dotty?

MRS. PERKINS. Y're all asleep. Come on, Polly. A few things in a bag. Now, Pa. Better put this light out p'raps. Is the front door shut? Look at the timetable, Pa. (*She is making for the door when* ALBERT *intercepts her.*)

ALBERT. Give me the diamond. I dunno what y're talkin' about.

MRS. PERKINS. Nay, I stick to this.

ALBERT. You can't! What nonsense! Give it here! This job's the making o' me. Let's have it.

MRS. PERKINS. Nay, it's mine an' I'll stick to it.

ALBERT. Yours!

MRS. PERKINS. Yes. Dimonds like this belongs to them as can get 'em. Nobody's honest with things like this. I got it an' y' shall all share. But it's mine. It's mine! Eh! It's a beauty. I'd stick to this if all the p'lice in London was after me.

ALBERT. Y'd do what?

MRS. PERKINS. Ay, an' Scotland Yard too.

ALBERT. Bah! *I'm* Scotland Yard.

MRS. PERKINS. What!

MISS PERKINS. Oh! Albert!

ALBERT. Didn't y' know? Didn't y' guess? Didn't y' understand? What did y' take me for?

MRS. PERKINS. D' y' mean to say – ?

ALBERT. I mean t' say it's 'igh time I was on my way back with this dimond. The gang's all rounded up by this time.

MRS. PERKINS. The gang?

MR. PERKINS. That feller was one of 'em, then? Where is he?

ALBERT. He was copped when he left 'ere. Y' didn't know y'r 'ouse was surrounded.

MRS. PERKINS. But 'ow did the dimond come 'ere? 'Oo threw it in?

ALBERT. I did.

MISS PERKINS. You!

MR. PERKINS. You did!

ALBERT. I did that.

MR. PERKINS. Why?

ALBERT. Becos they were after me. I was a dead man if I stuck to it then. I threw it in 'ere to gain time and knowin' the 'ouse.

MISS PERKINS. Well, I never!

ALBERT. They're a desp'rate lot.

MR. PERKINS. It's all most unusual. Never since I've been an 'ouse'older 'ave I –

MISS PERKINS. Oh, Albert! You might 'ave told me.

ALBERT. I 'ad my reasons.

MRS. PERKINS. Y're a detective, then?

ALBERT. I am that. So let's have it. I tell yer I must be off.

MRS. PERKINS (*holding up the diamond, but away from him*). Look at it, Albert!

ALBERT. I see it.

MRS. PERKINS. Can y' be honest? Look at it!

ALBERT. She's off 'er chump.

MR. PERKINS. She doesn't reely mean it. I've borne a 'igh character all my life.

MRS. PERKINS (*passionately*). It's my dimond.

MISS PERKINS. I'm ashamed of my ma.

MR. PERKINS. My employers 'as always put the utmost confidence in me.

ALBERT. What's she up to? Now, ma'am, you'll just 'and that over or –

MRS. PERKINS. Or?

ALBERT (*he produces a whistle*). I wouldn't 'andle yer myself.

MRS. PERKINS. That's it, is it?

ALBERT. That's it.

MRS. PERKINS. Then let it go the way it came. (*She throws it through the window.*)

MR. PERKINS. 'Old on. There's another pane gone!

ALBERT. O 'ell! (*He rushes out.*)

MISS PERKINS. You'll ruin us, Ma.

MRS. PERKINS (*dusting one hand against the other*). A good shuttance.

MISS PERKINS (*at the window*). Oh! I hope he'll find it. There he is, and a policeman's with him. They've got it, I think. Yes. Albert, Albert! I wish he'd look up. They're seeing if its damaged. There! He's waved his hand.

MRS. PERKINS (*she has settled into her chair*). Well, we've 'ad quite a busy evenin'.

MISS PERKINS. I don't know what Albert'll think of you.

MRS. PERKINS. 'E's not going to marry me, thank 'eaven.

MR. PERKINS. D' y' want t' know what *I* think of yer?

MRS. PERKINS. Go on. Y've no 'magernation.

MISS PERKINS. I never thought to be ashamed of my own mother.

MR. PERKINS. Wantin' in the very el'ments of morality. I wonder 'ow Sossiety 'd get on if they was all like you.

MRS. PERKINS. Polly, put up that blind. It's a bit chilly with them broken panes.

MISS PERKINS. Most unladylike as well.

(*They settle down into their chairs again.* MRS. PERKINS *takes up her darning and* MR. PERKINS *the paper. After putting up the blind* MISS PERKINS *returns to her puzzle.*)

MRS. PERKINS. 'Ow much did y' say it was worth, Pa?

MR. PERKINS (*gruffly*). Never mind.

MRS. PERKINS. Well, I 'ad my bit o' fun for onct.

CURTAIN

ANALYSING THE STRUCTURE OF THE PLAY

A play may be regarded as a conflict between two or more opposing forces or people. In *The Grand Cham's Diamond,* Ma Perkins is the dynamic force. In the first part of the play she is at odds with Pa and Polly. Then she takes on the villain in a duel of wits, while continuing to keep her husband and daughter at bay. Finally she holds out against Albert, her future son-in-law, as well as her family, when he tries to take the diamond from her.

An interesting point about these three scenes of conflict is that in the first one the conflict springs from differences in the ideas and character of the people. In the second scene the conflict is a more physical one. The villain wants the diamond, and Ma won't give it to him. In the third scene, with Albert, there is conflict on both planes – mental and physical.

The second scene climaxes when the shot is fired and the lights go out. The denouement or unravelling from this knot of tension finds Ma in possession of the clock and gem. Then in the third scene there is fresh interest with the introduction of a new character, Albert. We have heard about Albert and are eager to see him. The conflict between Albert and Ma for the possession of the diamond ends with Ma flinging it out of the window. This section of the play is closed when Polly looks out of the window and we know that Albert has the diamond and loves her.

What remains is that we in the audience, who have come to admire Ma, should have a final glimpse of her with her family settling down to the monotony of her life again. We are as pleased as she is to know that she has had her bit of fun "for onct".

FURTHER READING AND DISCUSSION

The Grand Cham's Diamond was first performed in 1918, when the author, Allan Monkhouse, was sixty years of age. While the play was his most popular work, he wrote others which you will enjoy reading. Perhaps the best of these are *The Education of Mr. Surrage,* a light comedy, and *The Conquering Hero,* one of the finest plays about the first World War.

An interesting discussion could centre around the treatment of the detective-story material in the play. You will have some among you who are specialists in this type of fiction and know Father Brown, Sherlock Holmes, and the other great amateur detectives of the "whodunit" literature. If you examine the play you will soon realize that the author is making fun of this literature. The play is a satire or travesty on stories dealing with valuable gems and thieves who steal them.

While the treatment of the melodramatic part of the play is farcical, our interest in Ma, Pa, Polly, and Albert as individuals is so great that the play on the whole is kept within the framework of comedy. It is true that the characters are drawn somewhat broadly, as in farce, but they remain essentially genuine. Moreover, the drama has a certain merit as a social document or play of ideas, commenting as it does on the dullness of suburban life. For this reason, too, it keeps above the plane of farce. Perhaps you will decide to call the play a comedy, with some of the ingredients of farce and melodrama added.

THINKING ABOUT THE PLAY

1. Show how skilfully, and in what a bright, humorous, and interesting fashion, we are told what we need to know in the first part of the play about the diamond, the thieves, their extradition, and the window and blind.
2. How are we prepared in the first part of the play to accept the things that Ma Perkins says and does in the last half?
3. The author gives us the name of Polly's suitor in the course of the play by an interesting device. Examine this carefully.
4. Pick out the most amusing moment in the play.

BROTHERS IN ARMS

MERRILL DENISON

COMEDY OF THE CANADIAN NORTH

This is one of the most famous and successful of Canadian one-act plays. It is notable, not for its plot, which is slight, but for its humorous dialogue, characterization, and ideas.

The story is simple. Major J. Altrus Browne and his wife, Dorothea, are at a hunting cabin in the north. The Major wants to return to the city in a hurry. He tries to get information about someone to drive him down from Syd White, backwoodsman, who is not very helpful until the last moment. The suspense created by this conflict is sufficient to tide us over the discussion of Charlie's whereabouts, of the war, and of the deer-shooting. The surprise comes when we learn that Syd might have driven the car all the time. This causes the Major's final outburst and brings the play to an end.

The Major must be convincing as a successful businessman and army officer. He must assume an air of self-importance and authority, and speak with a firm, pompous voice. His wife, Dorothea, is a wide-eyed, simple, and easily enraptured girl.

Since the comedy of the play is so broad that it verges on farce, both characters can be exaggerated to the point where they become absurdly and ridiculously amusing. The Major is a petty, bombastic little toy soldier, whom we delight to see frustrated. Dorothea is a silly creature who is just *thrilled* with everything. She has that overly bright, enthusiastic manner that bespeaks the empty mind.

Set against these two city folk are "the sturdy sons of the north", Syd White and Charlie Henderson. Two boys who can imitate the slow, heavy, rough speech of backwoodsmen will have a good time acting these parts.

Although *Brothers in Arms* was written in one sitting, we must not be deluded into thinking that one-act plays are easily created. Doubtless the ideas, the situation, and the characters had been simmering in the playwright's head for some time before the eventful day when the play was written. Merrill Denison spent many summers in north-eastern Ontario, and had doubtless listened on frequent occasions to "Dorotheas" rhapsodizing about the "wild virgin country" and "the simplicity of this big, free land". Doubtless, too, he had been amused to watch, on many occasions, encounters between these Dorotheas and their Majors and the backwoodsmen of the district. From such encounters, in all probability, the play was born.

The setting presents no difficulty. In a class or studio performance you can "fake" the stove and wall bunk. The bench, boxes, firewood, and lanterns can easily be found. Charlie Henderson should have an actual rifle.

The Major should be careful not to pace up and down too much like an animal in a cage. There should be just enough movement to punctuate and emphasize his high-strung, angry state of mind. He can move before or after he speaks, or while he is speaking. Rehearse his movements carefully, trying each method of delivering the lines and adopting the one that helps to point the meaning most effectively.

When the Major trips in the hole in the floor, where the boards have been removed, he need only catch his toe behind the other heel as he walks to have an effective fall.

I won't delay your pleasure any longer. In the first performance at Hart House Theatre, a man collapsed from laughing too much and had to be assisted from the hall. Thousands before you have enjoyed acting these parts and seeing the play. Now it's your turn.

CHARACTERS

J. ALTRUS BROWNE, *a business man*
DOROTHEA BROWNE, *his wife*
SYD WHITE } *backwoodsmen*
CHARLIE HENDERSON } *backwoodsmen*

Produced at Hart House Theatre, Toronto, April 1921, with the following cast:

SYD WHITE	Charles Thompson
DOROTHEA BROWNE	Heasell Mitchell
J. ALTRUS BROWNE	Walter Bowles
CHARLIE HENDERSON	Merrill Denison

BROTHERS IN ARMS

SCENE: *A hunting camp in the backwoods.*

TIME: *Dusk of a November evening, 1919.*

A room in an abandoned farmhouse used as a hunting camp during the deer season. There is a door and window in the far wall, a double-tiered wall bunk at the left and at the right a shanty stove. There is a bench beneath the window, a couple of upended boxes near the stove. The room is dirty and squalid.

The curtain rises showing DOROTHEA BROWNE, *a romantic young woman, seated on the bench, her chin in her hand, gazing wistfully into the fire. She shifts her pose so that she may watch her husband, who is pacing nervously up and down.*

J. ALTRUS BROWNE *is a business man with a penchant for*
efficiency. He served as a Major in the Army Service Corps 1

1. During the First World War there was a base camp at Sandgate, on the south coast of England near Folkestone. Major Browne served there in the Army Service Corps which, as its name implies, was a corps which "serviced" the army with supplies. Because he

---

during the late war and spent a most rigorous time at Sandgate. He looks forward to the next war.

DOROTHEA (*pleadingly*). Altrus, dear, won't you sit down You're so impatient.

BROWNE (*baring his wrist-watch with a click*). But Dorothea! We've been here half an hour and not a sign of this man who owns the car. (*Viciously.*) We'll miss that train as sure as . . .

DOROTHEA (*impatiently*). Oh, I know, dear . . . but don't you love it here? (*Rising, with an outflung arm gesture.*) This simple camp, its rustic charm . . . the great big out-of-doors? (*Goes to* BROWNE *and fondles his arm and lays her head on his shoulder.*) I don't want to go back to Toronto, Altrus. (*Emphatically.*) I'd like to live in a place like this forever

BROWNE (*with a tired indrawn breath*). But, my dear, we must go back.

DOROTHEA. Oh, yes, I know, dear. But this is our first trip together since we've been married. Since you came home from France.

BROWNE (*with controlled impatience*). Dorothea! I've explained to you that we must catch this midnight train. It is most important. If this man who owns the Ford ever turns up

DOROTHEA. But, dear . . . you can't do any good by walking around like that. Come and sit down beside me on this simple rough-hewn bench.

BROWNE (*growling*). I'm all right, thanks.

DOROTHEA (*her chin on her hand, pensively*). Oh, it's Canada and it's the wilds. Don't you love the wilds?

BROWNE. I do not! Might have known something like this would happen coming up to a God-forsaken hole twenty miles from a railroad. And if that chap doesn't turn up pretty soon . . .

DOROTHEA (*ecstatically*). I do hope he does. I'm just dying

---

remained at Sandgate, he saw no actual fighting and knew nothing of the reality and horror of war. Hence, "He looks forward to the next war." The word "rigorous" is used ironically.

to see one of those hunters. They must be such big, fine, simple men, living so close to nature all the time.

BROWNE. I'd like to see the one that drove us up. He'd do me.

DOROTHEA. Why, Altrus, he was only a common taxi-driver. I mean one of those coureurs-de-bois. One of those romantic figures we've read of in books about Canada. And we've seen them in the movies.

BROWNE. Taken in California, probably. (*Half to himself.*) If it took us five hours to drive up to the MacDougal's in the daytime, it will take us a good six to get down to that station tonight.

DOROTHEA (*half to herself*). I remember the hero in the "Land of Summer Snows". (*To* BROWNE.) It was about 2
Canada. (*To herself.*) A big, strong, silent man. (*To* BROWNE, *ecstatically.*) Oh, didn't you love him?

BROWNE. Unh?

DOROTHEA. Didn't you love him!

BROWNE (*absently, with puckered brows*). Love who?

DOROTHEA. That big, strong, silent man in the "Land of Summer Snows".

BROWNE (*deliberately*). My dear Dorothea! Can't you realize that if we don't catch that train at Kaladar tonight 3
I stand to lose twenty-five thousand dollars?

DOROTHEA. I know, dear. But I did hope we'd see a real Canadian frontiersman before we left.

BROWNE. We've got to see one before we leave. One frontiersman with a Ford.

DOROTHEA (*sobbing*). You never think of anything but your old business.

2. *Land of Summer Snows* is a fictitious name given to a silent film of the pre-war period. Note the alliterative title, which sounds attractive but is hardly complimentary to Canada.
3. You will find Kaladar on a map of Ontario; it is on Highway 7, seventy miles east of Peterborough. The play is set in a hunting cabin twenty miles north of Kaladar.

BROWNE (*going rapidly to her*). There, there, dear, there, there. I only worry about the business for your sake, dear.

DOROTHEA (*dabbing her eyes*). It's selfish of me . . . but I can't help being a romantic little fool. (*Blubbering lustily.*)

BROWNE. You're not a fool, dearest. Tell me you're not a fool.

DOROTHEA. Oh, but I am. (*Wiping her eyes.*) And ever since you met Jim MacDougal on the battlefields and wrote me of him, I've looked forward to coming here. During those horrible days of the war when you were at Sandgate, I've looked forward to coming here, where you would be safe and out of danger and we might find romance . . . romance in the land of Robert Service and Ralph Connor.

BROWNE. Yes, yes, dear.

DOROTHEA. I have wanted to see one of those noble men from whom they drew their characters.

(DOROTHEA *is sitting on the bench,* ALTRUS *kneeling beside her. Neither of them see* SYD WHITE *enter.* SYD *is a backwoodsman. He is wearing an old army tunic and a nondescript cap covered with red; his trousers are thrust inside a pair of heavy boots. He observes the pair on the bench, nods towards them and turns to place his gun against the wall. At the*

4. Jim MacDougal is a friend of Browne. He has a house or cottage near the cabin where the play takes place. He has invited Browne to make the hunting trip and to bring his bride with him. The sentences that follow should not be taken at face value. He and Browne had actually met at Sandgate and not on the battlefields. Dorothea's husband was in no danger. She is romanticizing about the war, as she does about everything else.
5. Robert Service (1874-1958) is famous for his poetry about the harsh and rigorous life of the Canadian North West during the early days. Ralph Connor (Charles William Gordon, 1860-1937), one of Canada's most popular novelists, wrote stories about pioneer life in his native Glengarry County and romantic novels about the years when the West was opening up.
6. Covered with red: so that he is easily seen by other hunters.

sound of the gun falling, DOROTHEA *starts and* BROWNE *rises quickly to his feet.*)

DOROTHEA. Oh!

BROWNE (*importantly to* SYD, *who is going on with his work*). My name is Browne, Major J. Altrus Browne. Mr. MacDougal told me that I'd find the man who drove me up from the station here.

SYD (*mildly interested*). Oh, he did, eh? (*Looks at the stove.*) Fire's kinda low, eh? (*Goes to the corner and gets some wood.*) You couldn't find no wood, I s'pose, to put on it. We jest rip a board off'n the floor. (*Going to the stove.*) Saves a feller quite a bit of time.

BROWNE (*trying to impress* SYD). I received a very important business communication this morning which makes it imperative that I return to Toronto tonight.

SYD. Oh, got to go back, eh?

DOROTHEA. And I do wish he would stay longer. But the Major is a business man, you know. (*She is trying to fit* SYD *into innumerable roles in fiction.*)

SYD. Oh, he is, eh? (*Filling his pipe.*) Kinda dark in here. (*Looks around.*) A feller might have a bit of light. (*Gets up and prowls around.*) They was a lantrun some place around here with the chimley cracked.

BROWNE (*impatiently and imperiously*). Never mind the lantern. We'll only be here a few moments, anyway.

SYD (*still searching under the beds*). Won't do no harm to have a bit of light. (*Finds the lantern and lights it; the globe is so sooty that just a glimmer shows.*) There, kinda helps make the place more cheerful.

BROWNE. Where is the man who drove us up from the station?

SYD (*hanging the lantern and sitting down behind the stove*). Well, that's kinda hard to say. When was it he druv you up?

BROWNE. Last Tuesday.

DOROTHEA (*helpfully*). And it rained the whole way. I loved it.

SYD (*politely*). Kinda wet, eh? (*To* BROWNE.) Last Tuesday? That musta been Charlie druv you up.

BROWNE. It doesn't matter what his name is. What I want to know is when he will be back.

SYD. Charlie it was. Charlie Henderson. That's who it'd be. He ain't here.

BROWNE. Yes! Yes! Yes! But when will he be here?

SYD (*lighting his pipe*). Well, that's kinda hard to say. The lads went over to Wolf Lake this mornin'.

BROWNE. This Charlie is with them?

DOROTHEA (*to* SYD). You know, I think your camp is adorable. It's so simple, and direct. So natural. (*With appropriate gestures.*)

SYD (*to* DOROTHEA). This here place?

DOROTHEA. Yes. Oh! I love it.

BROWNE. Dorothea!

SYD (*observing* BROWNE *walking near the corner by the head of the beds*). That floor ain't none too good since we've been using it for the stove.

BROWNE. Never mind about me. (*Exasperated.*) When will these men be back from Wolf Lake?

SYD. Well . . . that's kinda hard to say. It's most ten miles over there and the trail ain't none too good. But I figger they ought to be comin' in most any time now.

BROWNE. And this fellow Henderson will be with them?

SYD. No . . . he won't be with them. That is, it ain't likely.

BROWNE. Can't you understand that I have only five hours to catch that midnight train at Kaladar? And that I must find this fellow Henderson to take me down?

DOROTHEA (*to* SYD). And I simply hate to think of going back so soon.

SYD. Shame you can't stay till the end of the huntin' season. He might kill a deer.

BROWNE. Dorothea! Will you please try and keep quiet. (*To* SYD.) Now, when will Henderson be back? Answer me definitely.

(SYD *is cleaning his gun for several successive speeches. This adds to the hopelessness of* BROWNE*'s position.*)

SYD. Well . . . that's kinda hard to say. He went still-huntin' 7
over back of the big rock . . .

BROWNE (*almost frantic*). Yes, but you must know when he'll be here. I've got to have him drive down to that train tonight.

SYD. Oh . . . you want him to drive down to catch the midnight?

BROWNE. Yes, yes, yes. When will he be back?

SYD. Well . . . if he went back of the big rock he'd most likely leave about dark . . .

BROWNE. It's been dark half an hour. How long would it take him to get back?

SYD. I figger it'd take him about half an hour if he had a boat.

BROWNE. Half an hour, eh? Should be here, then, soon. (*Thinks.*) Did he have a boat?

SYD. No . . . he didn't have no boat.

BROWNE (*infuriated*). What in heaven's name are you talking about a boat for, if he didn't have one?

DOROTHEA. Don't be impatient, dear.

SYD. As I was sayin' – if he had a boat . . .

BROWNE (*screaming with rage*). But you said he didn't have one.

DOROTHEA (*helpfully*). But, dear, if he did have a boat.

BROWNE. Dorothea! will you kindly keep quiet and leave this to me? (*To* SYD.) Now, if it's within the range of human possibility, will you tell me when you expect Henderson back here?

SID (*laying down his gun and doing his best to be explicit*). Well, I figger it this way. If he had a boat . . .

DOROTHEA (*patiently*). He means that if he had a . . .

7. Still-hunting: hunting deer from a fixed position.

BROWNE (*disgustedly*). Let's forget about the boat. On foot, how long would it take him to get over here? Don't you realize that he's got to take me to that train? Will he be back in ten minutes? Twenty minutes?

SYD. Well . . . it's kinda hard to say. He mightn't have went back of the big rock at all. He might have picked up a fresh track and followed it west. But that ain't likely because most of the deer's scared off'n this side of the lake.

DOROTHEA. Oh! What scared them?

BROWNE. Dorothea! How many times must I ask you to keep quiet and not interrupt? I must find out when we can get out of here. (*To* SYD.) You feel sure that he went back of the big rock?

SYD. I figger that's most likely where he's went. And if he couldn't have got the loan of a boat . . .

BROWNE. He might have borrowed a boat then?

DOROTHEA (*helpfully*). Why, yes, dear, he might have *borrowed* a boat.

BROWNE. Is there some place he might have borrowed a boat?

SYD. No . . . there ain't.

DOROTHEA. You see, dear, he couldn't have got a boat anyway.

BROWNE. Good God!

SYD. Ain't no one's got a boat over here except Levi Weeks and he's got his'n up to Buck Lake.

BROWNE (*striding over to* SYD). Look here, we've established this point. He couldn't have gotten a boat.

SYD. Well . . . I wouldn't go as far as to say that. He might . . .

DOROTHEA. Dear, won't you sit down?

SYD. Yes, you'd best sit down. That floor ain't none too good.

BROWNE. Never mind about me. I can look out for myself all right.

DOROTHEA. But do be careful, dear.

BROWNE. Dorothea! (*To* SYD.) Now let's find out about

your friend Charlie.

SYD. He ain't no particular friend of mine. Kind of a brother-in-law, it seems to me. His half-sister Nellie married my stepbrother Aligan. My father's . . .

DOROTHEA. Why, you're related then.

BROWNE. Dorothea! (*Pleadingly.*) Do keep quiet. (*To* SYD.) He could walk back in an hour, couldn't he?

SYD. He might. But it'd depend on whether he got a deer or not. If he got a fawn and it wasn't too much to heft, he'd most likely try and drug it out.

BROWNE. From what I've seen of this country it's likely he never saw a deer.

DOROTHEA. Why, Altrus, they catch lots of wild things in the wilds.

SYD. Well . . . if he didn't get a deer the chancetes is he'd stay in the bush all night.

BROWNE. Do you mean to say that there is a possibility of his not returning at all?

DOROTHEA. We'd have to stay over then, wouldn't we?

SYD (*laughing*). I figger you would. He often stays out all night when he's still-huntin'. It ain't likely though. Charlie most often gets his deer. He ought to be here most any time now . . . if he's a-comin' at all.

DOROTHEA. I almost hope he doesn't come. You know, this is the first trip we've had together since we've been married. Since Altrus left his battalion.

SYD. You're his woman, eh? Married?

BROWNE. Dorothea, do shut up. Can't you realize what twenty-five thousand dollars means to us? (*She pouts.*)

SYD (*seriously*). If you'd really wanted to have gone, you shoulda went this morning.

BROWNE. I didn't know till four o'clock. (*Angrily.*) I should never have come up into this God-forsaken hole at all.

SYD (*mildly remonstrative*). This place ain't bad. The deer's about scared off what with the Finches running hounds all the year around, but they's still some left.

BROWNE (*disgustedly*). I'm not talking about the hunting.

I'm talking about the distance it is from the railroad.

DOROTHEA. That's why I love it. It's so far from everything.

SYD. Might be another twenty miles and do no harm.

DOROTHEA (*excitedly*). Oh, Altrus. He loves the wild, virgin country, too. Far, far from civilization . . . and phones . . . and motors.

BROWNE. I'd give a lot to see one, just one, now.

SYD. It's quite a ways from them things, but I figger it's just as well. Keeps folks outa here in the summer. City folks is a kinda bother.

DOROTHEA. I know. They encroach on the freedom of your life.

SYD. They's always tryin' to get a feller to work. One way and another they figger they's doin' a feller a favour to let him work for 'em.

DOROTHEA. I know, you want to be left alone to lead your own simple life.

BROWNE (*who has been walking like a caged lion and has neared the dangerous corner*). Simple is right. Now look here. I'm going to give Henderson ten minutes more.

SYD. He might be back in ten minutes. If he got a deer and didn't try to drug it out with him. (*Pause.*) And he come by the lower trail. (*Pause.*) And he didn't stop down to the MacDougal's to listen to that there phonograph. I'd figger he'd most like be about . . .

(DOROTHEA *screams and runs over to* ALTRUS *who has tripped in a hole and is rubbing his ankle, cursing softly to himself.* SYD *makes no change in position.*)

SYD. I told you to keep out of there.

DOROTHEA. Dearest, what have you done? Did you hurt yourself, dear?

BROWNE. My ankle. (*Hobbles.*) It's only a wrench probably.

8. Find three speeches in which we are prepared for the accident that happens to Browne.

SYD (*chuckling*). I kinda figgered you'd do that. You should've sot down. What did you do? Sprained it?

BROWNE (DOROTHEA *has helped him across to the bench where he sits rubbing the ankle*). I didn't do anything to it. (*Explodes.*) It was your infernal floor. Holes all over the place, because you're too damn lazy to chop down a tree for firewood.

SYD (*indignantly*). We hain't got no time to split firewood when we're huntin'.

DOROTHEA. Did you hurt yourself badly, dear? (BROWNE *winces.*) Oh, do hurry and tear up something clean for a bandage. And get some hot water.

SYD (*laughing*). There ain't no water nearer'n the lake and there ain't nothin' clean here. He ain't hurt bad.

DOROTHEA (*anxiously*). I hope not.

SYD. Why, he was lucky. One day last week one of the hounds fell down that there hole and broke his leg. We had to shoot him. You'd do best to sit quiet for a while. Have a chew? (*Offering* BROWNE *a plug which he refuses with a gesture of repugnance.*) To my way of thinkin' there ain't nothin' side of a good steady chew to quiet a feller's temper.

BROWNE. I'll just sit here and keep my weight off it for a few minutes. If Henderson isn't here in ten minutes, we'll go.

SYD. Have a chew?

BROWNE (*white with rage*). My God! I'd like to have had you in my battalion for about six months.

(DOROTHEA *rises.*)

SYD. Yes, you was lucky.

BROWNE. I'd teach you a few things if I had you in the army.

SYD. Was you in the war?

DOROTHEA. Oh, yes. Altrus was in the Army Service Corps for over a year. He was a major.

BROWNE. I'd teach you a few things.

SYD. I suppose you might.

BROWNE. I'd give you ten years if you ever said might again.

SYD. Perhaps you might . . . I was in the army.

DOROTHEA (*with dawning wonderment*). Dear, he, too, fought for his country in the Great War. You're brothers in arms.

BROWNE (*silencing her with a gesture*). What outfit were you ever with?

SYD. The 284th Battalion, but I didn't see no sense to it, so I left.

DOROTHEA. How could you leave? Altrus had a lot of trouble getting out. They were awfully mean about it.

BROWNE. Left? Do you mean you deserted?

SYD. No, I didn't desert. The head lads told me to come home. I couldn't get the hang of it like the rest of the lads. They were willin' to walk around doing nothin', but they wasn't no sense to it to my way of thinkin'.

DOROTHEA (*reminiscently*). I felt that sometimes. (*To* BROWNE.) Didn't you, dear?

BROWNE (*explosively*). Certainly not. (*To* SYD.) Why, the very thing you need is a few years in the army. Straighten you up, teach you discipline, make a man of you.

DOROTHEA (*to* BROWNE, *brightly*). It helped you a lot, didn't it, dear? (*To* SYD.) It really was wonderful what the army could do.

SYD. To my way of thinkin' it didn't do nothin' except help make a feller lazy. That's what I couldn't see no sense in. If they'd been somethun useful for a feller to do I'da stayed and helped them with their war, but they wasn't except in the clink.

DOROTHEA. Well, why didn't you get them to transfer you to the Clink Department, if you liked it and were useful there? Altrus got transferred to the Quartermaster's Branch. One is always so much more useful in work one likes.

BROWNE (*looking helplessly at his wife*). I suppose you spent most of your time in the clink?

SYD. No, not most of it. But a feller was doin' somethun useful there. When I wasn't in jail . . .

9. Clink: guardhouse or jail. Originally the name of a prison in Southwark.

DOROTHEA. Oh, who put you in jail?

SYD. One of them head lads. When I wasn't there we done nothin' but drill. One of them head lads'd get us out and walk us. 'Tweren't no sense to that. Walkin' a feller around just for the sake of walkin'.

DOROTHEA. It does sound silly, doesn't it, dear?

BROWNE. Dorothea! You know nothing about this at all. (*To* SYD.) Didn't you want to fight for your country?

SYD. To my way of thinkin', that's why I joint the army. But we wasn't doin' no fightin'. We wasn't doin' nothin' but follerin' them head lads around drillin'.

BROWNE. You had to be drilled. You had to learn the rudiments of soldiering.

DOROTHEA. But don't you think they overdid it, now and then, dear?

SYD. To my way of thinkin', they did. Why, them head lads'd make us clean our boots and then walk us around in the dust. Why didn't they keep us inside if they wanted our shoes shiny?

DOROTHEA. I remember all those clean-limbed young fellows
at Camp Dix walking along the dusty roads. It did seem a 10
shame. (*To* BROWNE.) You had a horse, didn't you, dear?

BROWNE. Dorothea! (*To* SYD.) But can't you understand that you had to learn the job of soldiering? Your job was to fight Germans and you had to learn how to do it.

SYD (*emphatically*). That's just what I figgered. All them Germans havin' to be licked and us wastin' our time follerin' them head lads around. They even tried to learn me how to use a gun.

DOROTHEA. How absurd. They didn't really, did they? They wouldn't try to teach a frontiersman to use a gun, would they, dear?

BROWNE. Certainly they would. All these things are very necessary from the standpoint of discipline, my dear.

10. Camp Dix: In the First World War, Camp Dix was a military camp at Wrightstown, New Jersey. It is now called Fort Dix.

SYD. That's what the head lads used to say. (*Looking at* BROWNE.) Was you a head lad in the war?

BROWNE. I was an officer.

DOROTHEA (*proudly*). Oh, yes, my husband was a major and he was much too valuable to go to the front. They kept him, quite against his own wishes, in Sandgate, all during the war, didn't they, Altrus?

BROWNE. Dorothea! Don't be absurd.

DOROTHEA. But you told me so yourself, dear.

SYD. I kinda figgered you was a head lad.

BROWNE (*sarcastically, evasively*). I suppose you told your officers what you thought of discipline?

SYD. Yes, I says to the head lad, I says, I wasn't goin' to waste my time doin' things they wasn't no sense in.

DOROTHEA. How courageous.

BROWNE (*dumbfounded*). You told one of your officers that?

SYD (*surprised*). Yes, I says to him, I says . . .

BROWNE. You were put under arrest, of course.

DOROTHEA. Would they arrest a man just for saying what he thought?

BROWNE. They generally shot them for that.

DOROTHEA (*with enthusiasm*). But dear, don't you love his sturdy independence? It's so Canadian.

BROWNE. That's not independence. It's insubordination. What crime did you commit to get you in the guardhouse?

SYD. 'Tweren't no crime.

BROWNE (*sharply*). But, man alive, you must have done something.

SYD. 'Tweren't no crime. I was out walkin' with my gun outside the tents where the lads slept and one of the head lads come around and ast me a lot of questions which I didn't know the answers for, because they was kinda riddles anyways, and he got mad and says to me I was guardin' the camp from Germans.

BROWNE. Why, you were on sentry duty and he was the officer of the day!

DOROTHEA. But, dear, he said it was at night.

SYD. Yes, it was at night. So I says to him, I says, all right, just to get rid of him, for I seen they wasn't no sense to it. They wasn't a German this side of the ocean and they wasn't no sense hangin' around in the cold. So I went in and went to bed.

BROWNE (*horrified*). You could have been shot for that. On sentry duty and deserted your post.

SYD. That's what the head lad says the next mornin'. Couldn't shoot a feller fer that. Wouldn't be no sense to it. I told the head lad, and he seen I was right. He come near to cryin' and says I could be his batman. But I wasn't going to stay up till four in the mornin' to pull anybody's boots off'n them, let alone one of them head lads, so he sent me to jail.

DOROTHEA (*romantically*). How cramping it must have been to a free out-of-doors spirit like yours. What did you do?

SYD. I liked it right well, but the head lads wouldn't let me stay when they found I was kinda enjoyin' it.

BROWNE. My heart bleeds for your officers.

SYD. Them head lads? Why, they didn't do nothin' but think up ways for us to waste our time.

DOROTHEA. You fought in France, of course? (*With a change of mood.*) Altrus always wanted to go to the front and fight, but they wouldn't let him leave England. I don't know what they would have done without him. He's so clever at business, you know.

SYD (*genuinely interested*). He is, eh?

BROWNE (*the conversation is becoming embarrassing*). How about this man, Charlie?

SYD. Well . . . he'd been here long ago if he coulda got a boat.

BROWNE (*he whimpers*). Back to the navy again?

DOROTHEA. But didn't you adore England? Oh, I love London.

SYD. London's quite a place, but to my way of thinkin' a feller can have just as good a time down here to Belleville.

DOROTHEA (*understandingly*). I know. You love the simplicity of this big free land.

BROWNE. Too simple-minded to like anything else. How did they get rid of you? Dishonourable discharge?

SYD. No, they wasn't nothin' dishonourable about it. They had a meetin' one day and I told 'em what they ought to do to my way of thinkin', and one of the old fellers, the head lad hisself, I figger it was, says I was incorr . . . incorr . . . incorr . . .

DOROTHEA. Incorruptible.

BROWNE (*explosively*). Incorruptible nothing. Incorrigible.

SYD. That's it. Says I was goin' home in disgrace. Ain't that just like the army? Why, when I got outside, the rest of the lads says I was a lucky stiff to be gettin' home at all. (*Gets up and listens.*) Someone's comin'.

BROWNE. I can hear no one.

SYD. Perhaps you ain't used to listenin' much in your business. We got a feller up here that got his eyes blew out in France can hear most a mile.

DOROTHEA. Someone is coming, Altrus. I can hear them. Listen! I do hope it's one of those men I've read about.

BROWNE (*peremptorily*). Is that Henderson? (SYD *nods his head.*)

DOROTHEA. Only the taxi-man. I'm so disappointed.

BROWNE. Well, I'm not. Now we can get something accomplished.

(*He rises, awaiting* CHARLIE*'s entrance, as if all would now be well.* SYD *rises and waits expectantly, showing an entirely new interest in life.* DOROTHEA *pettishly fingers a glove.* CHARLIE *comes in the door, carrying a gun, nods to* BROWNE *and his wife, and goes to the stove and warms his hands.*)

CHARLIE. Evenin'. Harye, Syd?

11. This sentence introduces a serious note in the comic picture of war that the play presents.

SYD. Any luck?

BROWNE. See here, you're the man who drove us up from the station, aren't you?

CHARLIE. Last Tuesday, wasn't it? (*Turns to* SYD *as if he had no further interest in* BROWNE.) Well, Syd, I got a nice four-year-old buck.

DOROTHEA. Oh, did you catch a buck?

BROWNE. See here, I've got to catch the midnight at Kaladar.

CHARLIE (*politely interested*). Got to catch the midnight, eh? You'd best be startin' soon.

SYD. Where'd you get him?

CHARLIE. In them hardwoods north of Dyer Lake.

DOROTHEA (*thrilled*). I'd love to have been there, wouldn't you, dear?

BROWNE. I would not. See here, Henderson!

SYD. How'd you get him, runnin'?

CHARLIE (*sitting down*). It was this way, Syd. About four o'clock I was about a mile north of Dyer Lake, a-standin' on top of a little rise, smokin'.

DOROTHEA. Isn't it exciting? I do wish we could have been there, don't you, dear?

BROWNE. Dorothea!

CHARLIE. I thought I seen somethin' move, but you know how you can look at a frozen deer and think it ain't nothin' but a tree.

DOROTHEA. Oh, do they freeze?

SYD. It ain't freezin' like ice. They stand still without movin' a hair. Just like that doe I missed yesterday.

BROWNE. Look here, Henderson. I stand to lose twenty-five thousand dollars . . .

CHARLIE. Twenty-five thousand dollars. Quite a lot of money. Just like that doe, it was, Syd. I looked again and seen him move his head. Why, he wasn't seventy-five feet from me.

DOROTHEA (*excitedly*). Weren't you awfully nervous? I know I would have been. I'm so excited.

SYD (*sucking on his pipe*). Afraid of scarin' him, eh?

CHARLIE. Yes. Well, I started to drug the rifle to me. Slow . . . slow . . . slow.

BROWNE. Drug it faster, in heaven's name. Shoot your blithering deer and listen to me.

SYD. But you got him, eh?

DOROTHEA. You got him?

CHARLIE. Yes, sir, I got him. I waits for him to move a bit so's I could get a sight on his shoulder. Didn't want to shoot him in the head.

DOROTHEA (*breathless*). No, you wouldn't want to do that.

CHARLIE. Well. I waited till his shoulder come across the sights and then I took a long breath and drug down on the trigger.

DOROTHEA and SYD. What happened?

CHARLIE. I shot him.

DOROTHEA. Did you kill it?

CHARLIE. Dead.

SYD. What did you do with him? Leave him in the bush?

CHARLIE. Cleaned him out and hung him up on a tree.

SYD. Quite a ways in, I suppose?

CHARLIE. No, he ain't very far from the big lake.

SYD (*nodding his head and sucking his pipe*). He ain't far from the lake, eh? Now Charlie, if you'd only had a boat . . .

(*The dialogue has worked* BROWNE *into a fine frenzy, and at the mention of the boat his control breaks down completely.*)

BROWNE. Oh, God! Let's get out of here. Dorothea, come on.

(*He picks up his coat and stick and marches out of the door.* CHARLIE *and* SYD *rise, very surprised, and* SYD *takes down the lantern.*)

SYD (*leaning out of the door*). That's a hard trail to follow in the dark. Best take the lantrun.

BROWNE (*outside*). I don't want your damned lantrun. Come on, Dorothea, we'll go back to the MacDougal's.

(DOROTHEA *goes to the door and waits.*)

CHARLIE. What's the matter with the old feller? Seems kinda crabbed.

SYD (*tersely*). He was a head lad in the war.

CHARLIE (*understandingly*). So that's what's the matter with him?

BROWNE (*from some distance*). Dorothea!

DOROTHEA. Yes, dear. (*To* CHARLIE.) Good-bye, I'm so sorry I have to go, but I have enjoyed your story so much.

BROWNE. Dorothea!

DOROTHEA (*to* SYD). And I did love your simple, beautiful camp. (*Calling.*) I'm coming, dear.

(DOROTHEA *goes, and* CHARLIE *looks around for wood.*)

CHARLIE. Seems a nice sort of woman.

SYD. About the pure hog's fat, I'd figger. They's some wood over there where Jim ties his hound. (CHARLIE *goes to the corner.*) The old lad fell down the hole a ways back.

(*The two men laugh heartily and* CHARLIE *carries a stick or two over to the stove, puts it in, and then turns questioningly to* SYD.)

CHARLIE. He wasn't thinkin' of going down to Kaladar, tonight?

SYD. Seemed kinda sot on it. Said he wanted you to take him down.

CHARLIE. I wouldn't go down for twenty dollars. Why don't you take him, you ain't doin' nothin'?

SYD. Talked like he wanted you, all the time.

CHARLIE. Don't see why you shouldn't take him. I'll call him. (*Going to the door.*) Hey! Hey! Hey! Back here!

BROWNE (*from some distance*). What is it?

CHARLIE. Come on back! (*To* SYD.) The chancetes is he might let you drive him in.

SYD. It's kinda hard to say. He seemed sot on havin' you.

(*The two men smoke, waiting for* BROWNE, *who comes in shortly in a very black mood.*)

BROWNE. Well, what is it now?

CHARLIE. We been thinkin'.

BROWNE (*wheeling*). No! it's impossible.

CHARLIE. No, it ain't impossible. We was wonderin' why you was so all-fired anxious for me to drive you down?

BROWNE. Anybody will do. They told me at the MacDougal's that you were the only person who owned a car.

CHARLIE. Shucks. Syd owns half as much of the car as I do. Why don't you get him to drive you down?

BROWNE. Syd? Syd? Syd who?

CHARLIE. Why, Syd, there. You been talkin' to him for the best part of an hour.

(DOROTHEA *comes in the door.*)

BROWNE. Him?

CHARLIE. Yes, him. Might as well drive the old lad in, Syd. You ain't got nothin' much to do.

SYD (*reaching for his coat*). No, I ain't got nothin' to do. Might just as well a started an hour ago. Been well on the way.

BROWNE. And you stayed here talking when you could have started with us?

SYD. Yes. (*Stopping with one sleeve on.*)

BROWNE (*his temper shot completely*). Why didn't you say you could drive us in? Why didn't you say you owned half the car? Why did you keep us here wasting valuable time?

SYD. I didn't keep you. I'da taken you in if you'd ast me to.

BROWNE. Well, why in hell didn't you?

SYD. You never ast me.

CHARLIE. No, you never ast him.

DOROTHEA (*helpful to the last*). Why no, dear. You never asked him once.

CURTAIN

WRITTEN TO ORDER

Brothers in Arms is a play written to order. It was the custom in the early years at Hart House Theatre to produce annually a "bill" of Canadian plays. For the April 1921 performance, a comedy was needed to complete the program, and Merrill Denison was asked to write one. *Brothers in Arms* was the result. It is said that the author was told what actors were available – and even what scenery would have to be used! In such a fashion plays are born.

Yet in a very real sense all plays are written to order. The dramatist, while he writes, sees his characters in his mind's eye impersonated by living actors, moving about and working out their mimic destiny on his imagined stage. He hears them speaking the words he is putting into their mouths. And not until an audience judges and approves his effort on a living stage is he entitled to call it a play.

It is in this respect, above all, that the play differs from the novel and poem. The novelist and poet write in the seclusion of their studies. But the dramatist engages in what is virtually a social project, with his audience, director, actors, and stage technicians, real or imaginary, constantly in his mind, giving him valuable criticism, suggestions, and assistance. The novel or poem is complete once it has left the creator's hand. But the play only begins to come to life when it is put into rehearsal. During the rehearsal period it undergoes many changes. If, when produced, it is found weak in certain respects, it is again revised, rehearsed, and presented for public approval. If at last the audience is satisfied, the dramatist can rest from his labours!

THINKING ABOUT THE PLAY

1. Divide the play into scenes or sections, as was done with *The Grand Cham's Diamond,* and show how our interest is sustained in each part.
2. Humour in the play stems from plot (amusing things that happen); from character (amusing and characteristic things that the players say or do); and from ideas (amusing statements that are made about the north country, the war, and other subjects). In the dialogue we have the words with which the characters react to amusing situations, or express themselves and their ideas. Give examples of (a) amusing incidents,

(b) amusing lines that are characteristic of the people, and
(c) amusing lines in which the characters express ideas.

3. In what way is romantic idealism satirized in the play?
4. The criticism has been made that the backwoodsmen were real a generation ago, but that they were the products of poverty, ignorance, and isolation, and have no reality today. Do you believe this, or do Syd and Charlie seem real to you? Have you met, or heard of, people like them? Discuss the question.
5. Dorothea says that the backwoodsmen must be "big, fine, simple men" because they live so close to nature. Comment on this statement. Is there any truth in the theory? If you think there is, you might look to the poetry of William Wordsworth and Walt Whitman, and to *Walden* by Henry Thoreau, to support the position you take.

A NIGHT AT AN INN

LORD DUNSANY

A FAMOUS THRILLER

This thriller was written in 1916 and produced in the same year in New York. Even the author, attending the first production, confessed that he was amazed at the hold his play had on the audience.

The four characters with speaking parts are clearly drawn. Most important of them is the Toff, a "dilapidated gentleman", the leader of the sailors who have stolen the idol's eye. For this part you must find someone in the class who can be the English gentleman in manner and speech. The Toff is always cool, self-possessed, and distinguished. He is resourceful and clever – "a deep one if ever there was one". Only when the horrible idol enters the room is his quiet, superior manner shaken. His speech should be cultured, well-modulated, clear, and pleasant.

Sniggers is nervous and easily frightened. His part is difficult to play. More than any of the other characters, he creates the mood and excitement of the drama. His tense remark, "It's lonely enough", must suggest the fear and terror of what is to follow. He is the first to come running back after the three of them leave the Toff. In the last moments of the play, when he returns after having seen the idol, he strikes the final note of terror. It is he who sees Bill die. He is the third to be called, and his exit provides a climax of horror that is set against the final calm departure of the Toff.

Therefore in choosing Sniggers it is important to find an actor who is sensitive, with a wide emotional range, and yet great control. Acting which is merely hysterical will communicate its hysteria in nervousness, giggling, and finally laughter on the part of the audience.

Albert is the most vigorous and assertive of the three sailors. He is the Toff's rival for leadership. He is boastful and self-confident.

Bill is a hearty soul. He is a "yes-man", loyal to the Toff, for whom he has the greatest admiration. He is courageous. It was he who stole the idol's eye from the temple. He kills two of the heathen priests, saving the Toff's life on both occasions.

Use costumes that are in keeping with the characters of the men. The Toff, for all he is dilapidated, must look like a gentleman. Of the three sailors, Albert should be the best dressed. Sniggers should be in mouse-like colours, suggesting his lack of courage.

Allan Sangster, Milne Studios

A setting for another of Lord Dunsany's plays, *The Golden Doom*, on the stage of the Central High School of Commerce in Toronto.

Bill can have bolder colours – perhaps a bright shirt and socks.

Begin with the three sailors speaking in low but clear voices to one another, creating tension from the moment the curtain goes up. Albert's story should be told dramatically, illustrated with vivid pantomime (gesture and movement). When the three return, knowing that the priests have found them, there is a big step-up in terror. This is relieved by some humour when the Toff speaks of how he will receive their visitors. The actors and audience are able to relax in preparation for the next shock.

Then we have the killing of the three priests. Follow carefully the suggestions given in the book for managing these killings.

When the priests are disposed of, the almost unbearable tension is released again. There is good fellowship among the murderers. Hopes are high. The actors feel free and happy. But perhaps not entirely so. The happiness might be a little uncertain and giddy.

Then the final grim episode begins, heralded by Sniggers's entrance and frightened, tearful pleas. Everything builds to the climax, the one big moment, when the idol enters. The four death exits merely complete the horror.

The players should keep the long build-up toward this climax in mind. Every moment they must know that they are moving toward the idol's entrance. Scenes of fear and violent action, followed by relaxing humorous scenes, all fit into a pattern of increasing suspense and horror that culminates at this point.

The entrance of the idol must be well staged, and a great deal of care should be given to making the mask and costume for the creature. It must be horrible, not merely grotesque and ridiculous.

The outlandish accent and wailing, long-drawn-out mysterious tones of the idol's voice, summoning the four to their death, should be carefully rehearsed. Each exit must be different and in keeping with the character of the player.

Here is *A Night at an Inn,* one of the best of all thrillers.

CHARACTERS

A. E. SCOTT-FORTESCUE (THE TOFF), *a dilapidated gentleman*

WILLIAM JONES (BILL), ALBERT THOMAS, JACOB SMITH (SNIGGERS) — *merchant sailors*

FIRST PRIEST OF KLESH

SECOND PRIEST OF KLESH

THIRD PRIEST OF KLESH

KLESH

A NIGHT AT AN INN

SCENE: *A room in an inn.* SNIGGERS *and* BILL *are talking,* THE TOFF *is reading a paper.* ALBERT *sits a little apart.*

SNIGGERS. What's his idea, I wonder?
BILL. I don't know.
SNIGGERS. And how much longer will he keep us here?
BILL. We've been here three days.
SNIGGERS. And 'aven't seen a soul.
BILL. And a pretty penny it cost us when he rented the pub.
SNIGGERS. 'Ow long did 'e rent the pub for?
BILL. You never know with him.
SNIGGERS. It's lonely enough.
BILL. 'Ow long did you rent the pub for, Toffy?

(THE TOFF *continues to read a sporting paper; takes no notice of what is said.*)

1. Pub: short for public house – a house for the sale and consumption of alcoholic beverages. A pub is a typical and popular English institution.

SNIGGERS. 'E's such a toff.

BILL. Yet 'e's clever, no mistake.

SNIGGERS. Those clever ones are the beggars to make a muddle. Their plans are clever enough, but they don't work, and then they make a mess of things much worse than you or me.

BILL. Ah!

SNIGGERS. I don't like this place.

BILL. Why not?

SNIGGERS. I don't like the looks of it.

BILL. He's keeping us here, because here those priests can't find us. The three heathen priests what was looking for us so. But we want to go and sell our ruby soon.

ALBERT. There's no sense in it. 2

BILL. Why not, Albert?

ALBERT. Because I gave those black devils the slip in Hull. 3

BILL. You give 'em the slip, Albert?

ALBERT. The slip, all three of them. The fellows with the gold spots on their foreheads. I had the ruby then and I give them the slip in Hull.

BILL. How did you do it, Albert?

ALBERT. I had the ruby and they were following me.

BILL. Who told them you had the ruby? You didn't show it.

ALBERT. No . . . but they kind of know.

SNIGGERS. They kind of know, Albert?

ALBERT. Yes, they know if you've got it. Well, they sort of
mouched after me, and I tells a policeman and he says, Oh, 4
they were only three poor heathens and they wouldn't hurt
me. Ugh When I thought of what they did in Malta to poor
old Jim!

2. This is Albert's first speech. Notice how startling and effective his "delayed entrance" into the conversation is.
3. The mention of Hull gives us the first indication of the route the three seamen have followed to escape from the heathen priests. They have come to the pub from Hull, which you can locate on your map of England.
4. Mouch is a variant of "mooch": to loaf or skulk; to slouch along.

BILL. Yes, and to George in Bombay before we started.

SNIGGERS. Ugh!

BILL. Why didn't you give 'em in charge?

ALBERT. What about the ruby, Bill?

BILL. Ah!

ALBERT. Well, I did better than that. I walks up and down through Hull. I walks slow enough. And then I turns a corner and I runs. I never sees a corner but I turns it. But sometimes I let a corner pass just to fool them. I twist about like a hare. Then I sits down and waits. No priests.

SNIGGERS. What?

ALBERT. No heathen black devils with gold spots on their face. I give 'em the slip.

BILL. Well done, Albert!

SNIGGERS (*after a sigh of content*). Why didn't you tell us?

ALBERT. 'Cause 'e won't let you speak. 'E's got 'is plans and 'e thinks we're silly folk. Things must be done 'is way. And all the time I've give 'em the slip. Might 'av 'ad one o' them crooked knives in him before now but for me who give 'em the slip in Hull.

BILL. Well done, Albert! Do you hear that, Toffy? Albert has give 'em the slip.

THE TOFF. Yes, I hear.

SNIGGERS. Well, what do you say to that?

THE TOFF. Oh . . . well done, Albert!

ALBERT. And what a' you going to do?

THE TOFF. Going to wait.

ALBERT. Don't seem to know what 'e's waiting for.

SNIGGERS. It's a nasty place.

ALBERT. It's getting silly, Bill. Our money's gone and we want to sell the ruby. Let's get on to a town.

BILL. But 'e won't come.

5. We are learning more about their escape. Their flight began in Bombay, where George was murdered; from there they fled to Malta, where Jim was killed.
6. Give 'em in charge: turn them over to the police.

ALBERT. Then we'll leave him.

SNIGGERS. We'll go to London.

BILL. But 'e must 'ave 'is share.

SNIGGERS. All right. Only let's go. (*To* THE TOFF.) We're going, do you hear? Give us the ruby.

THE TOFF. Certainly.

(*He gives them a ruby from his waistcoat pocket; it is the size of a small hen's egg. He goes on reading his paper.*)

ALBERT. Come on, Sniggers.

(*Exeunt* ALBERT *and* SNIGGERS.)

BILL. Good-bye, old man. We'll give you your fair share, but there's nothing to do here, and we must sell the ruby.

THE TOFF. I'm not a fool, Bill.

BILL. No, no, of course not. Of course you ain't and you've helped us a lot. Good-bye. You'll say good-bye?

THE TOFF. Oh, yes. Good-bye. (*Still reads his paper.*)

(*Exit* BILL.)

(THE TOFF *puts a revolver on the table beside him and goes on with his paper. After a moment the three men come rushing in again, frightened.*)

SNIGGERS (*out of breath*). We've come back, Toffy.

THE TOFF. So you have.

ALBERT. Toffy . . . how did they get here?

THE TOFF. They walked, of course.

ALBERT. But it's eighty miles. 7

SNIGGERS. Did you know they were here, Toffy?

THE TOFF. Expected them about now.

ALBERT. Eighty miles!

BILL. Toffy, old man . . . what are we to do?

THE TOFF. Ask Albert.

BILL. If they can do things like this, there's no one

7. More information! The pub is eighty miles from Hull.

can save us but you, Toffy . . . I always knew you were a clever one. We won't be fools any more. We'll obey you Toffy.

THE TOFF. You're brave enough and strong enough. There isn't many that would steal a ruby eye out of an idol's head, and such an idol as that was to look at, and on such a night. You're brave enough, Bill. But you're all three of you fools. Jim would have none of my plans, and where's Jim? And George. What did they do to him?

SNIGGERS. Don't, Toffy!

THE TOFF. Well, then, your strength is no use to you. You want cleverness; or they'll have you the way they had George and Jim.

ALL. Ugh.

THE TOFF. Those black priests would follow you round the world in circles, year after year, till they got the idol's eye. And if we died with it, they'd follow our grandchildren. That fool thinks he can escape from men like that by running round three streets in the town of Hull.

ALBERT. But you 'aven't escaped them neither, because they're 'ere.

THE TOFF. So I supposed.

ALBERT. You supposed?

THE TOFF. Yes. I believe there's no announcement in the society papers. But I took this country seat especially to receive them. There's plenty of room if you dig, it is pleasantly situated, and what is more important, it is a very quiet neighbourhood. So I am at home to them this afternoon.

BILL. Well, you're a deep one.

THE TOFF. And remember, you've only my wits between you and death, and don't put your futile plans against those of an educated gentleman.

ALBERT. If you're a gentleman, why don't you go about among gentlemen instead of the likes of us?

8. Explain "plenty of room if you dig".

THE TOFF. Because I was too clever for them as I am too clever for you.

ALBERT. Too clever for them?

THE TOFF. I never lost a game of cards in my life.

BILL. You never lost a game?

THE TOFF. Not when there was money in it.

BILL. Well, well!

THE TOFF. Have a game of poker?

ALL. No, thanks.

THE TOFF. Then do as you're told.

BILL. All right, Toffy.

SNIGGERS. I saw something just then. Hadn't we better draw the curtains?

THE TOFF. No.

SNIGGERS. What?

THE TOFF. Don't draw the curtains.

SNIGGERS. Oh, all right.

BILL. But, Toffy, they can see us. One doesn't let the enemy do that. I don't see why . . .

THE TOFF. No, of course you don't.

BILL. Oh, all right, Toffy!

(*All begin to pull revolvers.*)

THE TOFF (*putting his own away*). No revolvers, please.

ALBERT. Why not?

THE TOFF. Because I don't want any noise at my party. We might get guests that hadn't been invited. Knives are a different matter.

(*All draw knives.* THE TOFF *signs to them not to draw them yet.* TOFFY *has already taken back his ruby.*)

BILL. I think they're coming, Toffy.

THE TOFF. Not yet.

ALBERT. When will they come?

THE TOFF. When I am quite ready to receive them. Not before.

SNIGGERS. I should like to get this over.

THE TOFF. Should you? Then we'll have them now.

SNIGGERS. Now?

THE TOFF. Yes. Listen to me. You shall do as you see me do. You will all pretend to go out. I'll show you how. I've got the ruby. When they see me alone they will come for their idol's eye.

BILL. How can they tell like this which of us has it?

THE TOFF. I confess I don't know, but they seem to.

SNIGGERS. What will you do when they come in?

THE TOFF. I shall do nothing.

SNIGGERS. What?

THE TOFF. They will creep up behind me. Then, my friends, Sniggers and Bill and Albert, who gave them the slip, will do what they can.

BILL. All right, Toffy. Trust us.

THE TOFF. If you're a little slow, you will see enacted the cheerful spectacle that accompanied the demise of Jim.

SNIGGERS. Don't, Toffy. We'll be there, all right.

THE TOFF. Very well. Now watch me.

(*He goes past the window to the inner door, right. He opens it inwards; then, under cover of the open door, he slips down on his knees and closes it, remaining on the inside, appearing to have gone out. He signs to the others, who understand. Then he appears to re-enter in the same manner.*)

THE TOFF. Now, I shall sit with my back to the door. You go out one by one, so far as our friends can make out. Crouch very low to be on the safe side. They mustn't see you through the window.

(BILL *makes his sham exit.*)

THE TOFF. Remember, no revolvers. The police are, I believe, proverbially inquisitive.

(*The other two follow* BILL. *All three are now crouching inside the door, right.* THE TOFF *puts the ruby beside him on the table. He lights a cigarette. The door at the back opens so slowly that you can hardly say at what moment it began.* THE TOFF *picks up his paper. A native of India wriggles along the floor ever so slowly, seeking cover from chairs. He moves left where* THE TOFF *is. The three sailors are right.* SNIGGERS *and* ALBERT *lean forward.* BILL*'s arm keeps them back. An armchair had better conceal them from the Indian. The black* PRIEST *nears* THE TOFF. BILL *watches to see if any more are coming. Then he leaps forward alone – he has taken his boots off – and knifes the* PRIEST. *The* PRIEST *tries to shout but* BILL*'s left hand is over his mouth.* THE TOFF *continues to read his sporting paper. He never looks around.*)

BILL (*sotto voce*). There's only one, Toffy. What shall we do?

THE TOFF (*without turning his head*). Only one?

BILL. Yes.

THE TOFF. Wait a moment. Let me think. (*Still apparently absorbed in his paper.*) Ah, yes. You go back, Bill. We must attract another guest . . . Now, are you ready?

BILL. Yes.

THE TOFF. All right. You shall now see my demise at my Yorkshire residence. You must receive guests for me. (*He* 9 *leaps up in full view of the window, flings up both arms and falls to the floor near the dead* PRIEST.) Now, be ready. (*His eyes close.*)

(*There is a long pause. Again the door opens, very slowly. Another* PRIEST *creeps in. He has three golden spots upon his forehead. He looks round, then he creeps up to his companion and turns him over and looks inside of his clenched hands. Then he looks at the recumbent* TOFF. *Then he creeps toward him.* BILL *slips after him and knifes him like the other, with his left hand over his mouth.*)

9. At last the pub is definitely placed – in Yorkshire.

BILL (*sotto voce*). We've only got two, Toffy!

THE TOFF. Still another.

BILL. What'll we do?

THE TOFF (*sitting up*). Hum!

BILL. This is the best way, much.

THE TOFF. Out of the question. Never play the same game twice.

BILL. Why not, Toffy?

THE TOFF. Doesn't work if you do.

BILL. Well?

THE TOFF. I have it, Albert. You will now walk into the room. I showed you how to do it.

ALBERT. Yes.

THE TOFF. Just run over here and have a fight at this window with these two men.

ALBERT. But they're . . .

THE TOFF. Yes, they're dead, my perspicuous Albert. But Bill and I are going to resuscitate them. . . . Come on.

(BILL *picks up a body under the arms.*)

THE TOFF. That's right, Bill. (*Does the same.*) Come and help us, Sniggers. (SNIGGERS *comes.*) Keep low, keep low. Wave their arms about, Sniggers. Don't show yourself. Now, Albert, over you go. Our Albert is slain. Back you get, Bill. Back, Sniggers. Still, Albert. Mustn't move when he comes. Not a muscle.

(*A face appears at the window and stays for some time. Then the door opens and, looking craftily round, the third* PRIEST *enters. He looks at his companions' bodies and turns round. He suspects something. He takes up one of the knives and with a knife in each hand he puts his back to the wall. He looks to the left and right.*)

THE TOFF. Come on, Bill!

(*The* PRIEST *rushes to the door.* THE TOFF *knifes the last* PRIEST *from behind.*)

THE TOFF. A good day's work, my friends.

BILL. Well done, Toffy. Oh, you are a deep one!

SNIGGERS. There ain't any more, Bill, are there?

THE TOFF. No more in the world, my friends.

BILL. Aye, that's all there are. There were only three in the temple. Three priests and their beastly idol.

ALBERT. What is it worth, Toffy? Is it worth a thousand pounds?

THE TOFF. It's worth all they've got in the shop. Worth just whatever we like to ask for it.

ALBERT. Then we're millionaires now.

THE TOFF. Yes, and what is more important we no longer have any heirs.

BILL. We'll have to sell it now.

ALBERT. That won't be easy. It's a pity it isn't small and we had half a dozen. Hadn't the idol any other on him?

BILL. No, he was green jade all over and only had this one eye. He had it in the middle of his forehead and was a long sight uglier than anything else in the world.

SNIGGERS. I'm sure we ought all to be very grateful to Toffy.

BILL. And, indeed, we ought.

ALBERT. If it hadn't been for him . . .

BILL. Yes, if it hadn't been for old Toffy . . .

SNIGGERS. He's a deep one.

THE TOFF. Well, you see I just have a knack of foreseeing things.

SNIGGERS. I should think you did.

BILL. Why, I don't suppose anything happens that our Toff doesn't foresee. Does it, Toffy?

THE TOFF. Well, I don't think it does, Bill. I don't think it often does.

BILL. Life is no more than just a game of cards to our old Toff.

THE TOFF. Well, we've taken these fellows' trick.

10. Point out the play on words in this speech and the one which precedes it. Why is it fitting that the Toff should make the pun?

SNIGGERS (*going to window*). It wouldn't do for anyone to see them.

THE TOFF. Oh, nobody will come this way. We're all alone on a moor.

BILL. Where will we put them?

THE TOFF. Bury them in the cellar, but there's no hurry.

BILL. And what then, Toffy?

THE TOFF. Why, then we'll go to London and upset the ruby business. We have really come through this job very nicely.

BILL. I think the first thing that we ought to do is to give a little supper to old Toffy. We'll bury these fellows tonight.

ALBERT. Yes, let's.

SNIGGERS. The very thing!

BILL. And we'll all drink his health.

ALBERT. Good old Toffy!

SNIGGERS. He ought to have been a general or a premier.

(*They get bottles from cupboard, etc.*)

THE TOFF. Well, we've earned our bit of a supper.

(*They sit down.*)

BILL (*glass in hand*). Here's to old Toffy, who guessed everything.

ALBERT and SNIGGERS. Good old Toffy!

BILL. Toffy, who saved our lives and made our fortunes.

ALBERT and SNIGGERS. Hear! Hear!!

THE TOFF. And here's to Bill, who saved me twice tonight.

BILL. Couldn't have done it but for your cleverness, Toffy.

ALBERT and SNIGGERS. Hear! Hear!!

ALBERT. He foresees everything.

BILL. A speech, Toffy. A speech from our general.

ALL. Yes, a speech.

SNIGGERS. A speech.

THE TOFF. Well, get me some water. This whisky's too much for my head, and I must keep it clear till our friends are safe in the cellar.

BILL. Water? Yes, of course. Get him some water, Sniggers.

SNIGGERS. We don't use water here. Where shall I get it?

BILL. Outside in the garden.

(*Exit* SNIGGERS.)

ALBERT. Here's to the future!

BILL. Here's to Albert Thomas, Esquire.

ALBERT. And William Jones, Esquire.

(*Re-enter* SNIGGERS, *terrified.*)

THE TOFF. Hullo, here's Jacob Smith, Esquire, J.P., alias Sniggers, back again.

SNIGGERS. Toffy, I've been thinking about my share in that ruby. I don't want it. Toffy; I don't want it.

THE TOFF. Nonsense, Sniggers. Nonsense.

SNIGGERS. You shall have it. Toffy, you shall have it yourself, only say Sniggers has no share in this 'ere ruby. Say it, Toffy, say it!

BILL. Want to turn informer, Sniggers?

SNIGGERS. No, no. Only I don't want the ruby, Toffy . . .

THE TOFF. No more nonsense, Sniggers. We're all in together in this. If one hangs, we all hang; but they won't outwit me. Besides, it's not a hanging affair, they had their knives.

SNIGGERS. Toffy, Toffy, I always treated you fair, Toffy. I was always one to say, "Give Toffy a chance." Take back my share, Toffy.

THE TOFF. What's the matter? What are you driving at?

SNIGGERS. Take it back, Toffy.

THE TOFF. Answer me, what are you up to?

SNIGGERS. I don't want my share any more.

BILL. Have you seen the police?

(ALBERT *pulls out his knife.*)

THE TOFF. No, no knives, Albert.

ALBERT. What then?

THE TOFF. The honest truth in open court, barring the ruby. We were attacked.

SNIGGERS. There's no police.

THE TOFF. Well, then, what's the matter?

BILL. Out with it.

SNIGGERS. I take my oath . . .

ALBERT. Well?

THE TOFF. Don't interrupt.

SNIGGERS (*in tears*). Oh Toffy, Toffy, take it back. Take my share. Say you take it.

THE TOFF. What has he seen?

(*Dead silence, broken only by* SNIGGERS'*s sobs. Then steps are heard. Enter a hideous* IDOL. *It is blind and gropes its way. It gropes its way to the ruby and picks it up and screws it into a socket in the forehead.* SNIGGERS *still weeps softly, the rest stare in horror. The* IDOL *steps out, not groping. It steps away, then stops.*)

THE TOFF. Oh, great heavens!

ALBERT (*in a childish, plaintive voice*). What is it, Toffy?

BILL. Albert, it is that obscene idol (*in a whisper*) come from India.

ALBERT. It is gone.

BILL. It has taken its eye.

SNIGGERS. We are saved.

A VOICE (*off; with outlandish accent*). Meestaire William Jones, able seaman.

(THE TOFF *has never spoken, never moved. He only gazes stupidly in horror.*)

BILL. Albert, Albert, what is this?

(*He rises and walks out. One moan is heard.* SNIGGERS *goes to the window. He falls back sickly.*)

ALBERT (*in a whisper*). What has happened?

SNIGGERS. I have seen it. I have seen it. Oh, I have seen it! (*He returns to table.*)

THE TOFF (*laying his hand very gently on* SNIGGERS'*s arm, speaking softly and winningly*). What was it, Sniggers?

SNIGGERS. I have seen it.

ALBERT. What?

SNIGGERS. Oh!

VOICE. Meestaire Albert Thomas, able seaman.

ALBERT. Must I go, Toffy? Toffy, must I go?

SNIGGERS (*clutching him*). Don't move.

ALBERT (*going*). Toffy, Toffy! (*Exits.*)

VOICE. Meestaire Jacob Smith, able seaman.

SNIGGERS. I can't go, Toffy, I can't go. I can't do it. (*He goes.*)

VOICE. Meestaire Arnold Everett Scott-Fortescue, late Esquire, able seaman.

THE TOFF. I did not foresee it. (*Exits.*)

CURTAIN

LORD DUNSANY

Dunsany's plays are tales of wonder. Each one is a voyage of strange discovery to the reader. There is the story of Zoom-zoo-marma, the Queen, who fled the Hall of the Hundred Princes; of the Seven Beggars who became the Gods of the Mountains; of King Argimenes who overthrew King Darniak and the God Illuriel; of the two thieves at the Glittering Gate; of the wise King who found happiness in the Tents of the Arabs; and of the Golden Doom that befell the King in Zericon. (An illustration of a stage setting for *The Golden Doom* is shown on page 289.) Then there are amusing and ironic plays such as *His Sainted Grandmother, Fame and the Poet,* and *Atalanta in Wimbledon. A Night at an Inn* is different from his other plays. It is a thriller, a horror-piece, with elements of both mystery and irony.

There is a quality in the writing of Dunsany not to be found elsewhere in the theatre. Not only is his imagination "as elfish as moonlight mist", to quote Edwin Björkman, but his style is a perfect vehicle for his stories and ideas. His feeling for colourful and romantic words would be hard to match. Witness Coloono, the jungle city, and Mirsk, and sweet Thalanna in *The Tents of the Arabs.* His dialogue is infused with a kind of sharp, poetic beauty. His rhythms and phrases are essentially biblical. He resembles Coleridge in the subtle magic and delicate artistry with which he at once illumines and makes real the supernatural and the wonderful.

Edward John Moreton Drax Plunkett, Lord Dunsany, was born in 1878. According to his biographer, Edward Hale Bierstadt, he was the eighteenth Baron of his line, and his name and ancestry were said to be "the third oldest in Irish history".

Dunsany is allied to Yeats and the other playwrights of the Irish school in so far as imagination predominates in his writing. His first two plays were produced at the Abbey Theatre in 1909 and 1911. From then on, however, until his death in 1957, his reputation was essentially an international one. Obviously he found little inspiration in his native land, and this sharply differentiates him from the other dramatists of the Irish school.

THINKING ABOUT THE PLAY

1. See the discussion of tragedy that follows *Campbell of Kilmohr.* Is *A Night at an Inn* a tragedy?

2. Write the Toff's life story as you imagine it up to this point.
3. Select a passage in Albert's story about how he gave the priest the slip, that should bring a laugh from the audience.
4. "Supernatural" means "more than natural" – something that cannot be explained by ordinary causes. What is supernatural about the knowledge and movements of the priests? About the idol itself?
5. Sometimes productions of this play have made audiences laugh when they should be thrilled with horror. What directions should be given to the actors, especially to Sniggers, to prevent this reaction from the audience?
6. Discuss Bill's friendship with the Toff, giving examples to show his admiration for his leader, and his loyalty to him.

THE DARK LADY OF THE SONNETS

GEORGE BERNARD SHAW

TRYST WITH A DARK LADY

This is one of the most brilliant of Shaw's one-act plays, one which you will enjoy reading and acting. Its wit and comic invention are seemingly inexhaustible. What a master of rhythmic, pointed prose Shaw is! What a poet at heart!

The setting is a glamorous one: a midsummer's night in the royal gardens overlooking the Thames, with the palace in the background. We see the Beefeater on his lonely watch, we hear the clock chiming, and then the figure of Shakespeare approaches like a ghost – like the ghost of Hamlet's father on the battlements of the castle at Elsinore!

In an amusing opening scene Shakespeare fills his tablets (notebook) with the "jewels of common speech" spoken by the Beefeater, and learns the bitter truth about the double-dealing treachery of his friend and his mistress.

The palace door opens, lamplight streams from within, and the Queen of England, cloaked and mysterious, walking in her sleep, confronts Shakespeare. It was Shaw's brilliant idea that in her sleep she should be tortured by the thought of the blood of Mary Queen of Scots, the warrant for whose execution she had signed, and that Shakespeare, on seeing and overhearing her, should find the inspiration for the situation and the words (the tablets again!) of the famous scene in which Lady Macbeth walks in her sleep. Then follows a sparkling scene in which Shakespeare professes his love for the sleepwalker, not guessing who she is.

The play moves to its highest level of excitement as the Dark Lady enters and "comes stooping along the terrace behind them like a running thrush". She overhears them, and strikes them apart as they embrace. The Queen throws off her cloak and is revealed in all her outraged majesty. For some moments the lives of both the Dark Lady and Shakespeare are in danger, but the redoubtable Will is equal to the occasion. In what is perhaps the funniest passage in the play he expounds his claim to be "an honest gentleman of unquestioned parentage" (in contrast to the Queen's doubtful parentage) and with some "blunt honest speaking" calms her so that she regains her queenly dignity.

The scene that follows, in which the Dark Lady, asked by the Queen why she is there, tells her what it is like to be loved by the greatest poet of the realm – "this man that is more than man and less at the same time" – is the one that interested Shaw most, if we are to judge by the Preface to the play. Shaw's comment on what Shakespeare (whom he admits – with some qualifications – is a greater genius than he is) is like *as a human being* is fascinating. The Dark Lady says: "Oh, he is compact of lies and scorns. I am tired of being tossed up to heaven and dragged down to hell at every whim that takes him. I am ashamed to my very soul that I have abased myself to love one . . . that will write sonnets about me that no man of gentle strain would put his hand to. I am all disordered: I know not what I am saying to your Majesty: I am of all ladies most deject and wretched – "

The Dark Lady goes. Shaw has made his point about the son of an alderman and "the levity of genius". There remains only the request for the "boon of state" – a National Theatre. It was for a performance in aid of funds to establish such a National Theatre that the play was written.

The warder is summoned and reappears, the Queen leaves on a lively, happy curtain line, and the palace door closes. It is night in the garden again! The intruder, "the mightiest wonder" of her reign, is escorted by the warder to the Queen's palace gate.

So much for the story. Now some suggestions about casting the play. In choosing the Beefeater, you must establish the fact that he is a man of the people, in contrast to the Queen, the Lady of the Court, and the poet. Dialect, or slower, heavier speech will help. His name suggests that he is big and burly. Other things being equal, there is an advantage in having him solid as well as stolid. The Queen must have dignity and authority, the Dark Lady beauty and passion. However, the success or failure of the production of the play will rest chiefly with Will Shakespeare. The student who takes this part must be able to suggest the irrepressible spirits, the boundless self-confidence, and the delight in language that the part calls for. His long plea for a National Theatre is a challenging *tour de force* for any actor.

To simplify the staging, the palace might be offstage, perhaps with steps or a column or two showing. Then the cyclorama, or rear wall, lighted an intense night blue, with some trees or sculpture, could suggest the palace garden. An interesting idea is to have a garden wall on which the Beefeater can keep his watch. This will make the scene even more like the opening scene in *Hamlet,* and the Beefeater's silhouette against the night sky particularly effective.

The big problem in a night scene is to light the stage sufficiently that facial expressions can be seen. Shaw has provided moonlight, so you may improve on nature slightly by throwing some lighter blue light on the playing area, while keeping the sky its deep night blue. The problem is easily solved once the palace door opens – particularly if this door is well downstage. The stream of yellow lamplight will provide natural motivation for increased lighting in the playing area. This lighting can be continued throughout the play until the Queen's exit. When the palace door closes, night reigns again in the garden.

One of the pleasures of reading is that you are led from one delight to another. John Keats, in his famous sonnet that begins "Much have I travell'd in the realms of gold", tells of his excitement at discovering Homer's poetry. *The Dark Lady of the Sonnets* will lead you, if you do not yet know them, into two more "realms of gold" – the plays of Shakespeare and Shaw. John Middleton Murry wrote: "Next to Shakespeare's, [Shaw's] plays form the most impressive body of dramatic works in English." And again: "Shaw is a better critic of Shakespeare than either Goethe or Coleridge, because he is not hypnotized."

What did Shaw really think of Shakespeare? Referring to *As You Like It,* he said that he himself had never written anything "half so bad in matter", but "in manner and art nobody can write better than Shakespeare, because, carelessness apart, he did the thing as well as it can be done within the limits of human faculty."

The two Shakespearean plays that Shaw chiefly refers to are *Macbeth* and *Hamlet.* Before or after you read *The Dark Lady of the Sonnets,* you should read these two plays – or at least read prose versions of them such as can be found in books like Lamb's *Tales from Shakespeare.* Another idea is to have someone sketch the two stories in outline, and then to have the sleepwalking scene in *Macbeth* read or acted, followed by the scenes involving Hamlet and the Ghost of his father in Act I (Scene 1, Scene 2 – from Hamlet's soliloquy to the end – and perhaps Scenes 4 and 5).

Shaw knew his Shakespeare so well, and was himself such a master of words, that the play will be a pleasant lesson for us in discovering more about the magic of poetry. It will show us how to savour words, "as if tasting a ripe plum", how to tune our ears to catch a "vile jingle of esses", and how to relish the humour of "a snapper-up of such unconsidered trifles", the imaginative power of "fell sergeant . . . strict in his arrest", and the sheer beauty of "Frailty, thy name is woman!"

Here are a great Queen, the Dark Lady of the Sonnets, a Beefeater, and "the king of words" himself, in a comic action devised by the greatest English dramatist of the twentieth century.

CHARACTERS

THE BEEFEATER
WILLIAM SHAKESPEAR
QUEEN ELIZABETH
THE DARK LADY

First produced at the Haymarket Theatre, London, with the following cast:

THE BEEFEATER	Hugh B. Tabberer
WILLIAM SHAKESPEAR	Granville Barker
QUEEN ELIZABETH	Suzanne Sheldon
THE DARK LADY	Mona Limerick

THE DARK LADY OF THE SONNETS

Fin de siècle 15-1600. Midsummer night on the terrace of the Palace at Whitehall, overlooking the Thames. The Palace clock chimes four quarters and strikes eleven.

A BEEFEATER *on guard. A cloaked* MAN *approaches.*

THE BEEFEATER. Stand. Who goes there? Give the word.

THE MAN. Marry! I cannot. I have clean forgotten it.

THE BEEFEATER. Then cannot you pass here. What is your business? Who are you? Are you a true man?

THE MAN. Far from it, Master Warder. I am not the same [1] man two days together: sometimes Adam, sometimes Benvolio, and anon the Ghost.

THE BEEFEATER (*recoiling*). A ghost! Angels and ministers [2] of grace defend us!

1. Actors who appear in different plays on successive days are not "the same man" two days together. Adam, Benvolio, and the Ghost in *Hamlet* are three of the small parts that Shakespeare is said to have played. (According to tradition he was not a very good actor.) Adam is the faithful old servant in *As You Like It,* Benvolio is the friend of Romeo in *Romeo and Juliet,* and the Ghost is the ghost of Hamlet's father.
2. Angels and ministers . . . : this wonderful line is spoken by Hamlet when he first sees the ghost of his father.

THE MAN. Well said, Master Warder. With your leave I will set that down in writing; for I have a very poor and unhappy brain for remembrance. (*He takes out his tablets and writes.*) Methinks this is a good scene, with you on your lonely watch, and I approaching like a ghost in the moonlight. Stare not so amazedly at me; but mark what I say. I keep tryst here tonight with a dark lady. She promised to bribe the warder. I gave her the wherewithal: four tickets for the Globe Theatre.

THE BEEFEATER. Plague on her! She gave me two only.

THE MAN (*detaching a tablet*). My friend: present this tablet, and you will be welcomed at any time when the plays of Will Shakespear are in hand. Bring your wife. Bring your friends. Bring the whole garrison. There is ever plenty of room.

THE BEEFEATER. I care not for these new-fangled plays. No man can understand a word of them. They are all talk. Will you not give me a pass for The Spanish Tragedy?

THE MAN. To see The Spanish Tragedy one pays, my friend. Here are the means. (*He gives him a piece of gold.*)

THE BEEFEATER (*overwhelmed*). Gold! Oh, sir, you are a better paymaster than your dark lady.

THE MAN. Women are thrifty, my friend.

THE BEEFEATER. Tis so, sir. And you have to consider that the most open handed of us must een cheapen that which we

3. Globe Theatre: the theatre on the south bank of the Thames where many of Shakespeare's plays were performed.
4. In this speech, Shaw is defending his own plays and attacking the critics who condemned them because they were all "talk". He suggests that Shakespeare's plays were likewise "new-fangled" and difficult for the audiences of his day to understand, by contrast with a play like *The Spanish Tragedy* by Thomas Kyd, which was full of action and tremendously popular.
5. Een: a variant form of even. Shaw had "new-fangled" ideas about the reform of spelling: hence the spelling of "een" without an apostrophe and of "Shakespear" without an "e".

buy every day. This lady has to make a present to a warder nigh every night of her life.

THE MAN (*turning pale*). I'll not believe it.

THE BEEFEATER. Now you, sir, I dare be sworn, do not have an adventure like this twice in the year.

THE MAN. Villain: wouldst tell me that my dark lady hath ever done thus before? that she maketh occasions to meet other men?

THE BEEFEATER. Now the Lord bless your innocence, sir, do you think you are the only pretty man in the world? A merry lady, sir: a warm bit of stuff. Go to: I'll not see her pass a deceit on a gentleman that hath given me the first piece of gold I ever handled.

THE MAN. Master Warder: is it not a strange thing that we, knowing that all women are false, should be amazed to find our own particular drab no better than the rest?

THE BEEFEATER. Not all, sir. Decent bodies, many of them.

THE MAN (*intolerantly*). No. All false, all. If thou deny it, thou liest.

THE BEEFEATER. You judge too much by the Court, sir. There, indeed, you may say of frailty that its name is woman. 6

THE MAN (*pulling out his tablets again*). Prithee say that again: that about frailty: the strain of music.

THE BEEFEATER. What strain of music, sir? I'm no musician, God knows.

THE MAN. There is music in your soul: many of your degree have it very notably. (*Writing.*) "Frailty: thy name is woman!" (*Repeating it affectionately.*) "Thy name is woman."

THE BEEFEATER. Well, sir, it is but four words. Are you a snapper-up of such unconsidered trifles? 7

THE MAN (*eagerly*). Snapper-up of – (*He gasps.*) Oh! Im-

6. Frailty . . . is woman: one of the most memorable of Shakespeare's lines. Hamlet says it in the first of his four great soliloquies, in which he comments on the behaviour of his unfaithful mother (Act I, Scene 2).
7. A snapper-up . . . trifles: See *The Winter's Tale,* Act IV, Scene 2.

mortal phrase! (*He writes it down.*) This man is a greater than I.

THE BEEFEATER. You have my lord Pembroke's trick, sir.

THE MAN. Like enough: he is my near friend. But what call you his trick?

THE BEEFEATER. Making sonnets by moonlight. And to the same lady too.

THE MAN. No!

THE BEEFEATER. Last night he stood here on your errand, and in your shoes.

THE MAN. Thou, too, Brutus! And I called him friend!

THE BEEFEATER. Tis ever so, sir.

THE MAN. Tis ever so. Twas ever so. (*He turns away, overcome.*) Two gentlemen of Verona! Judas! Judas!!

THE BEEFEATER. Is he so bad as that, sir?

THE MAN (*recovering his charity and self-possession*). Bad? O no. Human, Master Warder, human. We call one another names when we are offended, as children do. That is all.

THE BEEFEATER. Ay, sir: words, words, words. Mere wind, sir. We fill our bellies with the east wind, sir, as the Scripture hath it. You cannot feed capons so.

THE MAN. A good cadence. By your leave. (*He makes a note of it.*)

THE BEEFEATER. What manner of thing is a cadence, sir? I have not heard of it.

THE MAN. A thing to rule the world with, friend.

8. Thou, too, Brutus!: As Brutus stabbed him, Julius Caesar cried out, "Et tu, Brute?" (Thou, too, Brutus?) Brutus was one of Caesar's closest friends.
9. Two gentlemen of Verona!: Proteus, one of the two gentlemen of Verona in Shakespeare's early play, betrayed his friend, just as Judas betrayed Christ.
10. We fill our bellies: Job 15:2 and 20:23.
11. You cannot feed capons so: In Act III, Scene 2, Hamlet, pretending to be mad, is talking to old Polonius, who asks him how he "fares". Hamlet replies that he eats the air, "promise-crammed"; "You cannot feed capons so."

THE BEEFEATER. You speak strangely, sir: no offence. But, an't like you, you are a very civil gentleman; and a poor man feels drawn to you, you being, as twere, willing to share your thought with him.

THE MAN. Tis my trade. But alas! the world for the most part will none of my thoughts.

(*Lamplight streams from the palace door as it opens from within.*)

THE BEEFEATER. Here comes your lady, sir. I'll to t'other end of my ward. You may een take your time about your business: I shall not return too suddenly unless my sergeant
comes prowling around. Tis a fell sergeant, sir: strict in his 12
arrest. Good een, sir; and good luck! (*He goes.*)

THE MAN. "Strict in his arrest"! "Fell sergeant"! (*As if tasting a ripe plum.*) O-o-o-h! (*He makes a note of them.*)

(*A cloaked* LADY *gropes her way from the palace and wanders along the terrace, walking in her sleep.*)

THE LADY (*rubbing her hands as if washing them*). Out, 13

12. Tis a fell sergeant . . . arrest: spoken by the dying Hamlet as he says farewell to his friend Horatio. The "fell" or cruel sergeant is death.
13. Out, damned spot: Shaw's brilliant, ironic invention in the play is to suggest that Shakespeare not only stole the "jewels" of "unconsciously musical speech" from common people like the Beefeater (as he, Shaw, did), but that the idea and much of the language of one of Shakespeare's greatest scenes (the sleepwalking scene in *Macbeth*) came to Shakespeare when he saw and heard the Queen of England sleepwalking in her palace garden, tormented by the thought of the blood of Mary, Queen of Scots, whose death warrant she had signed. Here Shaw pushes this "conceit" or fanciful idea further. Elizabeth was jealous of Mary's beauty, and Shaw suggests that Shakespeare overheard the Queen, while talking in her sleep, attack Mary's use of cosmetics (and later, false hair) and used her words in the famous scene (Act III, Scene 1) in which Hamlet attacks Ophelia and all women: "God made you one face; and you make yourself another."

damned spot. You will mar all with these cosmetics. God made you one face; and you make yourself another. Think of your grave, woman, not ever of being beautified. All the perfumes of Arabia will not whiten this Tudor hand.

THE MAN. "All the perfumes of Arabia"! "Beautified"! "Beautified"! a poem in a single word. Can this be my Mary? (*To the* LADY.) Why do you speak in a strange voice, and utter poetry for the first time? Are you ailing? You walk like the dead. Mary! Mary!

THE LADY (*echoing him*). Mary! Mary! Who would have thought that woman to have had so much blood in her! Is it my fault that my counsellors put deeds of blood on me? Fie! If you were women you would have more wit than to stain the floor so foully. Hold not up her head so: the hair is false. I tell you yet again, Mary's buried: she cannot come out of her grave. I fear her not: these cats that dare jump into thrones though they be fit only for men's laps must be put away. Whats done cannot be undone. Out, I say. Fie! a queen, and freckled!

THE MAN (*shaking her arm*). Mary, I say: art asleep?

(*The* LADY *wakes; starts; and nearly faints. He catches her on his arm.*)

THE LADY. Where am I? What art thou?

THE MAN. I cry your mercy. I have mistook your person all this while. Methought you were my Mary: my mistress.

THE LADY (*outraged*). Profane fellow: how do you dare?

THE MAN. Be not wroth with me, lady. My mistress is a marvellous proper woman. But she does not speak so well as you. "All the perfumes of Arabia"! That was well said: spoken with good accent and excellent discretion.

THE LADY. Have I been in speech with you here?

14. Mary! Mary!: See the discussion "Who was the Dark Lady?" which follows the play. You will note how well it served Shaw's dramatic purpose to use a Lady of the Court whose first name was the same as that of Elizabeth's great rival, the Queen of Scotland.

THE MAN. Why, yes, fair lady. Have you forgot it?

THE LADY. I have walked in my sleep.

THE MAN. Walk ever in your sleep, fair one; for then your words drop like honey.

THE LADY (*with cold majesty*). Know you to whom you speak, sir, that you dare express yourself so saucily?

THE MAN (*unabashed*). Not I, not care neither. You are some lady of the Court, belike. To me there are but two sorts of women: those with excellent voices, sweet and low, and cackling hens that cannot make me dream. Your voice has all manner of loveliness in it. Grudge me not a short hour of its music.

THE LADY. Sir: you are overbold. Season your admiration 15
for a while with –

THE MAN (*holding up his hand to stop her*). "Season your admiration for a while –"

THE LADY. Fellow: do you dare mimic me to my face?

THE MAN. Tis music. Can you not hear? When a good musician sings a song, do you not sing it and sing it again til you have caught and fixed its perfect melody? "Season your admiration for a while": God! the history of man's heart is in that one word, admiration. Admiration! (*Taking up his tablets.*) What was it? "Suspend your admiration for a space –"

THE LADY. A very vile jingle of esses. I said "Season your –"

THE MAN (*hastily*). Season: ay, season, season, season. Plague on my memory, my wretched memory! I must een write it down. (*He begins to write, but stops, his memory failing him.*) Yet tell me which was the vile jingle? You said very justly: mine own ear caught it even as my false tongue said it.

THE LADY. You said "for a space". I said "for a while".

THE MAN. "For a while". (*He corrects it.*) Good! (*Ardently.*) And now be mine neither for a space nor a while, but for ever.

15. Season your admiration for a while: spoken by Horatio (Act I, Scene 2) when he first tells Hamlet that he has seen the ghost of Hamlet's father.

THE LADY. Odds my life! Are you by chance making love to me, knave?

THE MAN. Nay: tis you who have made the love: I but pour it out at your feet. I cannot but love a lass that sets such store by an apt word. Therefore vouchsafe, divine perfection of a woman – no: I have said that before somewhere; and the wordy garment of my love for you must be fire-new –

THE LADY. You talk too much, sir. Let me warn you: I am more accustomed to be listened to than preached at.

THE MAN. The most are like that that do talk well. But though you spake with the tongues of angels, as indeed you do, yet know that I am king of words –

THE LADY. A king, ha!

THE MAN. No less. We are poor things, we men and women –

THE LADY. Dare you call me woman?

THE MAN. What nobler name can I tender you? How else can I love you? Yet you may well shrink from the name: have I not said we are but poor things? Yet there is a power that can redeem us.

THE LADY. Gramercy for your sermon, sir. I hope I know my duty.

THE MAN. This is no sermon, but the living truth. The power I speak of is the power of immortal poesy. For know that vile as this world is, and worms as we are, you have but to invest all this vileness with a magical garment of words to transfigure us and uplift our souls til earth flowers into a million heavens.

THE LADY. You spoil your heaven with your million. You are extravagant. Observe some measure in your speech.

THE MAN. You speak now as Ben does.

THE LADY. And who, pray, is Ben?

THE MAN. A learned bricklayer who thinks that the sky is at the top of his ladder, and so takes it on him to rebuke me for

16. As Ben does: Ben Jonson was Shakespeare's friend and great contemporary. Among his plays are *Every Man in His Humour*, *Volpone*, and *The Alchemist*.

flying. I tell you there is no word yet coined and no melody yet sung that is extravagant and majestical enough for the glory that lovely words can reveal. It is heresy to deny it: have you
not been taught that in the beginning was the Word? that the 17
Word was with God? nay, that the Word was God?

THE LADY. Beware, fellow, how you presume to speak of holy things. The Queen is the head of the Church.

THE MAN. You are the head of my Church when you speak as you did at first. "All the perfumes of Arabia"! Can the Queen speak thus? They say she playeth well upon the virginals. Let her play so to me; and I'll kiss her hands. But until then, you are my Queen; and I'll kiss those lips that have dropt music on my heart. (*He puts his arms about her.*)

THE LADY. Unmeasured impudence! On your life, take your hands from me.

(*The* DARK LADY *comes stooping along the terrace behind them like a running thrush. When she sees how they are employed, she rises angrily to her full height, and listens jealously.*)

THE MAN (*unaware of the* DARK LADY). Then cease to make my hands tremble with the streams of life you poured through them. You hold me as the lodestar holds the iron: I cannot but cling to you. We are lost, you and I: nothing can separate us now.

THE DARK LADY. We shall see that, false lying hound, you and your filthy trull. (*With two vigorous cuffs, she knocks the pair asunder, sending the man, who is unlucky enough to receive a right-handed blow, sprawling on the flags.*) Take that, both of you!

THE CLOAKED LADY (*in towering wrath, throwing off her cloak and turning in outraged majesty on her assailant*). High treason!

THE DARK LADY (*recognizing her and falling on her knees in abject terror*). Will: I am lost: I have struck the Queen.

17. In the beginning was the Word: John 1:1.

THE MAN (*sitting up as majestically as his ignominious posture allows*). Woman: you have struck WILLIAM SHAKESPEAR!!!!!!

QUEEN ELIZABETH (*stupent*). Marry, come up!!! Struck William Shakespear quotha! And who in the name of all the sluts and jades and light-o'-loves and fly-by-nights that infest this palace of mine, may William Shakespear be?

THE DARK LADY. Madam: he is but a player. Oh, I could have my hand cut off –

QUEEN ELIZABETH. Belike you will, mistress. Have you bethought you that I am like to have your head cut off as well?

THE DARK LADY. Will: save me. Oh, save me.

ELIZABETH. Save you! A likely savior, on my royal word! I had thought this fellow at least an esquire; for I had hoped that even the vilest of my ladies would not have dishonored my Court by wantoning with a baseborn servant.

SHAKESPEAR (*indignantly scrambling to his feet*). Baseborn! I, a Shakespear of Stratford! I, whose mother was an Arden! baseborn! You forget yourself, madam.

ELIZABETH (*furious*). S'blood! do I so? I will teach you –

THE DARK LADY (*rising from her knees and throwing herself between them*). Will: in God's name anger her no further. It is death. Madam: do not listen to him.

SHAKESPEAR. Not were it een to save your life, Mary, not to mention mine own, will I flatter a monarch who forgets what is due to my family. I deny not that my father was brought down to be a poor bankrupt; but twas his gentle blood that was ever too generous for trade. Never did he disown his debts. Tis true he paid them not; but it is an attested truth that he gave bills for them; and twas those bills, in the hands of base hucksters, that were his undoing.

ELIZABETH (*grimly*). The son of your father shall learn his place in the presence of the daughter of Harry the Eighth.

SHAKESPEAR (*swelling with intolerant importance*). Name not that inordinate man in the same breath with Stratford's

18. Stupent: amazed, astonished.

worthiest alderman. John Shakespear wedded but once: Harry Tudor was married six times. You should blush to utter his name.

THE DARK LADY } (*crying out together*). Will: for pity's sake –
ELIZABETH } Insolent dog –

SHAKESPEAR (*cutting them short*). How know you that King Harry was indeed your father?

ELIZABETH: Zounds! Now by – (*She stops to grind her teeth with rage.*)
THE DARK LADY: She will have me whipped through the streets. Oh God! Oh God!

SHAKESPEAR. Learn to know yourself better, madam. I am an honest gentleman of unquestioned parentage, and have already sent in my demand for the coat-of-arms that is lawfully mine. Can you say as much for yourself?

ELIZABETH (*almost beside herself*). Another word, and I begin with mine own hands the work the hangman shall finish.

SHAKESPEAR. You are no true Tudor: this baggage here has as good a right to your royal seat as you. What maintains you on the throne of England? Is it your renownéd wit? your wisdom that sets at nought the craftiest statesmen of the Christian world? No. Tis the mere chance that might have happened to any milkmaid, the caprice of Nature that made you the most wondrous piece of beauty the age hath seen. (ELIZABETH'*s raised fists, on the point of striking him, fall to her side.*) That is what hath brought all men to your feet, and founded your throne on the impregnable rock of your proud heart, a stony island in a sea of desire. There, madam, is some wholesome blunt honest speaking for you. Now do your worst.

ELIZABETH (*with dignity*). Master Shakespear: it is well for you that I am a merciful prince. I make allowance for your rustic ignorance. But remember that there are things which be true, and are yet not seemly to be said (I will not say to a queen; for you will have it that I am none) but to a virgin.

SHAKESPEAR (*bluntly*). It is no fault of mine that you are a virgin, madam, albeit tis my misfortune.

THE DARK LADY (*terrified again*). In mercy, madam, hold no further discourse with him. He hath ever some lewd jest on his tongue. You hear how he useth me! calling me baggage and the like to your Majesty's face.

ELIZABETH. As for you, mistress, I have yet to demand what your business is at this hour in this place, and how you come to be so concerned with a player that you strike blindly at your sovereign in your jealousy of him.

THE DARK LADY. Madam: as I live and hope for salvation –

SHAKESPEAR (*sardonically*). Ha!

THE DARK LADY (*angrily*). – ay, I'm as like to be saved as thou that believest naught save some black magic of words and verses – I say, madam, as I am a living woman I came here to break with him for ever. Oh, madam, if you would know what misery is, listen to this man that is more than man and less at the same time. He will tie you down to anatomize your very soul: he will wring tears of blood from your humiliation; and then he will heal the wound with flatteries that no woman can resist.

SHAKESPEAR. Flatteries! (*Kneeling.*) Oh, madam, I put my case at your royal feet. I confess to much. I have a rude tongue: I am unmannerly: I blaspheme against the holiness of anointed royalty; but oh, my royal mistress, AM I a flatterer?

ELIZABETH. I absolve you as to that. You are far too plain a dealer to please me. (*He rises gratefully.*)

THE DARK LADY. Madam: he is flattering you even as he speaks.

ELIZABETH (*a terrible flash in her eye*). Ha! Is it so?

SHAKESPEAR. Madam: she is jealous; and, heaven help me! not without reason. Oh, you say you are a merciful prince; but that was cruel of you, that hiding of your royal dignity when you found me here. For how can I ever be content with this black-haired, black-eyed, black-avised devil again now that I have looked upon real beauty and real majesty?

THE DARK LADY (*wounded and desperate*). He hath swore to me ten times over that the day shall come in England when black women, for all their foulness, shall be more thought on than fair ones. (*To* SHAKESPEAR, *scolding at him.*) Deny it if thou canst. Oh, he is compact of lies and scorns. I am tired of being tossed up to heaven and dragged down to hell at every whim that takes him. I am ashamed to my very soul that I have abased myself to love one that my father would not have deemed fit to hold my stirrup – one that will talk to all the world about me – that will put my love and my shame into his plays and make me blush for myself there – that will write sonnets about me that no man of gentle strain would put his hand to. I am all disordered: I know not what I am saying to your Majesty: I am of all ladies most deject and wretched – 19

SHAKESPEAR. Ha! At last sorrow hath struck a note of music out of thee. "Of all ladies most deject and wretched." (*He makes a note of it.*)

THE DARK LADY. Madam: I implore you give me leave to go. I am distracted with grief and shame. I –

ELIZABETH. Go. (*The* DARK LADY *tries to kiss her hand.*) No more. Go. (*The* DARK LADY *goes, convulsed.*) You have been cruel to that poor fond wretch, Master Shakespear.

SHAKESPEAR. I am not cruel, madam; but you know the fable of Jupiter and Semele. I could not help my lightnings 20
scorching her.

ELIZABETH. You have an overweening conceit of yourself, sir, that displeases your Queen.

SHAKESPEAR. Oh, madam, can I go about with the modest

19. Of all ladies . . . wretched: These are Ophelia's words (Act III, Scene 1) after Hamlet – angry and pretending madness – has left her, telling her to go to a nunnery and be no more "a breeder of sinners".

20. Jupiter and Semele: Semele was the mother, by Jupiter, of Bacchus. She asked Jupiter to appear in his majesty, but when he did she was stricken by lightning or died of terror. In his preface to the play, Shaw justifies the manner in which Shakespeare treats the Dark Lady. He says that Shakespeare was not cruel to her: "It was not cruelty that made Jupiter reduce Semele to ashes: it was the fact that he could not help being a god nor she help being a mortal."

cough of a minor poet, belittling my inspiration and making the mightiest wonder of your reign a thing of nought? I have said that "not marble nor the gilded monuments of princes shall outlive" the words with which I make the world glorious or foolish at my will. Besides, I would have you think me great enough to grant me a boon.

ELIZABETH. I hope it is a boon that may be asked of a virgin Queen without offence, sir. I mistrust your forwardness; and I bid you remember that I do not suffer persons of your degree (if I may say so without offence to your father the alderman) to presume too far.

SHAKESPEAR. Oh, madam, I shall not forget myself again; though by my life, could I make you a serving wench, neither a queen nor a virgin should you be for so much longer as a flash of lightning might take to cross the river to the Bankside. But since you are a queen and will none of me, nor of Philip of Spain, nor of any other mortal man, I must een contain myself as best I may, and ask you only for a boon of State.

ELIZABETH. A boon of State already! You are becoming a courtier like the rest of them. You lack advancement.

SHAKESPEAR. "Lack advancement". By your Majesty's leave: a queenly phrase. (*He is about to write it down.*)

ELIZABETH (*striking the tablets from his hand*). Your tables begin to anger me, sir. I am not here to write your plays for you.

SHAKESPEAR. You are here to inspire them, madam. For this, among the rest, were you ordained. But the boon I crave is that you do endow a great playhouse, or, if I may make bold to coin a scholarly name for it, a National Theatre, for the better instruction and gracing of your Majesty's subjects.

ELIZABETH. Why, sir, are there not theatres enow on the Bankside and in Blackfriars?

21. Not marble . . . shall outlive: This is the first line of one of the most beautiful of the sonnets, Sonnet 55.
22. You lack advancement: *Hamlet,* Act III, Scene 2.
23. Enow: enough.

SHAKESPEAR. Madam: these are the adventures of needy
and desperate men that must, to save themselves from perish-
ing of want, give the sillier sort of people what they best like;
and what they best like, God knows, is not their own betterment and instruction, as we well see by the example of the
churches, which must needs compel men to frequent them,
though they be open to all without charge. Only when there is
a matter of a murder, or a plot, or a pretty youth in petticoats,
or some naughty tale of wantonness, will your subjects pay
the great cost of good players and their finery, with a little profit to boot. To prove this I will tell you that I have written two 24
noble and excellent plays setting forth the advancement of
women of high nature and fruitful industry even as your
Majesty is: the one a skilful physician, the other a sister
devoted to good works. I have also stole from a book of idle
wanton tales two of the most damnable foolishnesses in the
world, in the one of which a woman goeth in man's attire and
maketh impudent love to her swain, who pleaseth the ground- 25
lings by overthrowing a wrestler; whilst, in the other, one of
the same kidney sheweth her wit by saying endless naughti-
nesses to a gentleman as lewd as herself. I have writ these to
save my friends from penury, yet shewing my scorn for such
follies and for them that praise them by calling the one As
You Like It, meaning that it is not as *I* like it, and the other
Much Ado About Nothing, as it truly is. And now these two

24. Two noble and excellent plays: these two plays are *All's Well That Ends Well* and *Measure for Measure*. In *All's Well That Ends Well,* Helena, using a prescription given her by her father, a noted physician, before his death, saves the life of the King of France and after many trials wins the love of Bertram. In *Measure for Measure* Isabella, the sister of Claudio, who is about to become a nun, saves her brother's life and preserves her honour in a difficult situation.
25. Groundlings: In the Elizabethan theatre the common people or "groundlings" stood in the pit (equivalent to the main floor of the theatre auditorium today). The lords and ladies were in the balconies.

filthy pieces drive their nobler fellows from the stage, where indeed I cannot have my lady physician presented at all, she being too honest a woman for the taste of the town. Wherefore I humbly beg your Majesty to give order that a theatre be endowed out of the public revenue for the playing of those pieces of mine which no merchant will touch, seeing that his gain is so much greater with the worse than with the better. Thereby you shall also encourage other men to undertake the writing of plays who do now despise it and leave it wholly to those whose counsels will work little good to your realm. For this writing of plays is a great matter, forming as it does the minds and affections of men in such sort that whatsoever they see done in show on the stage, they will presently be doing in earnest in the world, which is but a larger stage. Of late, as you know, the Church taught the people by means of plays; but the people flocked only to such as were full of superstitious miracles and bloody martyrdoms; and so the Church, which also was just then brought into straits by the policy of your royal father, did abandon and discountenance the art of playing; and thus it fell into the hands of poor players and greedy merchants that had their pockets to look to and not the greatness of this your kingdom. Therefore now must your Majesty take up that good work that your Church hath abandoned, and restore the art of playing to its former use and dignity.

ELIZABETH. Master Shakespear: I will speak of this matter to the Lord Treasurer.

SHAKESPEAR. Then am I undone, madam; for there was never yet a Lord Treasurer that could find a penny for anything over and above the necessary expenses of your government, save for a war or a salary for his own nephew.

ELIZABETH. Master Shakespear: you speak sooth; yet cannot I in any wise mend it. I dare not offend my unruly Puritans by making so lewd a place as the playhouse a public charge; and there be a thousand things to be done in this London of mine before your poetry can have its penny from the general purse. I tell thee, Master Will, it will be three hundred years and more before my subjects learn that man cannot live by bread alone, but by every word that cometh from the mouth of those whom God inspires. By that time you and I will be dust beneath the feet of the horses, if indeed there be any horses then, and men be still riding instead of flying. Now it may be that by then your works will be dust also.

SHAKESPEAR. They will stand, madam: fear not for that.

ELIZABETH. It may prove so. But of this I am certain (for I know my countrymen) that until every other country in the Christian world, even to barbarian Muscovy and the hamlets of the boorish Germans, have its playhouse at the public charge, England will never adventure. And she will adventure then only because it is her desire to be ever in the fashion, and do humbly and dutifully whatso she seeth everybody else doing. In the meantime you must content yourself as best you can by the playing of those two pieces which you give out as the most damnable ever writ, but which your countrymen, I warn you, will swear are the best you have ever done. But this I will say, that if I could speak across the ages to our descendants, I should heartily recommend them to fulfil your wish; for the
Scottish minstrel hath well said that he that maketh the songs 26
of a nation is mightier than he that maketh its laws; and the same may well be true of plays and interludes. (*The clock chimes the first quarter. The warder returns on his round.*) And now, sir, we are upon the hour when it better beseems a virgin queen to be abed than to converse alone with the naughtiest of her subjects. Ho there! Who keeps ward on the queen's lodgings tonight?

THE WARDER. I do, an't please your Majesty.

ELIZABETH. See that you keep it better in future. You have let pass a most dangerous gallant even to the very door of our royal chamber. Lead him forth; and bring me word when he is safely locked out; for I shall scarce dare disrobe until the palace gates are between us.

26. The Scottish minstrel hath well said: "Give me the making of the songs of a nation and I care not who makes its laws" (Andrew Fletcher of Saltoun, 1655-1716).

SHAKESPEAR (*kissing her hand*). My body goes through the gate into the darkness, madam; but my thoughts follow you.

ELIZABETH. How! to my bed!

SHAKESPEAR. No, madam, to your prayers, in which I beg you to remember my theatre.

ELIZABETH. That is my prayer to posterity. Forget not your own to God; and so goodnight, Master Will.

SHAKESPEAR. Goodnight, great Elizabeth. God save the Queen!

ELIZABETH. Amen.

(*Exeunt severally: she to her chamber: he, in custody of the warder, to the gate nearest Blackfriars.*)

WHO WAS THE DARK LADY?

Shaw wrote *The Dark Lady of the Sonnets,* as has been noted, to aid the cause of a National Theatre. In his Preface he tells us that the central idea of the plot was suggested by Dame Edith Lyttelton (who was originally to have written the play): "a scene of jealousy between Queen Elizabeth and the Dark Lady at the expense of the unfortunate Bard". Many of you will know that Shakespeare's one hundred and fifty-four sonnets are addressed only to a friend and to his mistress, a lady whose eyes were "raven black". They are formally dedicated to "Mr. W. H.", their "onlie begetter". The evidence of the sonnets points to the fact that the friend, who represented everything that the poet most admired, and his mistress, whom he loved passionately, betrayed him and became lovers.

> Beshrew that heart that makes my heart to groan
> For that deep wound it gives my friend and me!
> Is't not enough to torture me alone,
> But slave to slavery my sweet'st friend must be?
> (Sonnet 133)

Scholars differ as to who the friend was and who the Dark Lady was. It is impossible here to discuss the controversy at length, but if you are interested, you will find it absorbing reading. In a book published in 1964, *Shakespeare's Sonnets,* A. L. Rowse argues that the friend was Henry Wriothesley, the young Earl of Southampton, stepson of Sir William Harvey. J. Dover Wilson, in *Introduction to the Sonnets of Shakespeare*, also published in 1964, contends that he was William Herbert, Earl of Pembroke. You will see that Shaw believed he was the Earl of Pembroke.

As for the Dark Lady, one of the first theories was that she was Mary Fitton, one of the ladies of the court. (Shaw says that this idea was first advanced by a friend of his, Thomas Tyler.) But then her portrait was discovered; it showed that she was blonde! The most widely accepted suggestion thereafter was that the Dark Lady was Mistress Davenant, wife of a vintner (or wine merchant) in Oxford, and mother of Sir William Davenant, the dramatist. Shaw was prepared to accept this suggestion. With characteristic candour he admits that Mary Fitton was not the Dark Lady (*if* the lady's hair was "undyed"), but says that he introduced her as the Dark Lady out of loyalty to Tyler and to follow Dame Lyttelton's suggestion of presenting a scene of jealousy between Queen Elizabeth and the Dark Lady. This was easy if the Dark Lady was a maid of honour – almost impossible if she were a "tavern landlady".

Dover Wilson argues that the Dark Lady could not have been Davenant's mother, and maintains that she was a woman of Shakespeare's own class.

There you have it – the mystery. Who was the Dark Lady of the Sonnets?

A NATIONAL THEATRE

The weakness of the play (if it is a weakness) is that it ends with a plea for a National Theatre. Yet to anyone who loves the theatre this special pleading is heartening, just as the praise of the poet's magical power throughout the play is heartening.

Shaw has Shakespeare begin his request for a "boon of state" by saying that the theatres then in existence "give the sillier sort of people what they best like; and what they best like, God knows, is not their own betterment and instruction . . ." The theatres do this because their gain "is so much greater with the worse than with the better".

He expresses the hope that with a theatre endowed from the public revenue other men will undertake the writing of plays "who do now despise it and leave it wholly to those whose counsels will work little good to your realm. For this writing of plays is a great matter, forming as it does the minds and affections of men in such sort that whatsoever they see done in show on the stage, they will presently be doing in earnest in the world, which is but a larger stage."

Replying, the Queen tells Shakespeare that there are many things to be done before his poetry "can have its penny from the general purse", and that it will be three hundred years and more before her subjects learn "that man cannot live by bread alone, but by every word that cometh from the mouth of those whom God inspires." By this time every other country in the Christian world will have its playhouse at the public charge, and England will follow the example of other nations "only because it is her desire to be ever in the fashion, and do humbly and dutifully whatso she seeth everybody else doing." (Shaw cannot resist this "dig" at the English; he was forever making fun of them, and they took it in good spirit.)

In 1962, fifty-two years after Shaw wrote his play, the National Theatre became a reality. Its temporary home is the famous Old Vic Theatre; its permanent home will be an imposing structure on the south bank of the Thames adjoining the Royal Festival Hall. Sir Laurence Olivier is its first Director. On October 22, 1963, the inaugural production was staged – the play was *Hamlet* by William Shakespeare!

What of Canada – should we, too, have a National Theatre? A National Centre for the Performing Arts is being built in Ottawa. Should we have a national company of players as well, or is our country too vast to make their tours practicable? At present we have regional theatres, each with its own home and troupe of players, such as the Stratford Shakespearean Festival, the Théâtre du Nouveau Monde in Montreal, the Manitoba Theatre Centre, the Vancouver Playhouse, and the Neptune Theatre in Halifax. These playhouses have their "penny from the general purse". Is this enough, or would you prefer to have a company of our best players, with their home base in Ottawa, travelling across the land from theatre to theatre? What form should our National Theatre take?

SHAW LOOKS AT SHAKESPEARE

The special pleading for a National Theatre and the praise of the redeeming power of "immortal poesy" are the serious ideas that audiences have taken from *The Dark Lady of the Sonnets*. But Shaw had another and (for him) more important purpose in mind. At the end of the Preface he insists that the play's sketch of Shakespeare "is more complete than its levity suggests". He expresses anger at "the British Public" for taking his comic idea that Shakespeare appropriated words and phrases used by others ("as I do myself") as a disparagement of Shakespeare's "originality". "Why is Shakespeare made ridiculous by such a posterity?"

The Preface enlarges upon the ideas about Shakespeare that Shaw presents in his play. How does Shaw look at Shakespeare? "I am convinced," he writes, "that he was very like myself: in fact, if I had been born in 1556 instead of in 1856, I should have taken to blank verse and given Shakespear a harder run for his money than all the other Elizabethans put together."

Shaw insists that Shakespeare thought of himself as belonging to the upper class. "He thought of the Shakespears and Ardens as families of consequence, and regarded himself as a gentleman under a cloud through his father's ill luck in business, and never for a moment as a man of the people." This contention is the source of some of the most zestful comedy in the play.

At the same time Shaw claims that Shakespeare was not an enemy of democracy, as Shaw's friend Frank Harris claimed and as Tolstoi claimed. If mechanics and tradesmen had greasy clothes and rank breath and if they behaved like political imbeciles, this was merely "an observed fact". They were heirs to "the peculiar ills of poverty and slavery", and joint heirs, with the wealthy, "to all the failings of human nature". Shakespeare shows an "impartiality in judging classes", which is what one asks in "a great human poet", not by flattering the poor and denouncing the rich but in weighing them both "in the same balance". Shaw reminds us of how, in *King Lear*, Shakespeare mercilessly strips the purple from the " 'poor, bare, forked animal' that calls itself a King". In *The Dark Lady of the Sonnets* Shakespeare's friendly rapport with the Beefeater and his fearless blunt speaking to the Queen of England are proof of the impartiality of "a great human poet".

Of all the aspects of Shakespeare's character revealed in the play, perhaps the most fascinating is what Shaw calls "the irrepressible gaiety of genius". Shakespeare, he says, had no pity for himself. "There is nothing that marks the born dramatist more unmistakeably than this discovery of comedy in his own misfortunes almost in proportion to the pathos with which the ordinary man announces their tragedy." Shaw quotes Shakespeare's hundred and thirtieth sonnet, "My mistress' eyes are nothing like the sun", with its lines

> "And in some perfumes is there more delight
> Than in the breath that from my mistress reeks."

as an example of the kind of "compliment" from which the Dark Lady was never safe with Shakespeare. He asks whether any woman could have stood it for long, or "have thought the 'sugred' compliment worth the cruel wounds, the cleaving of the heart in twain", which seemed to Shakespeare a natural and amusing reaction.

It is here that Shaw discusses at length his comparison of the two lovers to Jupiter and Semele, referred to in footnote 20. What woman, he asks, could possibly endure a man "who *knows* and who is hugely amused at the absurdity of his infatuation for a woman of whose mortal imperfections not one escapes him"?

Shakespeare *was* Jupiter to his Semele, the Dark Lady. He knew his own greatness. "The timid cough of the minor poet was never heard from him.

> 'Not marble, nor the gilded monuments
> Of princes, shall outlive this powerful rhyme.' "

Closing the argument, Shaw stresses again the Shakespearean irony and the Shakespearean gaiety – "the grim delight in his own power of looking terrible facts in the face with a chuckle". He maintains that "this impish rejoicing in pessimism, this exultation in what breaks the hearts of common men" is "diagnostic of that immense energy of life which we call genius".

Shaw's final comment on Shakespeare in the Preface will explain Shakespeare's reference to four of the plays in his plea for a National Theatre. Shaw maintains that Shakespeare "reviled" the British public for ignoring his best work and admiring his "splendid commonplaces". But he says Shakespeare produced the commonplaces all the same, and made them sound magnificent "by mere brute faculty" for his art.

Then came a new development. The powerful acting and great popularity of Richard Burbage "enabled Shakespear to free himself from the tyranny of the box office, and to express himself more freely in plays consisting largely of monologue to be spoken by a great actor from whom the public would stand a good deal." Shaw points out that the great tragedies have continued to be popular as the vehicles of a long line of famous actors, from Burbage and Betterton to Forbes Robertson (and to Sir John Gielgud, Sir Laurence Olivier, and Christopher Plummer in our time). But Shakespeare had a real grievance: ". . . the plays which were written without great predominant parts, such as *Troilus and Cressida, All's Well That Ends Well,* and *Measure for Measure,* have dropped on our stage as dead as the second part of Goethe's *Faust* or Ibsen's *Emperor and Galilean.*" Shaw suggests that Shakespeare's discovery "that his most serious work could reach success only when carried on the back of a very fascinating actor" accounts for his dissatisfaction with the public and the theatre as expressed in his long speech to Queen Elizabeth.

This brings us to Shaw's philosophy of The Superman, which he develops in his longer plays: "But even if Shakespear had had no failures, it was not possible for a man of his powers to observe the political and moral conduct of his contemporaries without perceiving that they were incapable of dealing with the problems raised by their own civilization, and that their attempts to carry out the codes of law and to practise the religions offered to them by great prophets and law-givers were and still are so foolish that we now call for The Superman, virtually a new species, to rescue the world from mismanagement."

Here then, in *The Dark Lady of the Sonnets* and its Preface, you have a glimpse of two great men, Shakespeare and Shaw. The editor hopes that the reading of this play will be the beginning of a stirring adventure, and that you will go on to discover "the goodly states and kingdoms" over which both men rule.

THINKING ABOUT THE PLAY

1. Read the first scene in *Hamlet*. Then reread Shakespeare's speech in *The Dark Lady of the Sonnets* beginning "Well said, Master Warder . . .". Find two details in this speech that suggest that Shaw had the scene from *Hamlet* in mind when he conceived the setting and opening action of *The Dark Lady of the Sonnets.*
2. Why is Shakespeare called "The Man" for the first half of the play?
3. Select the sentences or passages in which Shaw (through Shakespeare) proclaims the importance of the poet in the world.
4. Read the sleepwalking scene in *Macbeth* carefully. Compare it with Queen Elizabeth's words as she walks in her sleep, and point out the words and phrases that Shaw wittily suggests "inspired" Shakespeare in writing this scene.
5. What, according to Shaw, is the difference between the poetic vision of Ben Jonson and Shakespeare?
6. Which, to you, is the most dramatic moment of the play? Which the most amusing?
7. For what reason does Shaw have Shakespeare insist that his father, the alderman, was more worthy than Queen Elizabeth's father?
8. What is the additional prophecy that Queen Elizabeth makes after saying that it will be three hundred years and more before a National Theatre is established?

THE PRIVATE EAR

PETER SHAFFER

A LONDON AND BROADWAY SUCCESS

Only rarely does a short play have the phenomenal success in the commercial theatre that *The Private Ear* has enjoyed. On a twin bill with another play by the same author, *The Public Eye,* it opened at the Globe Theatre, London, in May 1963, and ran for sixteen months. In October 1963, the two plays were brought to the Morosco Theatre in New York, where they ran for 163 performances. In Canada the plays have been performed by the Manitoba Theatre Centre in Winnipeg, and by the Crest Theatre and Merger Productions in Toronto.

Even before you read the play, it is hoped that you will have an opportunity to hear and become familiar with the selections from *Peter Grimes* and *Madame Butterfly* which are so integral a part of the play. In a class reading, when you come to these two passages, the music can be played while a narrator reads the description of the mime which accompanies the music.

A fully staged production will be difficult for high school students to carry off successfully. *The Private Ear* is a play that calls for professional actors with considerable experience and finesse.

In either a class reading or a full-scale production you may wish to make changes in the dialogue or mime. Some may regard Ted's language as questionable at times, and deletions can thus be made where they are considered necessary. This language is justified to some extent, however, by the fact that it characterizes Ted, revealing his crude and vulgar approach to life and love. It throws his personality into sharper contrast with that of Bob. The editor and publishers have respected the playwright's wish that the play should be printed virtually as it was presented on the stage.

The closing six-minute mime is extremely difficult to stage as described and yet maintain the essential mood of tenderness and muddled gentleness on Bob's part. The danger is that the comic and absurd elements – particularly in the final sequence of the mime – will rob us of our deep sympathy for Bob, and make us unwilling to accept at full value his gesture of renunciation and his bitterness and loneliness at the end of the play. The author tells us that the stage directions for this mime, used in the first production, need not be followed slavishly. In the 1965 production at the Crest Theatre the comic and absurd elements in the mime were played down, and the emphasis was placed on the tenderness, the embarrassment, and the humiliation felt by the two young people.

The music for the mime in this production could not have exceeded three minutes in length. The lovers (played by Frances Hyland and Heath Lamberts) never left the central armchair area. After the kiss and the confusion on the chair they both got up; there was an embrace, then Doreen's slap, her immediate gesture of regret, and the end of the music and the scene.

More will be said about *The Private Ear* following the play. Its most memorable feature is its poignant portrayal of a sensitive young non-conformist groping for meaning and beauty in life. The play is amusing and it is written with great skill and power; but it has been chosen, not so much for these qualities, but because it will speak directly to thousands of young people who love the world and its "beautiful people" as Bob does, and who are under pressure to conform to group standards which are less desirable than their own ideals. It has been chosen in the hope that it will encourage those who, like Bob, have bright, inquisitive, imaginative minds and a love of the arts to be stronger – to be themselves!

CHARACTERS

TED
BOB
DOREEN

Produced at the Globe Theatre, London, on May 10, 1962, with the following cast:

TED	Douglas Livingstone
BOB	Terry Scully
DOREEN	Maggie Smith

Directed by Peter Wood, with décor by Richard Negri.

THE PRIVATE EAR

SCENE: *Bob's bed-sitting-room in Belsize Park. A summer* 1
evening.

TIME: *The present.*

It is a fairly shabby attic room. The door to the stairs and entrance is down L. *In the corner up* L *there is a small kitchen, which can be closed off with a sliding door at the downstage side. In the living-room there is a dormer window at the back, looking out over a grimy roofscape and an area of sky. It opens french-window fashion and leads onto a small flat roof, bounded by a low wall. The kitchen has two windows, one in the back wall overlooking the roof and another in the wall separating it from the living-room. In the living-room there is a bed up* R, *made up as a sofa, a chest of drawers with a mirror on it* R, *and down* R *some shelves with books and a large rack of gramophone records. Above the bed hangs a large print of*

1. Belsize Park: a street in North-west London, near Hampstead Heath.

Botticelli's "Birth of Venus". The back wall L *of the window is used as a wardrobe and is screened off by curtains. There is a small dining-table* LC, *with a wooden armchair above it and an upright chair* L *of it. A leather-covered armchair stands* RC *and there is a stool down* C. *Under the window up* C *there is a rough box used as a step when going out to the flat roof beyond. Most noticeable are the large twin speakers of a stereophonic gramophone. The speakers are suspended from the sloping ceiling,* R *and* L *of the dormer window. The gramophone is down* R. *A large water-storage cistern is on a shelf over the kitchen door. In the kitchen there is a sink and drain-board, a refrigerator, a gas stove, a small table, and some dresser shelves.*

When the curtain rises, the stage is empty and in darkness. The noise of the water cistern can be heard. The lights come up. It is seven o'clock on a bright midsummer evening. The sun streams through the window. TED *marches in down* L. *He is aged about twenty-five or six, cocky and extroverted, fitted out gaily by Shaftesbury Avenue. His whole relationship to* BOB *shows an air of patronizing domination. He wears his hat and sunglasses, and carries a small transistor in one hand and a bunch of sweet peas in the other. The transistor is playing. He goes up* C, *looks out of the window, does a few dance steps, removes his hat, puts it on the bed, goes to the dressing-table, looks in the mirror, straightens his hair, then turns.*

TED (*calling*). Bob. (*He switches off the transistor.*) Bob.

BOB (*off* L). Hello.

TED. I've arrived – and to prove it, I'm here! Where are you?

2. Botticelli's "Birth of Venus": one of the most famous paintings of the great Italian master, Sandro Botticelli (1444-1510). Reproductions of it are available in many books of art. It is hoped that you will have an opportunity to see it and enjoy it. Venus, or Aphrodite, sprang miraculously from the foam of the sea and floated ashore at the island of Cythera in a seashell.
3. Shaftesbury Avenue: a street running north-west from Piccadilly Circus in the heart of London. The "best" men's shops are not located on it.

BOB. In the bathroom. What time is it?

TED. Ten past seven. What time is she coming? (*He puts the transistor in his pocket.*)

(BOB *runs in down* L, *closing the door behind him. He is a not very prepossessing boy of twenty-one. He is wearing a dressing-gown over underclothes and carries a towel.*)

BOB (*a North Country accent*). Half past. (*He goes to the table, takes a tablecloth and three mats from the table drawer, lays the cloth, and sets out the mats.*)

TED (*moving* C). Well, that's twenty minutes. You've got plenty of time. Just take it all nice and easy. I've bought you some flowers. Provides that chic touch to the décor you're a tiny bit in need of.

BOB. They're pretty. (*He goes into the kitchen and returns with a tray with paper napkins, glasses, water jug, and cutlery.*)

TED. You know, you ought to be flattered I'm here tonight playing cook for you. Do you know where I could have been? (*He takes out a photograph.*) With her. How about them for a pair of Bristols?

(BOB *puts the tray on the chair* L *of the table, crosses to* TED *and takes the photograph.*)

TED (*removes his sun-glasses and puts them in his breast pocket*). And that hair. It's what they call raven black. It's got tints of blue in it. Lustrous, as the ad says. You can't keep your hands off it. See the way she holds herself? (*He takes the photograph from* BOB.) That's what they used to call carriage, my boy.

(BOB *moves to the bed, puts the towel on it, picks up his trousers from the bed, and puts them on.*)

TED. Carriage. You don't see any carriage nowadays. Just fiddle and wiggle, that's all. 'Course, most of the girls you meet think they've got it – poor little nits. Toddling about on stilettos making holes in the lino. Carriage! Look at her. Miss Carriage.

BOB (*moving above the table*). Where did you meet her?

TED. Up the *Mecca* last night, twisting herself giddy with some little nit. I sort of detached her. She wanted a date for tonight, but I said: "Sorry, girl, no can do tomorrow. I'm engaged for one night only as chef to my mate Tchaik, who is entertaining a bird of his own. Very special occasion." So you be grateful. Greater love hath no man than to pass up a bird like this for his mate. (*He puts the photograph on the table and crosses to* R.)

BOB (*picking up the photograph*). What's her name?

TED. You won't believe it if I tell you. Lavinia. Honest. Lavinia. How's that for a sniff of class? The rest of it's not so good. Beamish. Lavinia Beamish. (*He takes the tissue paper from the flowers and picks up a small vase from the chest of drawers.*)

BOB. She's beautiful.

TED. Do you think so?

BOB. I do – yes.

TED. She's going to go off fairly quickish, though. (*He puts the paper in the waste-paper basket up* C.) In three years she'll be all lumpy, like old porridge.

BOB. I don't know how you do it. I don't, really. (*He puts the photograph on the table, then lays out the cutlery, etc.*)

TED. Just don't promise them anything, that's all. (*He moves to* R *of the table.*) Make no promises – they can't hang anything on you, can they?

BOB. I wouldn't know. I really am, by the way.

TED. What?

BOB. Grateful.

TED (*putting the flowers in the vase*). Oh, forget it. It's only a bird, isn't it? Come on, let's get on with din, then. Half past, you say? (*He puts the vase on the table then goes into the kitchen.*)

BOB. Quarter of an hour. That's if she comes at all. (*He takes his clean shirt from the line up* C, *removes his dressing-gown and dons the shirt.*)

(TED *comes from the kitchen with a salt cellar.*)

TED. Of course she'll come. Why shouldn't she? It's a free dinner, isn't it? (*He moves to the table, puts down the salt cellar and stares at the cutlery.*) Well, for God's sake! Is that what you call laying a table?

BOB (*anxiously*). What's wrong with it?

TED. It'd be great for the chimpanzees' tea-party. (*He points to the place settings.*) This one's got three knives, and this one's got three spoons. Well done.

BOB (*hurrying to the table*). Oh, Lord! (*He reaches out to rearrange the cutlery and upsets the vase.*)

TED. You're in a state, aren't you? (*He picks up the vase.*) Well, get a cloth.

(BOB *moves up* C, *collects a teacloth from the wall outside the window, returns to the table, and mops it.*)

TED (*picking up the photograph*). You've wet my Lavinia. I'll have to dry you out, luv. (*He crosses to the chest of drawers.*) Tchaik's in a state. Pit-a-pat, isn't it? Pit-a-flippin'-pat. (*He sticks the photograph in the mirror and turns.*) *Look*, what's up? It's just a girl, isn't it?

BOB. Yes.

TED. Well, then. What's so special? (*He moves to the table.*)

BOB. Nothing.

TED. All right. So she looks like a Greek goddess. (*He takes the cloth from* BOB *and goes into the kitchen.*)

BOB. Look, Ted, I didn't say that. I just said her neck reminded me . . . (*He gets his raincoat from the armchair, takes a bottle of wine from the pocket, places the bottle on the table, then moves to the wardrobe up* LC.)

TED (*coming from the kitchen*). All right, her neck. (*He picks up the bottle of wine.*) What's this?

(BOB *hangs his raincoat in the wardrobe.*)

BOB. It's called Rose. (*He pronounces it like the flower.*) The man in the Victoria said it'd go well with the lamb chops.

(TED *holds up the bottle, drops it and catches it with his other hand.*)

BOB (*running to* TED *with a cry*). Ted!

TED. Well, *he* didn't know what he was talking about, did he? Ignorant little nit.

BOB (*moving* RC; *alarmed*). What d'you mean?

(TED *backs* BOB *to the stool.* BOB *sits.*)

TED. Look and learn, will you? This is a *Rosé*. It's a light French wine. You drink it by itself, not with heavy meat like lamb. Get it? For that you want a claret or burgundy. That's a Burgogna or a – well, or a claret. In any case you've got to serve this cold, can't you read? "*Servir légèrement frappé.*" See? (*Pityingly.*) He's quite hopeless. I'll put it in the fridge. (*He goes into the kitchen and puts the bottle in the refrigerator.*)

BOB. Is it going to taste rotten, then?

(TED *picks up a filled carrier bag from the kitchen table and returns to the living-room.*)

TED. Well, it depends on what you like, doesn't it? (*He puts the bag on the table.*) Some people are happy with bottled cider or lovely limeade.

(BOB *looks worried.*)

TED (*seeing* BOB'*s face*). Oh, don't worry. *She* won't know the difference, anyway. What do we start with?

BOB (*rising and moving to the table*). Soup. I got a tin of mushroom. (*He takes the tin from the bag.*) It's quite good if you add milk.

TED. In a Works Canteen sort of way, I suppose. And what to follow?

4. This is a *Rosé:* In this speech Ted is drawing on his superficial knowledge both of wines and of the French language to patronize Bob. Notice that he mispronounces the French for burgundy.
5. Carrier bag: a shopping bag.
6. Works Canteen: a factory canteen or lunch room.

BOB. Chops. Lamb. (*He takes three chops from the bag, they are in cellophane.*) Do you have to unfreeze them first?

TED. They won't taste much, either way. Not out of those bins in the delly. They never do. You should always go to a 7
proper butcher, mate. (*He inspects the chops.*) A bit on the shaved side, aren't they?

BOB. They were the biggest they had.

TED. Well, just so long as I have that one. Let's hope *she's* got a genteel appetite. Probably will have. Most girls think its not really posh to eat a lot. (*He takes a tin of peas from the bag.*) These go with them?

BOB. Yes. Lamb and peas.

TED. You should have got petty pois – not these marrowfats. It's more chic. You know, the little ones. The other size are sort of com. 8

BOB. They're not, are they?

TED. Definitely. Com. C.O.M. *She* won't know, mind you, but it's just the difference between class and no class, that's all.

BOB (*upset*). It's going to be a right fiasco, isn't it? I'd better open them. (*He takes the tin of peas and goes into the kitchen.*)

TED. That's my job, isn't it?

BOB. I can do it. (*He picks up the opener, stands in the kitchen doorway and starts cutting away furiously at the tin.*)

TED (*replacing the soup and chops in the carrier bag*). Now look, don't get rattled: that's the worst thing you can do. Not with that pit-a-pat going, anyway. It's probably a good thing, anyway, not to have too much fancy food. That way she'll take pity on you, think you're not eating right and all that palaver. Needs a wife's good cooking. You know. In your case it's bloody time.

(BOB *cuts his finger on the tin and cries out.*)

BOB. Now look what I've done.

7. Delly: a delicatessen shop.
8. Com: common.

TED. Steady on. You really are in a state, aren't you? Put it under the tap for a moment.

BOB. There's a plaster in that drawer. (*He goes to the sink.*)

TED (*moving to the chest of drawers*). Well, pull yourself together for God's sake. (*He takes a plaster from a box in the drawer.*) You go on this way, the whole evening is going to be a flipping fiasco. You're not going to get far with any girl shaking blood over her cardigan. They're cowards that way. They can't stand the sight of blood on their woollies.

(BOB *comes from the kitchen and crosses to* TED.)

BOB. It's all right – just a nick.

TED. Give here. (*He puts the plaster on* BOB*'s finger.*) Now look, why don't you take yourself a snort and just sit down. I can cope in there. A gin and french, that's what you need.

BOB. There isn't any gin.

TED. I might have known. What are you going to give her first, then?

BOB. First?

TED. To drink.

BOB. Look, I said she had one drink. I didn't say she was a boozer, did I?

TED. You don't have to be a boozer to want a cocktail. It's the chic thing. No, it's not even chic. Even the suburbs do it. You can't ask *her* to sit down to eat just like that. You're really hopeless, aren't you?

BOB (*quietly, but with more firmness*). I asked you to help, you know. Not to make comments. (*He sits in the armchair, takes a pair of socks from the arm and puts one on. There is a large hole in it. He removes the sock, throws the pair on to the bed, rises, moves to the dressing-table and takes a clean pair of socks from the drawer.*)

TED (*moving up* C). Well, help's one thing. This is just bricks out of straw, isn't it? (*He moves to* R *of the table.*) Anyway, I didn't know I'd have to organize the whole bit. What's

9. A plaster: an adhesive bandage.

come over you? I know you've always been a bit on the twitch, but I've never seen you like this, all to pieces. What's she done to you? It's like the snake and the old guinea pig, isn't it? (*He puts finishing touches to the table.*)

BOB (*sitting in the armchair*). Don't be daft.

TED (*turning to him*). Are you really serious, Tchaik?

BOB (*avoiding* TED's *eye*). About what? (*He puts on the socks.*)

TED. This girl.

BOB. How can I be serious about someone I met for a few minutes?

TED. Well, I never know with you. You're deep. It's all that Celtic Twilight in your blood. That's not original, by the way. 10
Miss Story said it in the office last week. She said you were full of Celtic Twilight.

BOB (*removing his slippers*). Who's Miss Story? (*He puts on his shoes.*)

TED. You know – the old bag in accounts. She said you were mystic.

BOB. Yes, I'm sure. (*He struggles with his laces.*)

TED. Seriously, is there anything?

BOB. I told you, don't be daft. Why should there be?

TED (*tying* BOB's *laces for him*). Well, it's not every day you invite a girl to dinner, is it? Let's be honest. You go to hundreds of concerts, but you don't usually pick up a girl and invite her home for the old chops and vino, do you? So what gives?

BOB. I told you. We were next to each other.

TED. Yes?

BOB. I'd been watching her for ages out of the corner of my eye. She was absolutely beautiful. I couldn't believe it when she dropped her programme.

TED. Well, that was a piece of luck for you, wasn't it? Of course you handed it back with a mannerly bow?

10. Celtic Twilight: By reputation the Celts are sensitive, moody, and imaginative.

BOB. I didn't, as a matter of fact. I didn't like to – in case she thought anything. It just lay there between us for about ten minutes. And then it was the interval, and I had to make up my mind. She was just going out when I picked it up and gave it to her.

TED. And then what happened?

BOB. She said: "Thank you."

TED. Original.

BOB. Well, I asked her if she liked music, and she said, "Yes". It was a daft question, really, I suppose. I mean, she wouldn't have been there otherwise, would she? In the end it turned out she was on her own, and I asked her if she'd have a coffee with me after. I could hardly believe my ears when she said "Yes".

TED. Why not? Even goddesses get thirsty. So?

BOB. So we went to an Espresso in South Ken.

TED. And held hands over two flat whites?

BOB. Not exactly, no. As a matter of fact, I couldn't think of very much to say to her. We were out in the street again inside of ten minutes.

TED. So that's why you asked me tonight? To help out with the talk?

BOB. I suppose, yes.

TED. I really am flattered. (*He moves above the table.*) Your first date with her and you invite me along, too.

BOB. Well, you know what to say to women. You've had the practice, haven't you?

TED. There's no practice needed. You just say the first thing that comes into your head, as long as it's not dirt, of course. They don't much like dirt, though they'll go for that, too, if you present it right. You know – with a man-of-the-world smile.

11. Espresso: a coffee bar or shop.
South Ken: Royal Albert Hall, where the concert probably took place, is in South Kensington, a district in West London.
Two flat whites: *café au lait* – coffee with milk.

BOB. If I tried anything like that, I'd look like a seducer in a silent film.

TED (*going into the kitchen*). Well, you'd have to find your own style, of course. The important thing is, you've taken the plunge. You've invited a girl home. (*He removes his jacket and hangs it in the kitchen.*)

BOB. Oh, I had to, in this case. There's no question about that. She was . . .

TED. What? (*He picks up the tea-towel and tucks it round his waist as an apron.*)

BOB. You'll laugh.

TED. No, I won't. Go on. Well?

BOB. Well, the first girl I ever saw I wanted to see again. I mean, had to. She's got a look about her – not how people are, but how they ought to be.

TED (*coming into the room*). Steady.

BOB. No, I mean it. When I said her neck reminded me, you know what I was thinking of? (*He rises and moves* C.)

TED. Who?

BOB (*indicating the print on the wall behind the bed*). Her.

TED. Venus?

BOB. Yes. Botticelli would have been proud to paint her. She's got exactly the same neck – long and gentle. (*He moves to the picture.*) That's a sign.

TED. A sign?

BOB. Yes.

TED. What for?

BOB. Spiritual beauty. Like Venus. That's what this picture really represents. The birth of beauty in the human soul. My Botticelli book says so. (*He moves to the shelves down* R *and snatches up a Fontana Pocket Library edition, opens it and reads.*) Listen. "Venus, that is to say Humanity, is a nymph of excellent comeliness, born of heaven. Her soul and mind are Love and Charity. Her eyes, dignity. Her hands, liberality. Her feet, modesty." All signs, you see. (*He reads.*) "Venus is the Mother of Grace, of Beauty, and of Faith."

TED. And your bird's the mum of all that?

BOB (*replacing the book*). No, of course not. I'm not a fool. But that look of hers is ideal beauty, Ted. It means she's got grace inside her. Really beautiful people are beautiful inside. Don't you see? (*He takes his tie from the chest of drawers, and puts it on.*)

TED. You mean like after Andrews Liver Salts?

BOB. That's exactly what I mean.

TED. Oh, Tchaik, now seriously, come off it. I think that's daft. I mean it is, boy. (*He crosses to* BOB.) There's a lot of stupid, greedy little nitty girls about who are as pretty as pictures.

BOB (*turning*). I don't mean pretty.

TED. Then what? (*He ties* BOB*'s tie for him.*)

BOB. Well, what you called carriage, for instance. What your Lavinia's got. It's not just something you learn, the way to walk and that. It's something inside you. I mean real carriage, the way you see some girls walk, sort of pulling the air round them like clothes. You can't practice that. You've got first to love the world. Then it comes out.

TED. I see. Have you got any red-currant jelly? They always serve it with lamb in chic restaurants.

BOB. I've got some jam.

TED. What kind?

BOB. Gooseberry.

(*The doorbell rings.*)

BOB. There she is!

TED. So I hear. Calm down. All right, now listen. The last swallow of coffee and I'm away. Deadline at nine-thirty. Work to do at home. Got it? Nine-thirty you see me, nine-thirty-one you don't.

BOB (*moving to the wardrobe*). Look, it's not like that at all. (*He takes his jacket from the wardrobe.*)

TED. No? Well, if it isn't, it ought to be. Go on, then.

12. I see: Has Ted seen? Has he understood?

BOB (*putting on his jacket*). Yes. The soup's in a tin. (*He moves down* L.)

TED. You showed me. (*He hurriedly picks up* BOB'*s slippers, collects the dressing-gown and towel from the bed, bundles them into the wardrobe and closes the curtains. He then collects two cushions, puts them on the stool and sets the stool* R *of the table.*)

BOB. Good.

(*The doorbell rings.* BOB *stands at a loss down* L.)

TED. Why not just leave her standing there? She'll go away in five minutes.

(BOB *turns to go.*)

TED (*shouts*). Hi! (*He runs to* BOB, *tears a cleaner's label from* BOB'*s right sleeve, then bites the tape from the back of the collar.*) Go on! (*He gives* BOB *a push.*)

BOB. I wish I had a drink to offer her.

TED. Well, you haven't, have you?

(BOB *exits down* L. TED *crosses to the chest of drawers, tidies his hair, polishes his shoes on the back of his trouser legs, picks up the carrier bag and the tray, goes into the kitchen and closes the door.*)

(BOB *re-enters down* L *and stands aside.* DOREEN *enters down* L. *She is a pretty girl of about twenty, wearing an imitation ocelot coat. It is at once obvious that she is nervous also, and has no real pleasure in being there. Her reactions are anxious and tight, and these, of course, do nothing to reassure* BOB.)

DOREEN. I'm not too early?

BOB. No. Just right. (*He closes the door.*) Actually, it's only just half past. You're very punctual.

DOREEN. Unpunctuality's the thief of time, as my dad says. 13

BOB. To coin a phrase.

13. Unpunctuality's . . . time: What is the familiar saying on which this phrase is based?

DOREEN. Pardon?

BOB. Let me take your coat.

DOREEN. Thank you. (*She slips her coat off. Under it she is wearing a dress and a cardigan.*)

BOB (*taking the coat*). That's pretty.

DOREEN. D'you like it?

BOB. I do, yes. Is it real? I mean – real leopard.

DOREEN. It's ocelot.

BOB (*hanging the coat on the hook behind the door down* L). Oh! (*He imitates* TED.) Very chic.

DOREEN. Pardon?

BOB. Won't you sit down.

DOREEN (*moving to* RC *and looking at the table laid for three*). Is this all yours? Or do you share?

BOB (*moving below the table*). No, I live alone. There's actually a friend here at the moment. He's helping with the dinner. We work in the same office.

DOREEN. Can I help?

BOB. No, it's all done. Really. All you can do is sit down and relax. (*With an attempt at "style", he gestures at the armchair.*)

DOREEN. Thanks. (*She sits in the armchair.*)

(*There is a tiny pause.*)

BOB. Do you smoke?

DOREEN. I do a bit, yes.

BOB. Good! Tipped or plain? (*He crosses to the chest of drawers, picks up a cigarette box, opens it with a flourish, and offers it to* DOREEN.)

DOREEN. Well! That's luxury for you, isn't it – both kinds. Tipped, thank you. (*She takes a cigarette.*)

BOB. Allow me. (*He picks up a lighter from the chest of drawers and tries to snap it alight. It does not work. He fumbles with it, to no avail.*)

DOREEN. It's all right, I've got a match. (*She takes matches from her handbag and lights her cigarette.*)

(BOB *puts the lighter and cigarette box on the chest of drawers, crosses above* DOREEN *and sits on the stool.*

DOREEN *does not know what to do with her spent match and puts it in her handbag. There is a tiny pause.*)

BOB. So, how have you been?

DOREEN. Fine. You?

BOB. Yes. Can't complain. Er – you're a typist, aren't you?

DOREEN. Stenographer. The place that trained me said: "Never call yourself a typist: it's lowering."

BOB. Oh. What kind of things do you – well, stenog, I suppose?

DOREEN. The usual letters.

BOB. Yours of the tenth?

DOREEN. Pardon?

BOB. "Dear sir, in reply to yours of the tenth . . ." Things like that?

DOREEN. Oh, I see. Yes, that's right.

BOB. Do you mind it?

DOREEN. What?

BOB. Doing the same thing, day in, day out.

DOREEN. Well, there's not much choice, is there?

BOB. I suppose not.

DOREEN. You've got to earn your living, haven't you? Like my dad says, "It doesn't grow on trees."

BOB. No. Wouldn't they look odd if it did?

DOREEN. Pardon?

BOB. The trees.

DOREEN. Oh, yes. (*She looks nervously at him.*)

BOB (*plunging on*). Like when people say unpunctuality's the thief of time – like your dad says.

(DOREEN *is at a loss with her cigarette ash.*)

BOB. I always used to try and imagine unpunctuality in a 14
mask – you know – with a sack labelled "swag". That's what comes of having a literal mind. (*He looks for something to*

14. Bob, with his literal mind, imagines unpunctuality as a thief, wearing a mask, with a sack labelled "swag" (booty).

supply as an ashtray, rises, crosses to the chest of drawers, takes the lid from the plaster box and hands it to DOREEN.) I remember I had awful trouble at school one day with that poem which says, "The child is father of the man." I simply couldn't see it. I mean, how could a child be a father? (*He resumes his seat.*) I couldn't get beyond that. I don't think imagination's a thing you can cultivate though, do you? I mean, you're either born with it or you're not.

DOREEN. Oh, yes, you're born with it.

BOB. Or you're not.

DOREEN. Yes.

BOB. There ought to be a sign so parents can tell. There probably is, if we knew how to read it. I mean, all babies are born with blue eyes, but no one ever says there's a difference in the blue. And I bet there is. I bet if you looked really hard at six babies the first day they were born you'd see six different kinds of blue. Milky blue – sharp blue, you know, like cornflower colour – even petrol blue. And they each mean something different about characters. Of course, after the first day they all fade and become the same. It's a thought, anyway.

DOREEN. Oh, yes.

BOB. Daft one. Would you like a drink?

DOREEN. Well, I wouldn't say no.

BOB. Good! What would you like?

DOREEN. Whatever you suggest. I'm not fussy.

BOB. Gin and french?

DOREEN. That'd be lovely.

BOB (*rising and crossing to the chest of drawers*). Well, if you'll just excuse me. (*He picks up a Dimple Haig bottle and shakes out some sixpences into his hand.*)

DOREEN. What are you doing?

15. A Dimple Haig bottle: a whisky bottle with concave sides and "dimpled" glass.

BOB. I won't be a moment. (*He replaces the bottle.*)

DOREEN. Can I help?

BOB (*crossing to the door down* L). I won't be a second.

DOREEN. Where are you going?

BOB. Just round the corner. To the pub. It's only a step away. (*He opens the door.*)

DOREEN. Haven't you got any in?

BOB. No. I – (*inventing it*) I don't drink.

DOREEN (*rising*). You don't?

BOB. No.

DOREEN. Well, don't go on my account.

BOB. That's all right. I mean, I want to.

DOREEN. That's silly.

BOB. Why?

DOREEN. Because I don't drink, either. (*She resumes her seat.*)

BOB. You're just saying that.

DOREEN. No, honest. I don't.

BOB. Ever?

DOREEN. Well, at Christmas and that. But I don't want one now. I only said it to be sociable.

BOB. You sure?

DOREEN. Positive.

BOB. Well, that's all right then. (*He closes the door and pockets the coins.*)

DOREEN. Of course.

(*There is a pause.*)

BOB (*fingering* DOREEN'*s coat*). You know, I always thought an ocelot was a bird.

DOREEN. Did you?

BOB. Yes. I must have been thinking of an ostrich.

(TED, *playing the waiter, enters from the kitchen with two glasses of wine on a tray.*)

Geoffrey Frazer

Ted, playing the waiter, brings a drink for Doreen and Bob, in the Merger Productions presentation of *The Private Ear*.

TED (*crossing to* DOREEN). Cocktails, madame? A little chilled vino before din?

DOREEN (*delighted*). Ohh!

BOB. This is my friend, the one I told you about. Ted Veasey – Miss Marchant.

TED. Pleased to meet you.

DOREEN. How d'you do?

TED. Oh, *comme ci, comme ça*. You know, most people never answer that question – how do you do? That's because those who ask it don't really want to know. How do *you* do?

DOREEN. Oh, very nicely, thank you.

TED. That's all right, then. Do I have to call you "miss"?

DOREEN. Well, it is a bit formal, isn't it? Why don't you call me Doreen?

TED. Thanks. I will. If it's not too presumptuous. You see, I'm only the butler around here. (*He offers her a drink.*) Mademoiselle?

DOREEN (*hesitating to take a drink*). Well . . .

BOB. I'm afraid she doesn't drink.

TED. No?

DOREEN. Well, only on special occasions.

TED. Well, tonight's an occasion, isn't it? Of course it is. A real proper – (*in French*) "occasion". Come on. Do you good.

DOREEN. Well – just to be sociable. (*She takes the drink.*)

TED. That's it. (*He crosses to* BOB *and offers him the other drink.*) Tchaik?

BOB. Well, you know *I* don't.

TED. Don't what?

BOB. Drink.

TED. Since when?

BOB (*unhappily*). Well, always . . .

TED. First I've heard of it. You were sloshed last week. (*To* DOREEN.) He was.

BOB. I mean, not before dinner.

TED. What?

BOB. Not on an empty stomach. You know I don't.

TED. Well, waste not, want not, I say. (*He drinks.*) The servants you get these days. See you, my dear, in two shakes of a lamb's tail – or should I say, chop?

(TED *exits to the kitchen and closes the door.*)

DOREEN. He's funny.

BOB. Yes, he is. He's marvellous to have in the office. (*He crosses to* C.) I mean, he's always cheerful.

DOREEN. Aren't you?

BOB (*sitting on a stool*). Not always, no.

DOREEN. What office do you work for?

BOB. Import-export. I'm just a glorified clerk, really. At least that's what Ted keeps on telling me, and I suppose he's right.

DOREEN. Why, is he over you?

BOB. In a way he is, yes.

DOREEN. What way?

BOB. Well, he's just been promoted to look after a small department of his own. It means quite a bit of responsibility. He's going to go a long way, I think. I mean he's interested and keen – you know.

DOREEN. But aren't you?

BOB. Well, not so much as he is. He knows all about economics. Tariffs and that. I'm afraid it's all rather beyond me.

DOREEN. I like people who want to get on. Who've got drive. That's something I respect. My dad's got drive. That's one thing he has got.

BOB. What does he do?

DOREEN. Well, he's retired now. He used to be a Works' Manager.

BOB. Where?

DOREEN. Edmonton.

BOB. Oh.

DOREEN. He says, if you haven't got drive, you might as well be dead.

BOB. He's probably right. Is that drink all right?

DOREEN. Yes, it's lovely.

BOB. Good.

DOREEN. Cheerio.

BOB. Cheerio. (*Enviously, he watches her drink.*)

DOREEN. This is a nice room.

BOB. D'you like it?

DOREEN. Yes, I like large rooms.

BOB. So do I.

DOREEN. Most of the rooms you see today, they're tiny – like matchboxes.

BOB. Yes. (*He laughs obligingly, then rushes on eagerly.*) Mind you, that would suit some people. I saw a man in the

16. Edmonton: a district in North London.

Tube yesterday who looked exactly like a safety match. Thin 17
body like a stick, and a tiny black head. I remember thinking: Bryant and May could use you.

DOREEN. Pardon?

BOB. Bryant and May could use . . . (*He falls silent.*)

(DOREEN *stares at him unencouragingly.*)

BOB (*plunging on*). Mind you, it's not that large, really. Not when you have to eat and sleep all in the one. Still, it's hard finding places, and they're very tolerant here.

DOREEN. Tolerant?

BOB. I mean, they don't interfere with your private weaknesses – you know.

DOREEN. Pardon?

BOB. I mean your habits. I'm afraid I've got rather a weakness, and some people would get a bit shirty about it, but not
here. They let me play Behemoth all night, even past the music 18
hours. (*He indicates the stereophonic gramophone.*) That's him, of course. "Behemoth" means a great monster, you know. It's in the Bible.

DOREEN. What is it, then, a gramophone?

BOB. Stereo.

DOREEN. It looks lovely. Interesting, I mean.

BOB (*a new note of warmth and pride in his voice*). You should hear him. (*He rises and crosses to the machine.*) Do you know anything about these animals?

DOREEN. I'm afraid not, no.

BOB. Well, I shan't bother you with technical names, then. But I can tell you this is really the best machine a chap of my

17. Tube: the London subway.
    Bryant and May: English match manufacturers. This is a typical example of Bob's curious, eager invention.
18. Behemoth: In the Old Testament, this is a fanciful name for a huge creature living in marshes (Job 40: 15-24). In the Apocrypha it is a mythical beast, the male counterpart of Leviathan.

means could possibly afford, anywhere in the world. Of course, if you want to spend thousands, it'd be different. (*With an uncontrollable burst of true enthusiasm, he is off on his hobby-horse.*) Behemoth's a real marvel, I can tell you. Most big sets can't play properly below a certain level. You can't hear them properly, unless they blast you out of your seat. That's because they've got bad speakers. (*He moves up* C *and indicates the speakers.*) These things. Most speakers have only got between five and seven per cent efficiency. These have got between fifteen to twenty. Wharfedale Speakers. They're the best. I'm sorry: I promised not to give you technical names. It's the music that counts, anyway, isn't it? (*With great warmth.*) I'm glad you like music. (*He moves to the stool and sits.*) I can't tell you how glad I am to know that. You know, last week I'd been watching you for ages before you dropped that programme. I was watching you all through the Bach: and you were so wrapped up in listening, so concentrating, there were wrinkles all over your face.

(DOREEN *looks at him, startled and displeased.*)

BOB (*falters*). Well, I mean, they were very becoming – I love to see lines on people's faces. I mean, that's their life, isn't it? It's what's happened to them. Most girls you see have got so much powder and muck on, you can't tell anything's happened to them. You know, they're like eggs, their skins. Eggshells, I mean. You're different.

DOREEN. You mean I've got inner beauty.

BOB. Do I?

DOREEN. That's what a man told me once. Inner beauty. It was his way of saying he was off me.

BOB (*rising*). That's not what I mean at all. (*He moves down* R. *Desperately.*) You know the really wonderful thing about this machine? You can turn it up as loud as you like and all you hear is the faintest hum. (*He switches it on.*) Listen, I'm going to turn it right up. (*He turns the volume control as far as it will go.*) See?

DOREEN (*blankly*). Wonderful.

BOB (*switching off; happily*). You must have been listening to music for an awfully long time to like Bach. Most people come to him only after a bit. When I first started it was all the *Symphonie Pathétique* and *Swan Lake*. You know. 19

DOREEN (*who has heard of this*). Oh – yes.

BOB. That's why Ted calls me "Tchaik": it's short for Tchaikovsky. I was mad about his music once. I thought Bach was boring, like exercises. Then one day I was shaving – isn't it daft how things happen – I always play records when I'm
shaving, or in the bath – and I'd put on one of the Branden- 20
burgs, you know, the Fourth with two flutes, and suddenly – just suddenly – I heard what made it marvellous. It wasn't about love or victory, or those romantic things that change all the time. It was about things that don't change. D'you see what I mean?

(DOREEN *gives him a quick, tight smile, but says nothing.*)

BOB. Anyway, would you like to hear one? I've got all six.

DOREEN. Lovely . . .

BOB. Good. (*He crosses to the stool and moves it down* C, *facing the speakers.*) Well, if you wouldn't mind moving here, you'd enjoy it better. You'd be midway between the two speakers at just the right distance. Let me help you. (*He moves to* R *of* DOREEN *and takes the "ashtray".*)

(DOREEN *rises, moves to the stool and sits on it, with her back to the audience.*)

BOB. That's it. Now – behold. (*He removes the cover from the top shelf down* R, *revealing the rack of records.*)

19. *Symphonie Pathétique:* Tchaikovsky's most famous symphony.
    Swan Lake: his popular full-length ballet.
20. Brandenburgs: the Brandenburg Concertos, a series of six concertos for different instruments composed by Johann Sebastian Bach. They were written at the request of, and dedicated to, the Margrave of Brandenburg.

DOREEN (*impressed*). Help! Are all those yours?

BOB. Every one. (*He puts the cover on the floor down* R.)

DOREEN. But you must spend all your pay on records.

BOB. Well, you've got to spend it on something, haven't you? Which Brandenburg would you like? Or maybe you'd prefer the Goldbergs? Or the Musical Offering?

DOREEN (*who has never heard of any of these*). You choose.

BOB. No, it's your pleasure, madame.

DOREEN. Well, to be frank, I don't know that much about it. That old stuff isn't really me.

BOB. You mean you prefer Modern?

DOREEN (*seeing a gleam of hope*). That's right. Modern.

BOB. What d'you like? Stravinsky? Shostakovich?

DOREEN. Well, I don't quite mean that.

BOB. You mean something more tuneful?

DOREEN. Yes.

BOB. Benjamin Britten. Like me. I think Britten's the greatest composer in the world. I mean, he writes tunes, and makes wonderful sounds you can understand, not just plink-plonk. I hate all that twelve-tone stuff, don't you? It's sort of not – human. I know what I'll play you. (*He grabs an album.*) *Peter Grimes*. Decca's done the most marvellous recording of it ever. D'you know it?

DOREEN. I can't say I do.

21. The Goldbergs: the Goldberg Variations; a set of thirty variations for clavier or harpsichord written for Count Kaiserling, Russian Ambassador to the Saxony Court, at the suggestion of Bach's pupil, Johann Gottlieb Goldberg. Goldberg was in attendance on the Count, who had insomnia; he played for him to help while away his sleepless hours. Finding that Goldberg had been a pupil of Bach, the Count asked him to commission Bach to write some harpsichord music of a "pleasant, cheerful character".
The Musical Offering: a trio for flute, violin, and clavier, written by Bach as a "musical offering" to Frederick the Great.

BOB (*switching on the gramophone*). It's the greatest thing you ever heard. (*He takes the record from its sleeve and cleans it with a sponge.*) It's all about this lonely fisherman who lives by himself, and the village hates him because he's different, and has dreams and visions about what life should be. He dreams about this girl, Ellen – someone to share his life, you know, only he's not very good at expressing himself. (*He puts the record on the turntable.*) In the end the village turns against him and accuses him of killing his apprentice. There's a sort of manhunt at night – people calling and shouting, hurrying in with lanterns. They make up a posse, you know: it's terrifying.

(BOB *starts the record towards the end of the great lynch chorus in Act Three.*)

BOB. It's like a rising sea, getting wilder and wilder, up and up and up till it suddenly bursts over the town. I think it's the most marvellous thing I ever heard. Listen. (*He turns up the volume and listens to it, entranced, beating time to its hurtling rhythm and mouthing the words, which he clearly knows.*)

(DOREEN *watches* BOB *with something much less like involvement: she obviously detests the music.* BOB *has put it on very loudly: it becomes quite deafening as it boils up into the great shouts of "Peter Grimes!" punctuated by silence.*)

BOB (*explaining in a hushed voice*). That's his name – "Peter Grimes". They all just stand there and call it. Sssh!

(*The chorus yells "Grimes!" then there is a brief silence.*)

BOB (*singing*). "Peter Grimes!"

(TED *enters from the kitchen with three soup bowls on a tray.*)

TED (*facetiously*). Did someone call me?

(DOREEN *laughs and rises.*)

TED (*sets the bowls out on the table*). Turn it down, for God's sake, or you'll have the neighbours in. (*He bangs the tray as a gong.*) Come on, dinner up. (*To* DOREEN.) Madame! (*He indicates the chair above the table.*)

DOREEN. Ooh! Lovely. (*She sits above the table.*)

(BOB, *his face set, stops the gramophone.*)

TED (*putting the tray against the wall* L). *Potage à la* Heinz. *Champignon!* Note that g-n sound, that's pronouncing it proper. Followed by lamb chops *à la* Ted Veasey.

(DOREEN *laughs delightedly.* BOB *very elaborately switches off the set, puts the record in its sleeve and lays it on the machine. His movements are slow and mechanical.* TED *goes into the kitchen and returns with a plate of sliced Hovis.*)

TED. Hey, Tchaik, stop fussing with that damn thing, and come and be host. It's your party, isn't it? (*He puts the plate on the table. To* DOREEN.) Now, take a nice slice of Hovis, my dear, it gives body to the soup!

(BOB *moves to the stool to* R *of the table, and sits.*)

TED (*goes into the kitchen and returns with the bottle of wine*). And have a fill-up on the rosé. That's it. (*He pours wine for* DOREEN *and himself, then puts the bottle on the table.*) Here's to you!

(BOB *lifts his empty glass pointedly.*)

TED (*pours a drink for* BOB). And you, chum!

BOB (*responding quietly to the toast*). Thank you. To you. (*He drinks, keeping his eyes lowered.*)

(TED *puts down his glass, goes into the kitchen, and returns with a saucepan of hot soup and a ladle.*)

TED. You know, how you can stand that stuff, I'll never know. Opera! How so-called intelligent people can listen to it I just can't imagine. (*He serves soup into each bowl.*) I mean, who ever heard of people singing what they've got to say? (*He sings to the tune of the Toreador's song in "Carmen".*) "Will you kindly pass the bread?" "Have a bowl of soup?" "*Champignon*." "I must go and turn the gas off." (*He puts the saucepan in the kitchen and returns to the living-room.*) Well, for heaven's sake! If that's not a bloody silly way to go on, excuse language, I don't know what is. I wish somebody would explain it to me, honest. I mean. I'm probably just dead ignorant. (*He sits* L *of the table.*)

BOB (*very quietly*). You are.

(TED *looks at* BOB *in surprise.* BOB *has never said anything like this before.* BOB *looks at* TED *with calm contempt. There is a brief pause.* DOREEN *looks anxiously from one to the other.*)

TED. Come on. Drink up before it gets cold. (*He taps his bowl with his spoon.*)

(*All three lift their spoons. They freeze. The lights fade leaving only a pin-spot on* BOB*'s face. The following dialogue is heard through the loudspeakers from a tape-recording.*)

DOREEN. Lovely soup. Is it mushroom?

TED. Of course not – it's toadstool.

DOREEN. Oh, you are awful! It's a nice flavour.

TED. Well, let's say it shows willing, anyway. Warms you up on a cold night, like some others I could mention.

(*The recording revolves into high-pitched gabble.* BOB *puts down his spoon and drinks off an entire glass of wine, quickly. He picks up his spoon again, and freezes.*)

DOREEN. Ooh, lovely! Chops!

TED. D'you like 'em?

DOREEN. They're my favourite, actually – chops – they always were, ever since I was small. I always used to like the way there was a meaty bit in the middle of the fatty bit.

TED. Yes, I know what you mean. Here's some peas to go with them . . .

(*There is more high-pitched gabble.* BOB *takes some more wine and drinks it, then freezes again.*)

DOREEN. Ooh, lovely! Peaches!

TED. Yellow cling.

DOREEN. What's that?

TED. Their name.

DOREEN. It isn't.

TED. It is – yellow cling peaches. Say, what a name for your Chinese girl-friend. Yellow Cling Peach.

(DOREEN *laughs.*)

DOREEN. Did you cook all that yourself?

TED. Every scrap.

DOREEN. That's wonderful. All the boys I've met don't do anything like that.

TED. I'll bet all the boys you've met don't do anything – full stop.

DOREEN. Pardon?

TED. Nothing. What time is it, then? (*Louder.*) What time is it, then? What time is it, then?

(*The last line is recorded with an echo. The recording ends. The lights come up, but at a lower key. It is one hour later. The day has almost gone.*)

BOB. Nine o'clock.

(*They lower their spoons and resume the scene.*)

TED (*to* DOREEN). Some more vino, then?

DOREEN. I don't mind if I do.

TED (*picking up the bottle*). Well, what d'you know? There isn't any. Tchaik's taken it all.

DOREEN (*giggling*). I thought he didn't drink.

TED (*posh*). Not on an empty stomach. (*To* BOB.) You certainly make up for it on a full one.

DOREEN. Like my dad. Only that's cos he's got an ulcer. He can drink with his meal, but not before. If he drinks before, it's murder. He's chewed the carpet before now. Once 22 he tore a lump out of the fringe. Honest.

BOB. Poor chap.

DOREEN. Yes. He suffers terribly with it. Well, of course, he's a worrier. A natural worrier. He worries about everything.

TED. Does he worry about you?

DOREEN (*a little stiffly*). He's got nothing to worry about in that department.

TED. No?

DOREEN. No. I mean politics. Things like that. The way the world's going. I think his ulcer started to grow the day he was appointed to be branch secretary of the union.

TED. Well, that's enough to worry anybody. He's a union man, then?

DOREEN (*proudly*). All his life.

TED. Well, good luck to him.

DOREEN (*indignantly*). What d'you mean?

TED. I'm a Tory myself and I don't care who knows it. Bloody unions. If you ask me, they're doing their best to ruin the country.

DOREEN. That's just stupid.

BOB. Yes, I agree.

TED. You can shut up. You didn't even vote at the last election. Wherever you look you come back to the same thing. The unions. Always at the bottom of everything, the unions, demanding, demanding all the time. No settling day. Give them one thing, they want another, and another, and another, till we're all bust – which we pretty nearly are now. The unions. They make me bloody sick!

DOREEN. Well, I don't agree with you.

TED. Well, of course you don't agree. What do you know

22. He's chewed the carpet: an expression suggesting extreme pain.

about economics? About the real laws that govern industry? Nothing. What do you care? Damn all! Well?

DOREEN (*cowed*). Well – I don't know.

TED. 'Course you don't know.

DOREEN. Well, all the same . . .

TED. What?

DOREEN. My dad can remember the time when he had to fight to get twopence halfpenny a week.

TED. Your dad.

DOREEN. Yes, my dad.

TED. And how old a gentleman would he be, may one ask?

DOREEN. Well, he's getting on now.

TED. How old?

DOREEN. Sixty-one.

TED. Well, there you are then. (*He rises, crosses to the chest of drawers, takes a cigarette from the box, and lights it.*) That's all in the past, isn't it? Of course the unions were O.K. then: that was the bad old days. But it's become a cause now: the union right or wrong. Eh, it's all so old-fashioned, the bosses against the workers. I can tell you one thing: if the unions are going to run this country, I'm moving out. (*He moves up* C.) Because the rate they're going, they're going to bankrupt it completely and utterly inside ten years. Get the coffee, Tchaik. I'm worn out.

(BOB, *slightly tipsy, rises, goes into the kitchen and puts the kettle on the stove.*)

TED (*to* DOREEN). Come on, give a hand, luv. (*He sings to the tune of "Toreador".*) "That really was a very lovely meal – pass me the mats."

(DOREEN *gets the tray and helps* TED *to stack everything from the table.*)

DOREEN (*singing*). "The knives and forks and spoons . . ."

(*They both giggle.* BOB *comes from the kitchen.*)

TED (*singing*). "Where is the tray – pom, pom, ti pom – leave the flowers . . ." (*He hands the loaded tray to* BOB.)

You've gone very quiet. Are you all right?

BOB. I'm fine. (*He takes the tray into the kitchen.*)

TED (*picking up the vase*). It's all that wine.

(DOREEN *folds the cloth.*)

TED (*to* DOREEN). Did you know alcohol is what they call a depressant? (*He replaces the vase on the table.*)

DOREEN. No.

TED. That's something most people don't know. Most people think it's a stimulant, but they're wrong. Not in the long run, it isn't.

DOREEN. You know a lot, don't you? I like people who know things. (*She moves* RC.)

(TED *closes the kitchen door so* BOB *will not hear.*)

TED. Well, there's no good being an ignoramus, is there? You know things, you get on. (*He moves to* L *of her.*) Why don't you make yourself comfortable?

DOREEN. Thanks. (*She collects her handbag, crosses to the chest of drawers and puts the bag on them.*)

(TED *closes the curtains at the window to the kitchen.*)

DOREEN. That was a smashing dinner.

TED (*crossing to the stool*). Glad madame liked it.

DOREEN. I did, very much. You are clever. (*She lifts her skirt and pulls up her stocking.*)

TED. Oh, *ce ne fais rien!* (*He picks up the cushions from the stool and tosses them on to the bed.*) How d'you like Tchaik?

DOREEN (*without enthusiasm*). He's nice. (*She takes out her compact and attends to her make-up.*)

TED. Certainly is, and a very good son to his old mother, which is more than you are, I bet. I mean – daughter.

DOREEN (*turning to face him*). My mother's dead, smarty. And for your information, I look after my dad, which I bet is more than you do.

TED (*moving to* L *of her*). Me? I look after Number One.

DOREEN. Yes: I bet!

TED. Well, the way I see it, I'm enough to look after. I haven't got time to take on anyone else. (*He makes a quick movement with his right hand to his breast pocket.*)

(DOREEN *flinches.*)

TED (*takes out a comb and combs his hair*). Anyway, Tchaik's lucky: his old lady's in Warrington. Anyone can be a good son to someone living in Warrington. You go down there, have a couple of days, high tea, eggs and chips, quick kiss and you're away. Now me, my people live practically on the doorstep. Hounslow. Well, that's different, isn't it? You're flipping right, it is. "Why can't you live at home?" they say. (*He puts his comb in his pocket.*) Who the devil wants to? "You can have your own room," they say. My own room! I should just like to see me using my room for – well, for what I use a room. Am I being crude?

DOREEN. I think you are, yes. (*She moves to the armchair and sits, leaving her bag on the chest of drawers.*)

TED. Tsk, tsk, tsk, tsk! Dear me! You'll have to take me as you find me, then, won't you?

DOREEN. I'm not sure I find you very nice.

TED. No?

DOREEN. No.

TED. Well, that depends on what you're looking for, doesn't it?

DOREEN. Pardon?

TED. I find you smashing. I do, honest. I bet there's a lot of fun in you, once you loosen up.

(DOREEN *looks at him, startled.*)

TED. Oh, I don't mean that way. I don't know what you think of me.

23. Warrington: a county borough and market town on the Manchester Canal between Manchester and Liverpool.
24. Hounslow: an area in West London beyond Richmond and Kew Gardens.

DOREEN. Do you care?

TED. 'Course I do.

DOREEN. Well, if you're like most boys, your mind's on just one thing.

TED. Well, I'm not like most boys. I'm me. And my mind's on lots of things. What's *your* mind on, most of the time? That's when you're not looking after dad or going to Prom Concerts? What's with that, anyway? I don't get it. You're not the concerty type.

DOREEN (*rising*). You're Mr. Know-all, aren't you? (*She moves* C *and faces* TED.)

TED. Well, are you?

DOREEN. No, as a matter of fact, I was given a ticket by a girl friend. She couldn't go, and it seemed silly to waste it. (*She indicates the kitchen.*) Now he thinks I'm a music lover, and know about Bach and everything. Actually it was ever so boring. I realized I shouldn't have said "Yes" to him for tonight as soon as he asked me.

TED. What made you?

DOREEN. Well, I don't know. I don't get out that much. And he was very nice. Very courteous.

TED. I bet.

DOREEN. A blooming sight more better-mannered than what you are.

TED. Well, who's denying it? Tchaik's always had manners. He's one of Nature's gentlemen.

DOREEN. You're wicked, you know. You really are.

TED. I mean it. He's a good boy. He wouldn't hurt a fly – and that's not because he's a fly himself, either. Because he isn't. He's got feelings inside him I wouldn't know anything about – and you, neither.

DOREEN. Thanks.

TED. I mean it. Real deep feelings. They're no use to him,

25. He's got feelings . . . neither: We must admire Ted for his recognition of Bob's unusual qualities.

of course. They're in his way. If you ask me, you're better off without that dreamy bit.

DOREEN. What d'you mean?

TED. Dreams. Visions.

DOREEN. You mean he sees things?

TED. 'Course not.

DOREEN. What, then?

TED. Well, he has ideas about perfect women. He's got one about you.

DOREEN. He hasn't.

TED. He has. Why d'you think you're here? How many girls do you think he's ever asked here?

DOREEN. I dunno.

TED. One. (*He spells it.*) W-O-N. And she looked like the back of a bus. (*He crosses to her.*)

DOREEN. Well, what's he want with me, then?

TED. Nothing. You're a vision. You've got a long neck like Venus coming out of the sea.

DOREEN. Who?

TED. He thinks you're the dead spit of her. (*He goes to the head of the bed, takes down the picture of Venus, brings it, and shows it to* DOREEN.)

DOREEN. Oh. I haven't got a long neck like that.

TED. I know you haven't. Yours is the standard size, but he won't leave it at that. He's got to stretch it a bit. A long neck's a sign of a generous nature.

DOREEN. He's a bit nutty, isn't he?

TED. Not really.

DOREEN. I think he is. When he was talking about that record his eyes went all glary.

TED. Oh, that's nothing. Just the old Celtic Twilight in him. (*He replaces the picture crookedly on its hook.*)

DOREEN. Twilight?

TED. Just a phrase.

26. Crookedly: Why does the playwright use this adverb to describe Ted's action?

DOREEN. You don't half have a way of putting things. You've got a gift for words, haven't you?

TED (*moving to the armchair*). Always had. Words, languages. It's why I took up French in the evenings.

DOREEN (*admiringly*). I like that.

TED (*sitting on the armchair*). Do you? Most people would say it was getting above myself. Then most people just don't count. They've got no drive, no ambition, nothing. I bet your dad had some go in him when he was young.

DOREEN. He still does.

TED. 'Course. They do, those old ones. They've got guts. Not pampered and spoilt like the kids today.

DOREEN. That's what he says.

TED (*sarcastic*). I bet.

DOREEN. What d'you mean?

TED (*hastily*). Well, I mean, he's all right. You're a lucky girl.

DOREEN. Me?

TED. To have a sensible old dad like that. You should meet mine. Mr. Alcohol, one-nine-three-four. That's when he decided draught Guinness was the secret of life. Well, not decided 27
exactly. He hasn't decided anything since he married my mum, and then he was pushed into it by me, if you see what I mean. . . . She's not much better, mind.

DOREEN. Your mum?

TED. I was a middle-aged slave – or Ten Years in a Bingo Hall! That's when she goes out at all. Mostly she stays in with
the telly and a quarter bottle of Gordon's. Am I shocking you? 28

DOREEN. Of course not.

TED (*seriously*). Most people make me sick. They talk about us being sick. It's them. The old ones. Sick, sick, bloody sick! When I say I don't want a room at home, it's cos I can't

27. Draught Guinness: Guinness is a well-known beer; draught means unbottled or drawn from a barrel.
28. The telly: television.
Gordon's: Gordon's gin.

stand being with yobs. People who've given up. No – who've never started. They don't want to know. Not because they're old. Because they never did. Your dad sounds different. Like you. I could never be serious about a girl who was one of that lot.

DOREEN. I don't think you could be serious about anyone.

TED. That's where you're wrong. That's where you are utterly and completely wrong. You don't know me. I could be very serious about someone, if she helped me go places. . . . She'd have to have a bit of fun in her, too, mind.

(*Dance music is heard.*)

TED. Do you dance?

DOREEN. I do a bit, yes.

(TED *stands and takes from his pocket a transistor radio.*)

DOREEN. Oh! That's smashing.

TED (*starting to dance*). I bet you're a real hot pot of coffee on the floor.

DOREEN. Pardon?

TED. I bet you swing, Doreen girl. I bet you get really with it.

(BOB, *preparatory to bringing in the coffee, noiselessly opens the kitchen door and stands listening.*)

TED. You ever been to the *Mecca*?

DOREEN. No.

TED. You'd like that. It's really nice. Classy, you know. None of that cave-man stuff. Of course, if you do a bit of a wriggle, no one exactly minds.

(DOREEN *laughs.*)

TED. I'll take you there if you like.

DOREEN. When?

29. Bob . . . listening: Why does the playwright have Bob enter noiselessly and overhear the conversation that follows?

TED. Any time. You name it.

DOREEN. Well, I'm not sure I'd like it.

TED. 'Course you would. It's good clean fun, as they say. What about next Friday? They have a Late Night Special Fridays, eight to one.

(BOB *withdraws.*)

DOREEN. No, next Friday I'm busy. (*She crosses behind him watching him "twist".*)

TED (*not to be put off*). Friday after, then? (*He stops dancing.*) Well?

DOREEN (*suddenly capitulating*). All right. (*She crosses to* C.)

TED. Good. You'd better give me your phone number, then.

DOREEN. No, I'll meet you there.

TED. I can't have you going there on your own. I'll have to pick you up. That's if you don't live in Norwood, or some [30] lousy place like that.

DOREEN. No. Putney.

TED. You're lucky. That's just inside my cruising area. (*He switches off the transistor. Seriously.*) You're all right, you know. (*He moves to* R *of her.*) You've got it.

DOREEN (*sitting on the stool*). Got what?

TED. Oh, that certain something. It used to be called carriage.

DOREEN. Carriage?

TED. People call it class nowadays, but it's not the same thing.

DOREEN. Carriage. . . . What a nice word.

(BOB *comes from the kitchen with a tray of coffee for three.*)

TED (*sees* BOB – *with false breeziness*). Well – I'm away.

(BOB *crosses to* C.)

30. Norwood: a district in South London.

TED. I'll just have my coffee, and *allez*. (*He takes a cup of coffee and crosses to the chest of drawers.*) Love you and leave you.

DOREEN (*disappointed*). Oh! Why? (*She takes a cup of coffee.*)

TED. Duty calls. (*In an "executive" voice.*) All that work I took home from the office, clamouring for my attention.

DOREEN. Go on!

TED. Well, that's my story, and I'm stuck with it. No sugar?

BOB. Sorry. (*He puts the tray on the table and goes into the kitchen.*)

(TED *picks up a cigarette packet, puts his cup on the chest of drawers and crosses to* DOREEN.)

TED. Ciggy?

DOREEN. No, thank you.

TED (*offering her the packet*). Go on.

DOREEN. No, really.

TED (*sotto voce*). Telephone.

DOREEN. What?

TED (*through clenched teeth*). Number.

DOREEN (*understanding*). Oh. Got a pen? (*She takes the cigarette packet.*)

(BOB *comes from the kitchen.* TED *is about to give* DOREEN *a pen, sees* BOB *and crosses to the chest of drawers.*)

DOREEN (*very flustered*). It's lovely coffee.

BOB. It's only powdered. (*He puts a bowl of sugar on the table, then sits* L *of the table.*)

DOREEN. Well, you must have a way with it, then. It tastes like it's really ground. Like it's been perking for hours in one of those things. Really. Continental, you know. (*She becomes aware of the cigarette packet in her hand.*) Can I have the little girls' room?

BOB (*rising, moving to the door down* L *and opening it*). It's out on the landing.

(DOREEN *rises, puts her coffee on the table, crosses to the chest of drawers, picks up her handbag, takes the pen from* TED, *then crosses to the door down* L.)

BOB. I'll show you.

DOREEN. It's all right. I can find it.

(DOREEN *exits down* L. BOB *closes the door then leans against it, looking at* TED.)

TED (*after a pause*). Well, it's nine-thirty. I'm off. Count ten and I'll be gone. (*He moves to the table.*) I wish I was in your shoes. I do, honest. Not going home to my empty bed-sit. I tell you, mate, your card is definitely marked. We're frying tonight. What's the matter? (*He puts sugar in his coffee.*)

BOB. Nothing.

TED. Are you all right?

BOB. That's like "How do you do?" isn't it? There's no answer expected. (*He goes into the kitchen.*)

TED. What? Now pull yourself together, Tchaik. Don't start that pit-a-pat going again. What have you got to worry about? I've chatted her, and she told me she likes you a lot. She thinks you're the most courteous man she ever met. That's her actual word for you – courteous. If you ask me, it's time you stopped being so flipping courteous. Get off your knees. This is a girl, that's all. Not a goddess. And no girl wants to be worshipped, whatever she may tell you. You just give her a shove off her pedestal, you'll find she won't exactly resent it.

BOB (*coming from the kitchen*). Go home, Ted. (*He opens the door down* L.)

(TED *crosses the room in silence to the door, then suddenly slams it violently.*)

TED. I am going home. The only reason I'm still here at nine-thirty-two belting back my coffee, is because you seem in dire danger of jeopardizing your immediate succulent prospects. And that upsets me. It makes me feel I've wasted my time. After all, I've gone to no little trouble to ensure the success of this enterprise.

BOB. What?

TED. Well, haven't I? What do you think I've been doing here all evening?

BOB. I don't know. You tell me.

TED. What's the matter with you? You've been hitting the vino a bit, haven't you? You asked me here tonight to set it up for you. And that's what I've done. Just that. I've knocked myself out for you this past two hours, breaking her in nice and easy. Flowers on the table – chilled wine before din – the old sexy dance afterwards to get her in the proper receptive mood. To say nothing of cooking the meal itself. I'm not looking for thanks, mate.

BOB (*moving to* L *of the table*). Ted, what does it feel like to be a stupid, selfish, ignorant clod?

(*There is a very long pause.* BOB *crosses slowly to* C *below the table.* TED *remains by the door.*)

TED. Ignorant? That's twice in one night. That's a bit too much even for me. Ignorant. Selfish. That's lovely, that is. Selfish. . . . I didn't have to come here tonight, you know. I could have gone to one of a dozen places. I didn't have to be doing here. I could have gone up to the *Mecca*, the bowling alley, any place. But I didn't. I came here to help out my mate Tchaik, who had the pit-a-pats, and couldn't manage on his own. And that's all the thanks I get. That's all the thanks I bloody get! (*He crosses* R *for his hat.*) Well, I'll know better next time, won't I? I'll know better than to ever try and help someone else. (*He puts on his hat.*)

(BOB *has remained standing, not looking at him, shamefaced.*)

BOB. Help. You don't know what that is. Oh, you do your best as you see it. But what if that's nothing, what you see. You'll have lived in vain.

(*There is a small pause.*)

TED. You're sloshed, Tchaik. I'll excuse it because of that.

BOB. Excuse it? I don't want excuse from you. Bloody you . . . (*Controlling himself.*) Go home, Ted. You should never have come here in the first place.

(TED *puts on his sun-glasses. He whistles a few bars of "Toreador", then crosses to face* BOB.)

(DOREEN *enters down* L, *and stands down* L *of the table. Summoning up a jaunty exit* TED *pats* BOB *lightly on the shoulder, and exits down* L, *quickly, ignoring* DOREEN. BOB *stands looking after him. The light fades a little as the sun goes. Night falls during the rest of the play.*)

DOREEN. Where's he going?

BOB. Home.

DOREEN. Home?

BOB. Yes.

DOREEN. You mean he's not coming back?

BOB. I don't think so, no.

DOREEN (*unable to take it in*). You mean he's just gone off like that, without even saying good-night?

BOB. Well, yes. . . . He doesn't set much store on things like good-night. He had work to do at home, very urgent. Remember, he did say.

DOREEN. Did he?

BOB. Yes. And he won't let anything stand in the way of his work. That's what's called Drive.

DOREEN. Have you two had words, then?

BOB. No.

DOREEN. What about?

BOB. Nothing.

DOREEN. Was it over me, then?

BOB. Of course not.

(DOREEN *crosses* L, *opens the door and goes out on to the landing to look for* TED.)

BOB (*calling after her*). I mean – why should it be?

DOREEN (*off*). I don't know, I'm sure.

BOB. I've poured your coffee.

DOREEN. I think that's the rudest thing I've ever heard of.

BOB. It's getting cold.

DOREEN (*coming back on stage*). Ever, in my whole life.

BOB. He didn't mean it that way.

DOREEN (*closing the door*). Well, what way did he mean it, then?

BOB. How should I know? (*Pause. Sitting on the stool* C.) It's all my fault, really. I had too much to drink, and I can't really carry it, you see. Did you know that alcohol isn't really a stimulant at all, it's a depressant?

DOREEN. I know. I heard. (*She sits in the chair* L *of the table.*)

BOB (*smiling*). He means well, you know. He's good-hearted. Much more than me, really, if the truth were known. I'm not exactly fond of him, but you get attached out of habit. He knows a lot, and he's always laughing. We have a lot of laughs in the office, really.

DOREEN (*without enthusiasm*). That's good.

BOB. Yes.

DOREEN. What office would that be, then?

BOB. Import-export.

DOREEN. I mean the actual address.

BOB. Address?

DOREEN. Of your office.

BOB. Why?

DOREEN. No reason . . . I just asked.

BOB. I see.

(DOREEN *has been fiddling with the cigarette packet and pen half in and half out of her bag. Now she drops them both into it, and shuts it. A pause.*)

DOREEN. It must be nice having a friend in the same office. I mean, someone you're close to.

BOB. That depends what you mean by close, doesn't it?

DOREEN. Pardon?

BOB. We've been in the same room, but that doesn't make you close. No one in the office is close. That's what's wrong with them. You don't get to know anyone. But you're different. You know people at once, without having to try. I could tell that as soon as I saw you.

DOREEN. I don't know about that.

BOB. Oh, it's true. It's the obvious thing about you. Now, what would you say about me first sight. That I was a clerk?

DOREEN. Not specially, no.

BOB. Then what? Because I don't know. I suppose that's the point of education. Finding out who you really are. I never had that. (*He rises and moves* R.)

DOREEN. Why not?

BOB. Well, when I could have done, I didn't want it. I hated school. (*He picks up the "Peter Grimes" record, puts it in the album and puts the album on the rack.*)

DOREEN. So did I.

BOB. I hated it so much, I took the first job that came along.

DOREEN. What did you come down here for?

BOB. When dad died I came south. If I could start again, I'd *make* myself *study*. (*He moves up* C.)

DOREEN. Well, you could if you wanted. You're still young. You could go to night school.

BOB. No.

DOREEN. Why not? Your friend does.

BOB (*moving to* R *of the table*). Well, of course, he's got drive. Your lot go on about drive, but you can't have drive without enjoying your work. Now Ted does. When he leaves the office he's as fresh as a daisy, but when I come home I've hardly got the energy to grill a chop, let alone pick up a French book; and what have I done? Filled in about sixty invoices. What a way to spend your day: and some of those people have been doing it for thirty years. Taking endless dictation. Typing thousands of meaningless letters. Tenth of the inst. and eleventh ultimo. C.I.F. – E. and O.E. Thanking you in anticipation. Your esteemed order. Are you going to spend the rest of your life typing nonsense? Top copy and two carbons?

DOREEN. Well, like I say, we haven't got much choice, have we?

BOB (*kneeling on the stool and facing her*). Yes, we have. We must have. We weren't born to do this. Eyes. Complicated things like eyes, weren't made by God just to see columns of twopence-halfpennies written up in a ledger. Tongues. Good grief, the woman next to me in the office even sounds like a typewriter. A thin, chipped old typewriter, always clattering on about what Miss Story said in Accounts and Mr. Burnham said back. It's awful! Do you know how many thousands of years it took to make anything so beautiful, so feeling, as your hand? People say I know something like the back of my hand, but they don't know their hands. They wouldn't recognize a photograph of them. Why? Because their hands are anonymous. They're just tools for filling invoices, turning lathes round. They cramp up from picking slag out of moving belts of coal. If that's not blasphemy, what is? I'll tell you something really daft. Some nights when I come back here I give Behemoth a record for his supper. That's the way I look at him sometimes, feeding off discs, you know. And I conduct it. If it's a Concerto I play the solo part, running up and down the keyboard, doing the expressive bits, everything. I imagine someone I love is sitting out in the audience watching; you know, someone I want to admire me. Anyway, it sort of frees things inside me. At great moments I feel shivery all over. It's marvellous to feel shivery like that. What I want to know is, why can't I feel that in my work? Why can't I – oh, I don't know – feel bigger? There's something in me I know that's big. That can be excited, anyway. And that must mean I can excite other people, if only I knew what way. I never met anyone to show me that way.

(*There is a pause.*)

DOREEN. Well.

(*Pause.*)

BOB. Well. So.

(*Pause.*)

DOREEN. I suppose I must be going then.
BOB. Yes.

(DOREEN *rises.*)

BOB. You're quite pretty, you know.
DOREEN. Thank you. (*She moves towards the door, down* L.)
BOB (*crossing to her*). I mean very pretty, really. . . . Please stay just a little longer.
DOREEN. I'm afraid I can't. My dad'll be worrying about me. (*She takes her coat from the hook.*)
BOB. Does he worry that much about you?
DOREEN. Yes, he's a natural worrier.
BOB. Well, how about one more record before you go?
DOREEN (*putting on the coat*). Worries about everything.
BOB. One for the road, as they say.
DOREEN. Old people always do, don't they?
BOB (*desperately*). Something more tuneful and luscious! Madame Butterfly! . . . (*He runs to* R, *takes the record from the rack and switches on the gramophone.*) D'you know the Love Duet? You'll like that. I know it's awfully corny, but I do love all that fudgy sort of music. At least I have great sort of cravings for it. (*He takes the record from its sleeve.*) Like I suppose some people have for chocolates. (*He drops the sleeve on the floor and holds out the record.*) Try a bit.
DOREEN (*opening the door*). Well, really, it is getting rather late.
BOB (*moving appealingly towards her*). It only takes three minutes.
DOREEN (*closing the door*). Well – all right.

(BOB *crosses to the gramophone and puts the record on the turntable: the start of the Love Duet from "Madame Butterfly". We hear the quiet orchestral music before "Vogliatemi bene, un bene piccolino".*)

BOB. You know what's happening, don't you? Pinkerton – that's the American sailor – has married this Japanese girl in spite of her family and the priests and everybody. This is the first time they are alone together.

MIME

There now ensues a six-minute sequence in which not a word is spoken. The following is a movement-by-movement description of what was done at the first production. It need not be slavishly followed. The mood must be tender, at times comic and even absurd – but always real. It must never suggest a revue sketch. And it must end in humiliation and embarrassment for both.

The lights dim, except for the area C, *around the gramophone and around the armchair. As the singing starts,* BOB *stares at the turntable.* DOREEN *remains by the door. After a moment he turns and motions her to sit in the armchair. Gingerly* DOREEN *complies. She sits.* BOB *starts conducting the music: she stares at him, and he becomes self-conscious, stops, shyly crosses above her to the stool* C, *and sits. She relaxes, pushing her shoes off and stretching.* BOB, *plucking up a little courage, moves the stool a little nearer to her. She looks at him: he moves it yet nearer. She picks up her handbag from the floor at her left and deliberately moves it to the right side. He now moves the stool close to her left side.* DOREEN *smiles, looks approvingly at the turntable, and herself begins to conduct, looking round at the speakers and mouthing, "Lovely!" As she listens, the boy touches her sleeve. She turns and he abruptly turns the motion into a gesture miming: "Would you like a cigarette?" Eagerly, she nods.* BOB *rises, crosses to the chest of drawers, picks up the cigarette box and matches.* DOREEN *takes a cigarette and* BOB *puts the box on the floor. He opens the box of matches, but he is looking at her and the box is upside down: the matches spill. Together they pick them up from the carpet, and then he strikes one and lights her cigarette. Fascinated by her prettiness, he stares at her: the flame of the match burns between them until she gently blows it out. They stare at one another. She offers him a puff of her cigarette. He declines – then accepts – takes a puff: then a big one and chokes a little. He takes her hand and begins to study it with intense concentration.*

Suddenly DOREEN *is sorry for the boy. She closes her eyes and lowers her face to be kissed. He looks at her, uncertain what to do. Slowly, hardly daring, he raises himself from the floor to kiss her. He nearly does so, but suddenly she thinks she has burnt her coat with the cigarette in her left hand. She wets her finger and rubs the spot.* BOB *jumps up, gets the plaster-lid "ashtray" from the chest of drawers, and hands it to her, again kneeling* R *of her. All is well with her coat: she adopts her former pose of invitation. This time* BOB *raises himself and is about to kiss her lips: at the last moment switches to her forehead. She opens her eyes a little impatiently and tugs at the collar of her coat. It is a little hot, isn't it? She undoes the buttons and tape of her coat.* BOB *rises to help her out of the coat, which he places over the back of her chair.* DOREEN *rises, straightens her dress, and putting her right leg under her, sits and again offers her lips. This time* BOB *responds more confidently: he kisses her. Then liking it, he tries again, sitting on the arm of the chair and pressing her back. The eagerness of his response surprises and alarms the girl. She struggles to free herself, pushing herself forward so that* BOB *falls down behind her and is trapped across the arms of the chair behind her back.* DOREEN, *sitting on her right leg, finds she cannot move. She struggles to free it – then rises precipitately and moves to* R *of the table.* BOB *rises and follows her. He is rumpled and desperate: he is no longer listening to the passionate, undisturbable lovers singing so ecstatically on the gramophone. Slowly, his mind full of how* TED *would cope under these circumstances, he begins to follow her round the room: as slowly she retreats up stage, backwards, to the corner of the room. She stumbles back on to the bed. The boy falls softly on top of her, and tries with a muddled gentleness to show her passion. She tries haplessly to avoid him. Finally she pushes him away and moves away from him down* C.

BOB *stares after her. Then he, too, gets up and comes towards her with a gesture at once desperate and supplicating. Puccini's Love Duet rises to its climax. As the final climactic chord crashes over the room,* DOREEN *slaps his face – then, horrified, takes it between her hands, trying to recall the blow. He moves away from her across the stage,* R*: she from him,* L. *By the chest of drawers he turns and appeals to her, saying he is sorry. We cannot hear this because of the music. He slowly goes to the turntable and lifts the stylus just before the quiet closing music of the duet finishes.*

BOB. I'm sorry.

DOREEN. That's all right. (*She crosses to* RC, *sits on the stool, puts on her shoes and picks up her handbag.*)

BOB. No, no, it isn't. It isn't at all. Actually, you see, I've brought you here under false pretences. I should never have asked you. You see, I didn't really tell you everything about myself. That was wrong of me. Please forgive me.

DOREEN. What d'you mean?

BOB. Well, you see, actually I'm engaged. (*He picks up the cigarette box and matches.*)

DOREEN. Engaged?

BOB. Yes. To be married.

DOREEN (*really surprised*). *You* are?

BOB (*defiantly*).Yes. Yes. So I shouldn't have asked you here. I'm sorry.

(DOREEN *stares at* BOB, *who is not looking at her.*)

DOREEN (*pointing to the photograph in the mirror*). Is that her?

BOB (*looking at the photograph*). Yes.

DOREEN. Can I see?

(BOB *goes to the mirror, takes down the photograph and hands it to* DOREEN.)

DOREEN. She looks lovely.

BOB. Yes, very. That's really raven black hair. It's got tints of blue in it. You can't really judge from a photo.

DOREEN. What's her name?

BOB. Er – Lavinia. It's rather an unusual name, isn't it? Lavinia. I think it's rather distinguished.

DOREEN. Yes, it is.

BOB. Like her. She's distinguished. She's got a way with her. Style, you know. It's what they used to call carriage.

(DOREEN *gives him a startled look.*)

DOREEN. Carriage?

BOB. In the old days.

DOREEN. I see.

BOB (*taking the photograph from her and putting it on the chest of drawers*). Well – no harm done, I suppose.

DOREEN (*rising*). No, of course not.

BOB (*picking up her coat*). Here's your coat.

(DOREEN *looks at him, touched for the first time by a feeling of sympathy she cannot analyse.* BOB *helps* DOREEN *on with her coat.*)

BOB. I wonder why I thought ocelot was a bird. I wasn't thinking of an ostrich. It was those pictures you see of ladies in Edwardian photos with long, traily feathers in their hats. Is there such a thing as an osprey?

DOREEN. I wouldn't know. (*With a smile.*) It's not really ocelot, you know. It's lamb dyed. And it's not really cold enough for fur coats, anyway, is it, yet? I was showing off.

BOB. I'm glad you did.

(DOREEN *moves to the door down* L. BOB *overtakes her and opens the door.*)

DOREEN. Well, it's been lovely.

BOB. For me, too.

DOREEN. I enjoyed the music. Really.

BOB. Did you?

DOREEN. Perhaps we'll meet again. At a concert or somewhere.

BOB. Yes.

DOREEN. I'm glad about your girl. She looks lovely.

BOB. She is.

(*They stare at one another, nervously.*)

DOREEN. Well, good night. (*She moves to the door.*)

BOB. Good night. (*He moves quickly to* R *of her.*) Fabian and Carter.

DOREEN. Pardon?

BOB. The name of the firm. Where Ted works. You wanted to know it. Fabian and Carter. Bishopsgate two-four-three-seven. Good-bye.

(DOREEN *gives* BOB *a quick smile and exits down* L. BOB *closes the door, switches on the light, turns and surveys the empty room, then walks aimless across it. He stops by the gramophone and puts the stylus on the record. We hear the first strains of "Madame Butterfly". He stands by it as it plays, and looks down at the turning record. After a moment he crouches behind the turntable, lifts the stylus, then, with infinite slowness, staring at it, he moves the needle right across the record, then again across, making a terrible sound and damaging the record beyond repair. He puts the stylus on the record and "Madame Butterfly" is heard again, but now there is a deep scratch clicking the music, ruining it.* BOB *stares at it as it plays, with an expressionless face. The lights slowly dim to black-out as –*

THE CURTAIN FALLS.

THE NEW YORK CRITICS

What did the New York critics think of *The Private Ear,* and of Peter Shaffer's dramatic skill as shown in his twin comedies? Some excerpts from their reviews on October 10, 1963, will be enlightening. They will help you to read more deeply into the meaning of the play, to understand better the difficult art of playwriting, and to familiarize yourself with something of the language and "approach" of criticism, so that you will be able to comment more intelligently on plays that you see and hear – whether film, stage, radio, or television.

Robert Coleman, in the *New York Mirror,* described the *Madame Butterfly* sequence of *The Private Ear* and the finale of the play, as "tender and touching, wryly amusing". In the *New York Post,* Richard Watts, Jr., said of the play: " . . . it is raised beyond the commonplace by the sympathetic insight of its character-drawing and the believable combination of the comic and the compassionate in the writing and the playing." After praising Shaffer's "authentic light touch, his gift for witty urbanity", he again mentions the play's characterization: " . . . it is the important feature of *The Private Ear* that not only the sad young man is touching and entirely credible, but the girl and the brash youth whom she prefers receive friendly as well as comic attention."

In the *New York World-Telegram and The Sun,* Norman Nadel wrote: "*The Private Ear* offers a lad so unworldly that you're inclined to laugh unless you've known – or been – such a lad, and then you smile." He then tells the story of the play to the closing mime. "[Doreen] is indifferent to his stereo, his Wharfedale speakers, to Britten's *Peter Grimes* and succumbs only in passing to *Madame Butterfly*. His clumsy pass is parried, and he sees her off – to Ted – then finds the one way to punish himself most painfully, as he ruins a beloved recording."

Speaking of both plays, and of Peter Shaffer's talent as a playwright, John McClain in the *Journal American* said that the author "has the gift of a splendid ear for dialogue, an abiding sense of the ridiculous . . . ". John Chapman in the *Daily News* wrote: "They are silky-smooth, literate, witty and irresistibly human. . . . And, because they look into the little weaknesses and vulnerabilities of human beings, they often are touching as well as funny."

Richard Watts, Jr., had high praise for the two "delightful" London comedies: "Mr. Shaffer, who attracted admiring local attention with his first drama, *Five Finger Exercise*, several seasons ago, demonstrates his first-rate skill again, and also his deft versatility, by writing a pair of plays that differ vastly in mood and manner but have in common a most winning quality of humor, sympathy, fresh characterization, imaginative observation, and brightly artful entertainment."

Robert Coleman was equally enthusiastic: "With *The Private Ear* and *The Public Eye* Peter Shaffer has achieved a remarkable *tour du force*. In these one-acters he has created characters and situations that almost assume the proportions of full-length stature. It takes deft writing to do that, and Shaffer has the skill of a magician. . . . Here is entertainment for sophisticates, and playgoers looking for superior theatre."

The most interesting and perceptive comment on Shaffer's unusual gifts as a playwright was made by Norman Nadel:

> The heart has no secrets from Peter Schaffer. Perhaps that is because he does not spy on it, but waits to be invited in.
>
> He is one of those rare playwrights who has uncontested access to the intimate feelings of the people he observes, and writes about. Through wisdom, sensitivity and compassion, he gently uncovers what others must dig and probe to find. Through these same merits, plus an exceptional skill at fashioning a play, he communicates these private emotions to his audience.
>
> *The Private Ear* and *The Public Eye* . . . are open-hearted plays that speak gentle truths in terms of humor, innocence, poignancy, sophistication and a full awareness of life.
>
> They are not ambitious dramas about mighty themes; on the contrary, they are quite modest. But they are thorough. At the conclusion of each, you know that you have been a guest at [a] lucid moment of truth. . . .

TWO OTHER PLAYS BY PETER SHAFFER

Peter Shaffer first rocketed to fame with *Five Finger Exercise*, which was a hit in London under Sir John Gielgud's direction, and ran for seventeen months. The London newspapers voted it the best play of the 1958-9 season by a new playwright. In New York it ran for ten months, and won the New York Drama Critics' Award as the best foreign play presented during the 1959-60 season. This was followed by the success of *The Private Ear* and *The Public Eye* in 1962-3.

In the summer of 1964 Shaffer's spectacular pageant-play, *The Royal Hunt of the Sun,* had its premiere at the Chichester Festival. It was highly praised, particularly by Bernard Levin in the *London Daily Mail*: "The greatest play of our generation. I do not think the English stage has been so graced nor English audiences so privileged since Shaw was in his heyday half a century ago."

The play was put into the repertory of the National Theatre at the Old Vic. A Broadway production, with Christopher Plummer as its star, opened on October 26, 1965, and ran for 261 performances. Writing in the *New York World Telegram and The Sun* on October 27, Norman Nadel said: "For Shaffer it is a triumph. No Englishman in this century, save Shaw and Christopher Fry, has achieved such sensible beauty with words, such noble clarity of ideas. *The Royal Hunt of the Sun* might well be a masterpiece." In *The New York Times,* Harold Taubman wrote: "*The Royal Hunt of the Sun* is a brave and daring try to expand the narrow horizons of a theatre too often constricted by small minds and limited imaginations. Mr. Shaffer's work is sometimes static and sometimes pretentious and arty, but its partial success is more commendable than victory in a routine venture."

The editor was fortunate to see the memorable production of *The Royal Hunt of the Sun* at Chichester. Set in sixteenth-century Spain and Peru, the play is based on the incredible story of Pizarro and his Spanish conquistadors, seeking the glittering gold of the Incas. They fight their way through swamp and jungle and scale the Andes to capture the young ruler of the Incas, Atahuallpa. Then, against a background of treachery and violence, the play tells of the strange friendship that grew between the aging conqueror and his young hostage – a friendship that ended cruelly and tragically.

This is a play that will nourish your spirit and enlarge the horizons of your mind. It is hoped that many of you will read it.

STAGING THE PLAY

Our photograph shows the setting for the performances by Merger Productions on the "thrust" stage of the Colonnade Theatre in Toronto in July 1966. The Colonnade is a circular theatre; its circular stage projects into the auditorium, and the audience sits on

Geoffrey Frazer

A setting for *The Private Ear* on the "thrust" stage of the Colonnade Theatre in Toronto.

three sides of the stage in rising tiers of seats around it. In this theatre, there is only one entrance and exit for the players. If you compare the setting with the one described in the text you will see that some sacrifices had to be made in such a theatre. It was impossible to convey the impression that the room was an attic, with a dormer window looking out on roofs and sky. It was also impossible to show the kitchen. This was unfortunate, because when the kitchen door is open at the beginning of the play the two boys can pass in and out through it, talking to one another as they prepare the meal.

However, the essential details of the setting are shown in the photograph. The two most important are the armchair and the footstool. The armchair was moved back to the table for the meal, where Ted sat in it. In the *Peter Grimes* scene, Bob moved the footstool midway between the two speakers, and Doreen sat on it, back to the audience, while Bob played and "conducted" the music from the opera; he and Ted also used it while talking to Doreen, placing it beside the armchair. The other essential items (from left to right) are the hi-fi set and records, the chest of drawers, the print of Botticelli's "Birth of Venus", the bed (made up to look like a sofa), the curtained wardrobe, and the table and chairs.

The only difficult lighting problem in producing the play occurs in the dinner scene in which the actors "freeze", the lights fade, and a pin-spot lights Bob's face while the recorded dialogue of Ted and Doreen revolves into "high-pitched gabble". In the Merger Production, Bob sat in the chair beside the table; the spot beam used was wider than a pin-spot and lighted much of his body. The author calls for lighting in a lower key after the dinner scene, since it is an hour later and the day has almost gone. Then, after Ted leaves, the sun sets and night falls during the scene between Doreen and Bob. These changes will be more effective if there is a window through which we can see the sky darken into night. During the final mime the lights dim except in the central area around the armchair.

It is interesting to note that the device of the "freeze" – the suspension of motion – combined with the spotting of a single important character, takes the place of the older and traditional blackout or lowering of curtains to denote the passage of time. The device is doubly effective because Bob's isolation is heightened by the tape-recording of fragments of dialogue from his two visitors – each fragment increasing, as noted, to a high-pitched gabble – while he broods and drinks the wine.

You will undoubtedly have an expert in handling sound equipment to whom you can turn for help in this tape-recording sequence. Indeed, sound is of the greatest importance in the play, and you need the best help and equipment available. Two of the most significant scenes are those in which Bob plays the excerpts from *Peter Grimes* and *Madame Butterfly*, trying to share with the girl the wordless world of rapture in which he lives. These musical passages must sound thrilling and compelling. In the final moment of the play the scratch effect can be played off stage, with Bob "faking" the action on stage. Then, again off stage, a second scratched recording of the "Butterfly" music can be played as the lights dim.

THINKING ABOUT THE PLAY

1. What characteristic do Ted and Doreen's father have in common?
2. Comment on the author's skilful use of the word "carriage" throughout the play.
3. There are two arbitrary or unmotivated lighting cues. The first is the black-out (except for the pin-spot) in the "freeze"

during the dinner. The second is the dimming of lights, except for the centre area, before the final mime. Why is this second light cue an arbitrary and unmotivated one?

4. Trace the dramatist's handling of the situation in which Ted tries to get Doreen's telephone number after she has agreed to go dancing with him at the Mecca. In your answer, comment on the playwright's skill in creating tension and dramatic conflict with this situation.
5. Peter Shaffer, like most of England's "angry young men" writing for the theatre, is on the side of labour and against the economic, social, and political "establishment". Yet he is a playwright first of all; the "message" takes second place to characterization and plot.

   Show that this is the case in the dinner argument about unions. Under the heading of characterization describe what this argument tells us about the background, outlook, and character of each of the three players. Under the heading of plot, show how it sharpens the conflict between Ted and Bob, and adds new depth to the relationship between Ted and Doreen.
6. Bob's comments on unpunctuality (footnote 14) and on the man who looked like a safety match (footnote 17) demonstrate his bright, fanciful imagination, and his sharp powers of observation. Find other examples of these qualities.
7. Bob is the playwright's mouthpiece for some penetrating comments on life and people. He is a natural philosopher. Note his comments on ideal beauty, on "real" carriage, on Bach's music, and on wrinkles. Can you find any others?
8. One of the major themes of the play is its protest against the dullness and monotony in the work and lives of many people. Trace the development of this theme in the play to its climax in Bob's long speech just before the final mime.
9. Bob, like Peter in *Nobody Waved Good-bye*, is a bright drop-out. He lacks an education, which, he says, helps one to find out "who you really are". Discuss the part that education, or the lack of it, plays in the lives of the three young people. In Bob's case, relate it to the theme of protest which you have discussed in question 8.
10. Comment on the pleasant and commendable aspects of Ted's character. Refer to what he says and does, and to what Doreen and Bob say to him and about him.

11. In trying to win Doreen's favour, Ted says that he could be very serious about someone "if she helped me go places . . . ". Bob pleads his case in much the same way. Find his parallel statement, and discuss what each statement reveals about the character of the speaker.
12. In the big confrontation scene between Bob and Ted, Bob accuses his "friend" of being "a stupid, selfish, ignorant clod". Shortly after, he utters a sweeping condemnation of Ted and all people like him: "Oh, you do your best as you see it. But what if that's nothing, what you see. You'll have lived in vain." This is the central issue of the play – the way of life exemplified by each of these two boys. Is Bob justified in his attack on Ted?
13. Prepare an answer to the critic who claimed that the play is "glibly carpentered" and "shallow in content".

A RESOUNDING TINKLE

N. F. SIMPSON

A NEW KIND OF PLAY

We close our volume with an outstanding example of a new kind of theatre, the "Theatre of the Absurd". Herbert Whittaker, drama critic of the Toronto *Globe and Mail*, tells you about the ideas and techniques of this new theatre in the note that follows the play. As he explains, our version of *A Resounding Tinkle* is a shorter one-act version of the longer play, which he directed at Hart House Theatre. In shortening the play, Simpson has cut out most of the "detachable parts". What remains is wildly absurd, but closely knit and well-constructed. If you approach it as you would approach *Alice in Wonderland* – as sheer, happy nonsense – you will enjoy it. Indeed, as Robert Allan pointed out in his introduction to the CBC *Festival* production of the play, *A Resounding Tinkle* has an advantage for us that *Alice in Wonderland* no longer possesses. It is of our time, and the things it parodies are in common coinage, while so many of Lewis Carroll's targets have become blurred with time.

The characters, situations, and dialogue are so absurd and so far removed from reality that you will appreciate some help here (and in the footnotes) in following what happens. The characters, for the most part, belong to that odd group of people who keep strange pets. The Paradocks have kept dwarf elephants for years, and their friend Nora Mortice and her family have kept snakes. The central situation is that the Paradocks have just received an elephant that is too big, and Nora's family a snake that is too small. They agree to exchange their pets.

A further plot complication is provided by the arrival of Uncle Ted, who has just changed his sex. Uncle Ted comes to visit them, spending a long day on the train, in order to hear a "modern" religious service on their radio. They entertain "him" by giving him a couple of good "reads". While he is there, Nora's boy brings her snake – in a pencil box!

On Uncle Ted's departure, Bro sets out in his gumboots to take the elephant to Nora. While he is away, the playwright skilfully fills in the time first of all by having their quarrelling continue as if it is a radio play, in heightened, unnatural or surrealistic fashion, with the elephant becoming a dinosaur; and then by a telephone conversation with the mad neighbour, Mrs. Stencil, who is raising money to buy spectacles and parachutes for eagles.

Bro returns. The curtain is delayed for a few moments while this preposterous appeal from Mrs. Stencil to help the eagles is considered gravely. Then the truth is revealed! First we hear the end of the play as in the radio play and hear of Bro's problems with the dinosaur; then, in the real play we discover that he has not been able to get the elephant through the gate! But Middie has the last word: "It was got *in*."

The play, thus, has a definite form or shape. The thin plot is filled out with a series of comic expressions, ideas, and arguments, which keep recurring and weaving in and out like themes in a symphony.

A Resounding Tinkle is not mere suburban nonsense. Under the surface it has a serious comment to make on our life and normal behaviour. Too many of us are wasting our lives, as the Paradocks do, with conversation that is inane and full of platitudes, with endless foolish bickerings, and with concern over things that are petty and trivial. Our lives become a resounding tinkle.

This is not an easy play to read or to perform. In the longer version of *A Resounding Tinkle* the author-character says: "The retreat from reason means precious little to anyone who has never caught up with reason in the first place; it takes a trained mind to relish a *non-sequitur*."

You will enjoy class readings of the play, but you will be bold indeed if you attempt a full-scale production. It takes a highly trained professional cast to cope with the wildly improbable situations with sober-faced gravity. The CBC *Festival* production had two such actors in Helen Burns (wife of Michael Langham, director of the Stratford Shakespearean Theatre) and Eric House. The reviewer in *The Globe and Mail,* November 14, 1963, had this to say of their performances: "To tip the wink that this is nonsense is to destroy it. In Helen Burns and Eric House, you have the perfect comedians – artists who know how to extract your giggles without nudging you in the ribs while doing so. Miss Burns is wonderfully blank but capable of subtle colourings and expression. Mr. House is a masterpiece of discouraged dimness, while being endlessly sensitive and, well, brilliant about it. Who better to introduce The Paradocks to the television audience?"

Here then, for your pleasure, are the Paradocks in Wonder-suburban-land.

CHARACTERS

BRO PARADOCK
MIDDIE PARADOCK
UNCLE TED

Produced at the Royal Court Theatre, London, April 2, 1958, with the following cast:

BRO PARADOCK	Nigel Davenport
MIDDIE PARADOCK	Wendy Craig
UNCLE TED	Sheila Ballantine

Directed by William Gaskill

A RESOUNDING TINKLE

TIME: *The present.*

SCENE: *The living-room of the Paradocks' suburban home. Evening.*

A door back C *leads to a small entrance hall, where coats and hats are hanging. There is a window* R *of the door, from which anyone standing on the front doorstep can be seen obliquely. A window* R *looks out onto the garden. The fireplace is* L. *A sofa stands* LC *with a small table* L *of it, on which there is a radio-receiver. A low coffee-table stands in front of the sofa. On it, there are some rug-making materials. There is an armchair* RC *and a sideboard up* R. *Several bottles are on the sideboard. Small tables stand down* R *and down* L. *There is a telephone on the table down* L. *Built-in bookshelves fill the wall* L *of the door. A standard lamp is above the window* R. *In the hall there is a hall-cupboard and a hat-stand with hats and coats on it. Other suitable dressing may be added at the discretion of the producer.*

When the curtain rises, it is not yet dark, and the window curtains are undrawn. A fire is burning in the grate. BRO *and*

MIDDIE PARADOCK *have just come in. A shopping basket full of books is on the coffee-table. Both* BRO *and* MIDDIE *are staring out of the window* R *into the garden.*

MIDDIE. It'll have to stay out.

BRO (*turning away from the window*). What are the measurements?

MIDDIE (*continuing to stare through the window*). You don't need measurements. A thing that size in a semi!

BRO (*moving to the sideboard*). I thought we were living in a bungalow. (*He picks up two small adjustable spanners from the sideboard.*)

MIDDIE. People think you're trying to go one better than everybody else.

BRO. What are these doing here? When did we order adjustable spanners?

MIDDIE (*without turning*). They were samples.

1. Paradock: Observe the suspense created by the opening scene of the play as Middie and Bro stare out the window at "it".
   Look up the word "paradox" in your dictionary; you will then know why the author chose the surname he gave to Bro and Middie.
2. Semi: One of the comic subjects of the play is the argument between Middie and Bro as to whether they live in a bungalow or a semi (a semi-detached house is one of two houses that are joined together and form a single unit with a single roof). A semi has a second story, and a bungalow doesn't. In English cities there are many streets of semi-detached houses; for this reason, bungalows have more social prestige. Hence Middie's remark in her next speech.
3. Spanners: A spanner is a wrench. This opening quarrel about the spanner is an excellent one to launch us into the amusing bickering between husband and wife that goes on (in a less foolish manner) in many homes. Men pride themselves on knowing something about tools and mechanical matters in general.

BRO. What do they think we want with two? 4

MIDDIE (*turning away from the window and beginning to put books from the shopping basket on to the bookshelf*). One of them is probably for loosening things.

BRO. You can do that with any spanner.

MIDDIE (*with a handful of small identical books*). I've brought in some more of these in case Uncle Ted comes. I expect he'll ask for critical essays with his coffee. 5

BRO (*after a pause*). There's no difference between them. You can use either of them for tightening and you can use either of them for loosening.

(MIDDIE *puts the last book on the shelf, picks up the basket and moves to the door.*)

MIDDIE. One is probably bigger than the other or something.

(MIDDIE *exits up* C *to* L, *leaving the door open.*)

BRO. They're *adjustable,* Middie. (*He puts the spanners on the sideboard, goes to the armchair* RC, *picks up a newspaper, sits and reads.*)

MIDDIE (*off*). Or smaller or something.

BRO. The plain fact is that we don't need adjustable spanners and are never likely to. (*He pauses.*) It would be interesting to know what would have happened if *I'd* answered the door and let them foist adjustable spanners on to us.

4. They: This is the first reference to the mysterious "they" – the strangers – those from the outside world who intrude upon the lives of the players. You will find the "they", or the stranger, in many of the plays of the Theatre of the Absurd. In perhaps the greatest of these plays, *Waiting for Godot* by Samuel Beckett, the stranger is Godot (or God), for whom the two tramps wait in vain.
5. Critical essays with his coffee: One of the delightful comic ideas in the play is this fondness of Uncle Ted for a "read". It reappears after Uncle Ted arrives. Is the author satirizing those who like to improve their minds by taking their culture in "digest" or capsule form?

MIDDIE (*off*). We don't have to use them if we don't like them.

BRO (*after a pause*). We shall have them unloading a complete tool-kit on us before we know where we are.

MIDDIE (*off*). They won't be around again.

BRO. I hope you're right – that's all I can say.

MIDDIE (*off*). I wish it were.

(MIDDIE *enters up* C *from* L, *and as though attracted compulsively towards it, crosses to the window* R.)

I wish that were all you could say. Except that then we'd have you saying it all day long, I suppose, like a mentally deficient parakeet. (*She looks steadily through the window.*)

BRO. What a typical woman's remark. A parakeet saying the same thing over and over again wouldn't necessarily be mentally deficient. If that's all it's been taught how can it say anything different?

MIDDIE. Look at it.

BRO. It may be educationally subnormal – but that's another matter.

MIDDIE. Look at its great ears flapping about.

BRO (*after a pause*). It's only once a year for goodness sake.

MIDDIE. Surely they know by now what size we always have.

BRO. Perhaps they've sent us the wrong one.

MIDDIE (*crossing above the armchair to the sofa*). It's big

6. Parakeet: A parakeet is a species of parrot; the word is now applied to the smaller kind, especially those having long tails. The word is also used to allude to humans and their chattering. Notice that the duel of the sexes continues here – "What a typical woman's remark." Both Middie and Bro resemble parakeets, saying the same thing over and over again.
7. Look at . . . flapping about: Our curiosity about the "it" is increased by this reference to "its great ears flapping about". Notice the *non sequitur* – the speeches not following one another logically. Bro is talking about the parakeet, Middie about the strange creature in the garden.

enough for a hotel. (*She picks up a magazine from the coffee-table and sits on the sofa.*) If you had a hotel or a private school or something you wouldn't need a thing that size. (*She looks through the magazine.*)

BRO. I suppose not.

MIDDIE. And supposing it goes berserk in the night? I'm not getting up to it.

BRO. Why should it go berserk any more than a smaller one?

MIDDIE. We shall have old Mrs. Stencil round again if it 8
does – threatening us with the R.S.P.C.A.

BRO. You should have been in when they came with it, then you could have queried the measurements.

MIDDIE. I can't think what we're going to call it. We can't 9
call it Mr. Trench again.

BRO. The only time we've not called it Mr. Trench was three years ago when we had to make do with a giraffe.

MIDDIE. And look at the fuss we had before they'd take it in part exchange.

BRO. Of course they made a fuss. There was something wrong with it.

(MIDDIE *puts the magazine on the coffee-table, then picks up her rug-making materials and works on the rug. She does this intermittently throughout the evening.*)

MIDDIE. Imagine calling a clumsy great thing that size Mr. Trench.

BRO. Why not?

MIDDIE. We can't go on year after year calling it Mr. Trench.

8. Mrs. Stencil: We shall hear more of Mrs. Stencil later. The R.S.P.C.A. is an extension of the mysterious "they" – probably the Royal Society for the Prevention of Cruelty to Animals.
9. We can't call . . . again: Here we are introduced to another diverting subject in the play: the naming of their elephants, past and present.

BRO. You talk as if it were the same animal every time.

MIDDIE. You can hear the neighbours, can't you? They'll think we never launch out.

BRO. I know what you want to call it.

MIDDIE. It looks all the time as if we're hard up for a name to give the animal.

BRO. You want to call it Oedipus Rex, don't you?

MIDDIE. It's better than Mr. Trench year after year. At least it sounds as if we knew what was going on in the world.

BRO (*contemptuously*). Oedipus Rex! (*He wags a finger archly through the window.*) Ah, ah! Only the *edible* blooms, remember, Oedipus.

MIDDIE. If you say it in that tone of voice – of course it sounds ridiculous.

BRO. Oedipus! Not all your weight on that glass, eh?

MIDDIE. Anything would sound ridiculous if you said it like that.

BRO. It isn't Mr. Trench we want a change from.

MIDDIE. The only thing to do is ring up the Zoo. Tell them to come and collect it.

BRO. And be without an elephant at all?

MIDDIE. Tell them to come and collect it and the sooner the better. I'd rather not have one.

BRO. That's only your point of view.

MIDDIE. We did without one the year we had a giraffe instead.

BRO. I know we did without one the year we had a giraffe

10. Oedipus Rex: Oedipus the King. See footnote 14, *The Western Hero*, p. 124.
11. Only the edible . . . Oedipus: Bro makes fun of the name by cautioning "Oedipus" to eat only the flowers in the garden that are edible.
12. Not all . . . glass, eh?: Two speeches later Bro tells us the truth – that "it" is an elephant. Here he almost gives the secret away. He warns "it" – archly – not to put all its weight (the weight of its trunk) against the window.

instead. And look at the trouble we had getting it changed. I don't want that all over again.

MIDDIE. It's the R.S.P.C.A. I'm worried about.

BRO. They haven't been round yet. In any case you wouldn't get the Zoo at this time. They'll be closed.

MIDDIE. I don't know why they couldn't send us what we asked for in the first place.

BRO. Is it any use trying to get hold of Eddie on the phone?

MIDDIE. Yes. Ring Eddie up. Or Nora. Nora'd be sure to know what to do. They used to keep pigeons and things. They had a room full of nothing else but different kinds of birds when they were all living at number eighty-nine, and white mice and things..

BRO. It'll have to stay outside tonight.

MIDDIE. I'm not having it in the kitchen, if that's what you're leading up to.

BRO. If it starts straying all over the place during the night, we shall have the R.S.P.C.A. making a lot of difficulties.

MIDDIE. Not if we get it changed first thing. Get on to Nora. 13

BRO. If we're getting it changed first thing in the morning, where's the sense in thinking up a name like Oedipus Rex for it now?

MIDDIE. Because I'm not calling it Mr. Trench six years running. You can if you like. I'm not.

BRO. I didn't want to call it Mr. Trench the year it was a giraffe. That was your idea. It was your idea it would make a pleasant change to give the name to a giraffe instead of an elephant. Now you complain about calling it Mr. Trench six years running.

MIDDIE. I think we'd be better off without it.

BRO. How would we?

MIDDIE. I do really. I think we'd be better off without. We've done nothing except bicker ever since they came with it.

BRO. We weren't in when they came with it.

MIDDIE. That's the whole point.

13. Get on to Nora: Telephone Nora.

(*Both relapse into silence.* BRO *reads his paper. After a few moments he looks up.*)

BRO. If we're going to change the name at all, I can't see what you've got against "Hodge" for that matter.

MIDDIE. "Hodge" is all right for a monkey.

BRO. We'll go through some names and see what we can agree on. "Hodge".

MIDDIE. "Hodge" for a monkey. "Gush" for an elephant.

BRO. "Admiral Benbow".

MIDDIE. "Hiram B. Larkspur".

BRO. "Playboy".

MIDDIE. "Killed-with-kindness Corcoran".

BRO. "New-wine-into-old-bottles Backhouse".

MIDDIE. " 'Tis-pity-she's-a-whore Hignett".

BRO. "Lucifer".

MIDDIE. "Stonehenge".

BRO. "Haunch".

(*There is a pause.*)

MIDDIE
BRO } (*almost simultaneously*). "Splinter".

BRO. Thank goodness we can agree on something. Now I can ring Eddie. (*He puts his paper on the floor, rises, crosses to the telephone down* L, *lifts the receiver and dials a number.*)

MIDDIE. Why ring Eddie when you've got Nora who's had some experience with animals? She could probably suggest something.

BRO. So you keep saying.

14. " 'Tis-pity . . . Hignett": *'Tis Pity She's a Whore* is a play by Thomas Ford (1586 - 1640?). Note that the names in this amusing game grow longer and more ridiculous to this point. Then follow the powerful words Lucifer and Stonehenge, both rich in associations, and finally Haunch and Splinter, as a humorous anti-climax. If you like words and their sounds and qualities, you will enjoy this passage.

MIDDIE. Well?

BRO (*into the telephone*). Is that Mrs. Mortice? . . . Oh . . . Yes, will you? Tell her Bro Paradock would like a word with her. (*He waits.*)

MIDDIE. You've decided to ring Nora, then?

BRO (*ignoring* MIDDIE; *into the telephone*). Hallo . . . Nora? . . . Yes, thank you, Nora. And how are you? . . . Oh? . . . And what's that, Nora? . . . A what? . . . No! I can't believe it. Hold on a moment, Nora. Wait till I fetch Middie to the phone.

MIDDIE. Don't tell me they've got ours.

BRO (*to* MIDDIE). It's her snake. It's too short.

MIDDIE. Too short for what? (*She rises, moves to* BRO *and takes the receiver from him.*)

BRO. She says they're worried about the R.S.P.C.A. (*He moves* LC.)

MIDDIE (*into the telephone*). Nora? . . . Yes, Bro was telling me. Isn't it maddening? . . . Yes. . . . Yes. . . .Yes, and do you know they've done exactly the same with us. . . . No – about ten times too big. You'd think they'd know by now, wouldn't you? A thing that size in a semi of all things.

BRO. This is a bungalow, for the fiftieth time. 15

MIDDIE (*to* BRO). Oh, for God's sake! (*Into the telephone.*) No, Nora, I was talking to Bro. He won't have it we're living in a semi. If I've got the deeds out once to show him, I've got them out a hundred times . . .

BRO. I wouldn't have bought the place without looking pretty closely . . .

15. This is a bungalow . . . time: Here, while Middie is talking to Nora on the telephone, the family quarrel becomes sharpened by being shared with an outsider, and the joke about whether they live in a semi or a bungalow is worked over to develop all its ridiculous possibilities. One cannot push absurdity beyond checking the deed to find the kind of house one lives in! The final word is that Bro has not set foot upstairs since they moved in – because it is a bungalow.

MIDDIE (*into the telephone*). Just a moment, Nora. He's got to have his say out.

BRO. I wouldn't have bought it without looking pretty closely at the deeds to see if there was any mention of its being semi-detached. It's one of the things I always look for.

MIDDIE (*into the telephone*). I'm sorry, Nora. I've started Bro off on his hobby-horse again . . .

BRO. You just read things into them once you've made up your mind.

MIDDIE (*into the telephone*). He's got a thing about this being a bungalow, Nora. He hasn't set foot upstairs since we moved in. . . . Exactly, Nora. . . . It's just the same with us, of course. We're stuck with the thing like you. . . . We shan't get the Zoo at this time. . . . We shall just have to keep it till the morning. . . . Not indoors, no. We've got it out at the back. . . . Yes, I should think so, Nora. . . . You're perfectly justified . . .

(BRO *tries to attract* MIDDIE'*s attention.*)

BRO. Why not ask her if she'd like to have Mr. Trench and we'll take the snake off her?

MIDDIE (*to* BRO). What? (*Into the telephone.*) No, it's something Bro just said, Nora. I think he's thought of something. I'll get him to tell you. (*She puts her hand over the mouthpiece. To* BRO.) You talk to her; she's on about this snake of hers.

(BRO *takes the receiver from* MIDDIE, *who moves* LC.)

BRO (*into the telephone*). What do you say to that, Nora? . . . How about it? . . . Oh, I thought Middie told you. It was just an idea I had – I thought perhaps we could help each other out if I came round with our Mr. Trench and took the snake off you. . . . Are you? . . . Yes – Middie wants to change the name of ours this year. . . . "Oedipus Rex". . . . Of course it is, Nora – and for an elephant this size. Middie doesn't seem to see that. . . . Yes. . . . No – don't bother about changing the name, Nora. We can do all that ourselves when we get it home.

..."Bees' Wedding"?...Oh, yes. I should think that must look 16
rather good on a snake. Wait a moment, Nora – I'll ask Middie. (*To* MIDDIE.) She's called her snake "Bees' Wedding". What do you think? Shall I tell her to take it off the snake and keep it for Mr. Trench when I take him round?

MIDDIE. That'll mean we shall have to find a name to fit the snake out with.

BRO. Let's see what "Bees' Wedding" looks like on Mr. Trench, first. (*Into the telephone.*) Hold on a moment, Nora.

(MIDDIE *and* BRO *look out for a few moments through the window* R *into the garden.*)

What do you think?

MIDDIE. Wait till he turns round.

BRO. Remember she's got the upstairs as well.

MIDDIE. Yes – well, it's better, anyway, than "Mr. Trench" for him.

BRO. I'll just tell her to keep "Bees' Wedding" for Mr. Trench, then.

MIDDIE. Ask her about "Mr. Trench" on the snake; see what she thinks.

BRO (*into the telephone*). Nora? . . . Yes, it fits beautifully. . . . Tailor-made, Nora. . . . Would you, Nora? I was going to ask you if you wouldn't mind doing that . . . (*To* MIDDIE.) She's trying it on the snake now.

(*There is a knock at the front door.* MIDDIE *exits up* C, *closing the door behind her.* BRO *waits, humming to himself.*)

(*Into the telephone.*) Oh, splendid, Nora. . . . No – no trouble at all. . . . That's better still. . . . In about half an hour, then. . . . Yes. Good-bye, Nora. (*He replaces the receiver.*)

(MIDDIE *enters up* C.)

16. I should think . . . snake: Now follows an amusing extension of the "names" comedy – trying names *on* the animals to see if they fit, as one would try on clothes.

MIDDIE (*moving to the sofa*). It was lucky we rang her up. (*She sits and works on her rug.*)

BRO. Did she say how short this snake was?

MIDDIE. She didn't give any measurements, if that's what you mean.

BRO. I thought perhaps you might have thought to ask her what the measurements were.

MIDDIE. Why didn't you ask her for the measurements yourself, as far as that goes?

BRO. How was I to know whether you'd asked already?

MIDDIE. You heard me talking to her.

(*There is a pause.*)

BRO. Who was that at the door?

MIDDIE. It was two comedians. They wanted to come in and amuse us.

BRO. That's the second time this week. Where are they now?

MIDDIE. I sent them next door.

BRO. Not to Mrs. Gride?

MIDDIE. I said we've already been amused, thank you.

BRO. Mrs. Gride is going to be pleased – having comedians foisted on to her.

MIDDIE. She wasn't above sending the undertaker in to us, was she?

(*There is a pause.*)

BRO. Were both of them funny?

MIDDIE. How should I know?

BRO. I just wondered if one was funnier than the other.

MIDDIE. They just asked if they could come in and be comic for a few minutes.

17. It was two comedians: In the sequence that follows we have the only reference to the two comedians who are so important in the long version of the play. Notice the juxtaposition of "comedians" and "undertaker", and the neighbour's unpleasant name. Do you consider the joke about the "Hoover" on page 417 a good one?

(*There is a pause.*)

The last time we had them in here I was picking up jokes in the Hoover for days afterwards.

BRO. I suppose they didn't say how comic they were going to be?

MIDDIE. I didn't ask them.

(*There is a pause.*)

BRO. I'm wondering if we've done the right thing about this snake of Nora's.

MIDDIE. You haven't done it yet.

BRO. What happens if it turns out to be about two inches long?

MIDDIE. You can always have them lengthened.

BRO. I know you can have them lengthened. But you don't get the thickness then. (*He crosses to the door and opens it.*) What have you done with my gumboots? 18

MIDDIE. What do you want gumboots for to go down the road a few doors with an elephant? Where are your other shoes?

BRO (*standing in the doorway*). These are my other shoes I've got on.

MIDDIE. And I should come straight back with Mr. Trench. We don't want Mrs. Stencil asking a lot of questions.

BRO. I notice you've agreed to keep "Mr. Trench" for it now you know it's a snake.

MIDDIE. And what are you going to bring it back in? You can't trail a snake on a lead like a canary.

BRO. In any case I thought we'd settled on "Hodge" for a name.

18. Gumboots: Boots made of gum or India rubber. The following passage (to Bro's exit) contains a "reprise" of the comic names theme. Notice also the mention of Mrs. Stencil again, to prepare us for her later telephone conversation with Middie, and also the complete absurdity of "You can't trail a snake on a lead like a canary."

MIDDIE. "Hodge" for a jackal. "Gush" for an anaconda.

BRO. "Admiral Benbow".

MIDDIE. "Hiram B. Larkspur".

BRO. "Playboy".

MIDDIE. You're just thinking up names at random.

BRO. How else can I think them up?

MIDDIE. You can wait till you've seen how short it is.

(*There is a pause.* BRO *turns to go out of the door.*)

BRO. I hate this job.

MIDDIE. You say that every year.

BRO. I've never had to do it before.

MIDDIE. You say it about other things.

(BRO *exits to the hall and re-enters almost at once.*)

BRO. If it comes to that, how do you know it *is* an anaconda?

MIDDIE. What else would it be? We shall have the R.S.P.C.A. round while you stand there.

BRO. Good God!

(BRO *exits to the hall and shuts the door behind him.*)

MIDDIE (*moving her head slowly from side to side.*) "Admiral Benbow"!

(BRO, *after a few moments, re-enters. His coat collar is turned up. He turns it down and shakes water from his jacket, then picks up his newspaper, sits in the armchair and reads.*)

You're not back already?

BRO. I'm not going in this rain.

MIDDIE. It's barely started yet.

BRO. I'm not going out in it. I haven't got a hat suitable for going out in the rain. You know that.

19. I haven't . . . the rain: Bro abandons his first attempt to take the elephant to Nora because he hasn't a hat suitable for going out in the rain. This "plants" the idea of the big mock-heroic rain-hat passage later in the play.

MIDDIE. You've got an eyeshield.

BRO. You gave it away.

MIDDIE. I don't mean the one I gave away. I mean the one you wear for tennis.

BRO. But that's to keep the sun out of my eyes.

MIDDIE. Couldn't you wear it back to front?

(*A knock is heard at the front door.*)

(*She rises and moves to the door.*) That would be too ingenious for you, I suppose.

(MIDDIE *exits to the hall.* BRO *reads the newspaper.* MIDDIE *returns with an unopened telegram, which she hands to* BRO.)

(*She sits on the sofa and works at the rug.*) It's Uncle Ted and that motor-scooter again I expect. I shall be glad when we see the last of that craze.

BRO (*opening the telegram*). What's he up to this time?

MIDDIE. He's probably been parking his motor-scooter on
that piece of waste ground again behind Rachmaninov's Sec- 20
ond Piano Concerto.

BRO. Who does that belong to?

MIDDIE. It doesn't belong to anybody. It's just a piece of waste ground.

BRO. Then they can't stop him parking his motor-scooter on it if it doesn't belong to anyone.

MIDDIE. I suppose they can't.

BRO (*reading the telegram*). "Arriving Euston twelve-ten 21
send sandwiches." (*He ponders.*) The last time we had a tele-

20. On that piece . . . Concerto: The nonsense becomes wilder and more absurd as the play proceeds.
21. Arriving Euston . . . sandwiches: Here we have another comic idea – a coded telegram. Notice how illogical the dialogue is. There is no way of telling whether a telegram is in code. This one is, so they can set their minds at rest.

The joke is developed further on Uncle Ted's arrival. The

gram like this it was worded very differently.

MIDDIE. Perhaps we ought to take it back and get it seen to.

BRO. No. If they start playing about with the wording we shan't know where we are. It's in code. We should never decipher it.

MIDDIE. How can you tell whether it's in code?

BRO. There isn't any way of telling. Either it is or it isn't. This one is.

MIDDIE. Thank heaven for that, then. We can set our minds at rest.

BRO (*rising*). Lucky I spotted it. (*He puts the telegram on the coffee-table.*)

MIDDIE (*glancing through the window*). Do you know it's stopped raining?

BRO. I'll get across to Nora's then with the elephant. (*He moves to the door.*) What have you done with my gumboots?

MIDDIE. What do you want gumboots for to go down the road a few doors with an elephant? Where are your other shoes?

BRO. These are my other shoes I've got on.

MIDDIE. And I should come straight back with Mr. Trench. We don't want Mrs. Stencil asking a lot of questions.

BRO. I notice you've agreed to call it "Mr. Trench" now you know it's a snake.

MIDDIE. And what are you going to bring it back in? You can't trail a snake on a lead like a canary.

BRO. In any case I thought we'd settled on "Hodge" for a name.

telegram meant that he had changed his sex. Ted had handed it in in code, provided the code number, and asked that it be decoded before being sent. But this had not been done.

22. I'll get across . . . elephant: This is Bro's second start to take the elephant to Nora. Before he leaves we have the gumboots again, Mrs. Stencil, the snake-canary line, the threat of the R.S.P.C.A., and the names game – all satirizing the merry-go-round of meaningless repeated conversation that we sometimes overhear.

MIDDIE. "Hodge" for an antelope. "Gush" for a boa constrictor.

BRO. "Admiral Benbow".

MIDDIE. "Hiram B. Larkspur".

BRO. "Playboy".

MIDDIE. We've been through all this before. For goodness' sake pull yourself together. We shall have the R.S.P.C.A. round while you stand there.

BRO. Perhaps we shall. Perhaps we shan't.

(BRO *exits.* MIDDIE *rises, goes to the fireplace, tidies the hearth and puts some coal on the fire.*)

(BRO *re-enters. He seems to have been thrown momentarily off balance, and speaks as though dazed.*) 23

There was somebody at the door.

MIDDIE. Who?

BRO (*moving to* R *of the sofa*). I told him he'd better wait. (*He pauses.*) He wants me to form a Government.

MIDDIE. What does he look like?

BRO. He says he's working through the street directory.

(MIDDIE, *who has sized up the situation in her own way, quickly completes the tidying of the hearth, picks up two bottles from under the table* L *of the sofa, and hands them to* BRO.)

MIDDIE (*motioning towards the sideboard*). You might do something about all these bottles. What does it look like if the Cabinet arrive suddenly?

BRO. He was wearing an old raincoat.

MIDDIE. He was very likely trying it on for size. (*She*

23. Bro re-enters . . . dazed: Bro returns, bewildered, having forgotten completely about his intention to take the elephant to Nora. A man at the door has asked him to form a government! For the next three pages, until the appearance of Uncle Ted, the playwright skilfully works comic variations on this theme, with the counter theme of the old raincoat to provide variety and surprise.

smoothes the loose cover on the sofa.)

BRO (*beginning to move abstractedly among the bottles*). What would he be doing trying an old raincoat on for size?

MIDDIE. It might not be as old as the one he had before. (*She pauses.*) The coat he had before may have been in tatters for all you or I know. It may have been black with grease.

BRO. I doubt it. I very much doubt it.

MIDDIE. Or mud or something.

BRO. Mud possibly. But not grease.

MIDDIE. Why not grease? (*She goes into the hall, leaving the door open, and is seen foraging among the coats.*)

BRO (*crossing to the fireplace*). There's no grounds for thinking it's grease any more than mud. (*He takes a pipe from the mantel-piece and begins thoughtfully filling it.*) How can I start forming a Government at six o'clock in the evening?

(MIDDIE *comes in to* R *of the sofa holding up a torn and dirty raincoat.*)

MIDDIE. Look at this thing. How do you know his mightn't have been in a worse state than this one? Look – what's that but grease? Look at the sleeves. And his was probably as bad or worse. (*She returns the coat to the hall.*)

BRO. How can I start forming a Government at six o'clock in the evening?

MIDDIE (*coming into the room*). You'd be saying the same thing if it were six o'clock in the morning. (*She closes the door, moves to the sofa and sits.*)

BRO. It's the Prime Minister's job.

24. Mud . . . not grease: Have you heard of people who argue strenuously about subjects that are purely "if"? Middie is told that the man outside was wearing an old raincoat. She makes her first guess to explain this: he was trying it on for size. Why? She makes her second guess: that an earlier coat was in tatters, or black with grease or mud. Bro agrees to mud, but objects strongly to grease. So they quarrel again, this time about an "if" twice removed from possibility.

MIDDIE. That's one way of shelving your responsibilities, I suppose.

BRO. It's not a question of shelving anything. I just don't want the job. And in any case where would I begin forming a Government? We don't know anybody.

MIDDIE. You could make a start by asking Uncle Ted when he gets here. And in the meantime there's a man at the door waiting for your answer.

(*There is a pause.*)

BRO. How do I know he isn't wanted by the police?

MIDDIE. Why should he be?

BRO. If he is we ought to turn him over.

(MIDDIE *rises and peers from behind a curtain through the window next to the door.*)

MIDDIE (*coming away*). If he's a criminal, he's in plain clothes. That's all I can say. (*She sits on the sofa.*)

BRO. I'm going to turn him over and be on the safe side.

MIDDIE. You may never get another chance to form a Government.

BRO. That goes for anything I ever choose not to do.

MIDDIE. So what's it to be?

BRO (*crossing to the door*). I'll see what he's got to say.

(BRO *exits, closing the door.* MIDDIE *works at her rug.* BRO *re-enters, goes to the armchair, picks up his newspaper and sits.* MIDDIE *waits expectantly.*)

(*Casually.*) It was someone having a joke. 25

MIDDIE. I would have recognized him through the window.

25. It was someone having a joke: This is a new development in the comic situation. According to Bro, the man at the door was playing a joke on him, pretending that he was approaching him on behalf of the Whigs (the old name for the English Liberal party), and that Bro looked like Gladstone. Middie remembers the year 1868 from her school history book – the year when Gladstone formed his first ministry. She also remembers that Gladstone's mission was to pacify Ireland (by

BRO. He was disguising his voice. (*He pauses, glancing through his newspaper.*) He said he thought I looked like Gladstone.

MIDDIE. And did you?

BRO. That sort of thing cuts no ice with me.

MIDDIE. You should have led him on. You should have pretended to think it was eighteen sixty-eight.

BRO. It was all of a piece with his asking me to form a Government in the first place.

MIDDIE. I hope you didn't start saying, Your mission was to pacify Ireland?

BRO. It cuts no more ice with me, that sort of thing, than Gladstone would have done if I'd been Queen Victoria. And God knows there's little enough of the Empress of India about me.

MIDDIE. It would have been playing into his hands to say, Your mission was to pacify Ireland.

BRO. I know it would have been playing into his hands.

MIDDIE. I can't think why I didn't recognize him.

BRO. I've told you he was having a joke with us.

MIDDIE. I suppose he thought he could talk you round. Like last time when they had you voting for some candidate who refused to stand.

BRO. He said he was round canvassing for the Whigs.

MIDDIE. You should have let him come in for a few moments to try your overcoat on.

BRO. He'd never have got into it.

MIDDIE. Exactly.

BRO. He was broader across the shoulders than I am. He probably still is. I doubt whether he could even have worn it like a cloak.

giving the Irish Home Rule). From here on until Uncle Ted enters, the conversation moves from absurdity to absurdity. First Middie pursues the idea of the man trying on Bro's overcoat – for what purpose she is not sure. Then she reproaches Bro for not forming a government. Finally time and identity become confused. Is it 1868? Is Bro Gladstone?

MIDDIE. You don't see what I'm leading up to, do you?

BRO. It would have looked thoroughly ridiculous on him.

MIDDIE. I know your overcoat would have been too small for him. Of course it would have looked ridiculous. It looks ridiculous on you most of the time. But don't you see that if he'd tried it on in here, I could have seen at a glance he wasn't a man of your build? After a time I might have been able to narrow it down still further. As it is I don't know what to think. (*She pauses.*) What happened about the Government? Did you agree to form one or not?

BRO. He didn't approach me any more.

MIDDIE. I see. It didn't occur to you to raise it?

BRO. I've no desire whatever to form a Government.

MIDDIE. And while you're sitting there not wanting to form a Government, he's probably next door. Asking Mrs. Gride's husband.

BRO. He's very likely forgotten all about it by now.

MIDDIE. If he's forgotten all about it already, how do we know he was genuine in the first place? It could have been any old Tom, Dick or Harry asking you to form a Government. (*She pauses.*) It looks to me as if you've let yourself in for something with your bland assumptions about it being someone having a joke with us.

(UNCLE TED, *a young woman, elegantly dressed, enters quietly with the obvious intention of surprising* BRO *and* MIDDIE *who continue talking, unaware of her presence. She stands waiting for one of them to look up.*)

You'll be getting a man round before you know where you are with papers to prove it's eighteen sixty-eight.

BRO. But not that I'm Gladstone.

MIDDIE. If it's eighteen sixty-eight, it makes precious little difference whether you're Gladstone or not. (*She looks up, sees* UNCLE TED *and is momentarily speechless with astonishment.*) Uncle Ted! (*She rises.*) Why, you've changed your sex! (*She draws* UNCLE TED *down* C.)

(UNCLE TED *strikes an attitude which invites appraisal.* BRO *rises.*)

You look lovely – doesn't he, Bro? But why ever didn't you let us know?

UNCLE TED. Surely you got the telegram I sent you? (*She crosses to the fireplace, removes her gloves, looks in the mirror over the mantelpiece and pats her hair.*)

BRO. We got one – but it was in code.

UNCLE TED (*turning*). Oh, no! What a fool of a man!

(BRO *reacts.*)

No – not you, Bro. It's that idiot at the post office.

BRO. We were wondering if you were having trouble with the motor-scooter again.

UNCLE TED. I told him when I handed it in that it wasn't to go off without being decoded first.

MIDDIE. They're not very reliable.

UNCLE TED (*putting her gloves and handbag on the coffee-table*). I gave him the code number and everything. It isn't as if he had to break it down letter by letter himself or anything. So I suppose you hadn't quite expected such a change? (*She sits on the sofa.*)

MIDDIE. We shall get used to it. It just seems funny calling you "Uncle Ted". But you must be dying for a read.

UNCLE TED. Yes, I'd love a book, Middie. I haven't opened one since I got into the train at four o'clock this morning.

(MIDDIE *goes to the bookshelves, takes out a number of books and arranges them on a tray.* BRO *sits in the armchair.*)

26. But . . . dying for a read: This is the first "read" sequence. Instead of food and drink, Uncle Ted is given a book. As you read the passage, you might work out an equivalent in terms of normal visiting conversation. For example, "Yes, I'd love a cup of tea, Middie." The by-play between Middie and Bro while Uncle Ted has his "read", particularly about the conversation about the conversation, is engaging.

BRO. What sort of a journey did you have this time, Uncle Ted?

UNCLE TED. The usual kind, Bro. I just got into the train, and from then onwards it was just a matter of moving in roughly the same direction practically the whole time until I got out of it at Euston.

(MIDDIE *brings the tray of books to* UNCLE TED *and puts it on the coffee-table.*)

Ah, thank you, Middie.

MIDDIE. There are some nice critical essays, if you'd like one of those. Or biography. Or I've got some textbooks in the cupboard . . . ?

(UNCLE TED *rises and takes a small book.*)

UNCLE TED. No – I think I'll have this book of poems, Middie. I feel as if I could really do justice to a good poem after travelling up to Euston since four o'clock this morning. Thank you, Middie. (*She sits on the left arm of the sofa and reads silently and intently.*)

MIDDIE (*crossing to* BRO; *in an undertone*). I wonder what the next craze is going to be?

BRO (*in an undertone to* MIDDIE). Next craze?

MIDDIE. When she gets tired of her new sex.

BRO. Oh. As long as she doesn't go back to the motor-scooter.

(*There is a pause.*)

MIDDIE. Perhaps we shall be able to have that conversation presently.

BRO. Which conversation?

MIDDIE. Don't you remember we promised ourselves the next time Uncle Ted came up to have a nice long conversation about the conversation we had at the Wordsworths'? When we were all talking about what we'd been talking about at the Hunters' the week before?

BRO. We had the conversation about that last time Uncle Ted was here.

MIDDIE. So we did.

(UNCLE TED *looks up from her book, closes it, and holds it out to* MIDDIE.)

BRO. Better?

(MIDDIE *crosses, takes the book and puts it on the tray.*)

UNCLE TED. That was just what I wanted, Middie. I felt like some verse after that wretched stuffy compartment.

(MIDDIE *sits on the sofa.* UNCLE TED, *from where she sits, looks across the room through the window into the garden.*)

So your elephant came?

MIDDIE. Yes. And look at it.

UNCLE TED (*rising*). Don't you usually have a dwarf elephant? (*She crosses to the window* R *and looks out.*)

BRO. They sent us the wrong one.

27. So your elephant came: From this point until the discussion changes to rain-hats (footnote 28), the playwright returns to the central comic idea of the play. This idea has the humour that comes from exaggeration and contrast: the Paradocks have an elephant that is too large, Mrs. Mortice (Nora) a boa constrictor that is too small. They are going to exchange them; the first part of the exchange is completed in this passage. After Uncle Ted has been brought up to date on the situation, Nora's boy arrives with the snake. We've been kept guessing throughout the play about how big it is. Now we know; it is in a pencil box! And it must be kept in the box, lest it eavesdrop! Your sense of humour will be tickled by the absurd repetitions, particularly by the *non sequiturs* about Mr. Trench (with Bro going on about the name, and Middie and Uncle Ted fearful lest it go berserk in the night), and by the wonderful nonsense about the small snake – you can have it lengthened, but then you won't get the thickness!

UNCLE TED. What on earth for?

BRO. We shan't know till we get the measurements from them.

MIDDIE. I can see its great ears flapping about from here.

UNCLE TED. Why didn't you query the measurements when it came?

BRO. We weren't in when they came with it.

MIDDIE. What do they think we want with an elephant that size?

BRO. It's big enough for a hotel.

MIDDIE. People think you're trying to go one better than everybody else.

UNCLE TED (*crossing to the sofa*). Never mind. It's only once a year. (*She sits on the sofa beside* MIDDIE.)

BRO. Or a private school. If we had a private school, or a hotel, we might be glad of an elephant that size.

UNCLE TED. You're not calling it "Mr. Trench" again, I hope.

BRO. Why not "Mr. Trench"?

UNCLE TED. Six years running? You can't call an elephant "Mr. Trench" six years running. It looks as if you were hard up for a name to call the animal or something.

BRO. It isn't the same animal every time, you know.

MIDDIE. If it goes berserk in the night, *I'm* not getting up to it.

BRO. As far as that goes it wasn't I who wanted to call it "Mr. Trench" the year it was a giraffe.

UNCLE TED. If it's going to go berserk in the night you'd have been better off with a smaller one.

MIDDIE. I'm not getting up to it.

BRO. It was Middie's idea it would make a pleasant change to give the name to a giraffe instead of an elephant.

MIDDIE. I think we'd be better off without it.

UNCLE TED. And be without an elephant at all?

BRO. It seems a bit late now to start complaining about calling it "Mr. Trench" six years running.

MIDDIE. I think we'd be better off without an elephant. We've done nothing except bicker ever since they came with it.

(UNCLE TED *takes a cigarette from her handbag, and lights it.*)

UNCLE TED. You weren't in when they came with it.

MIDDIE. That's the whole point!

(*There is a silence for a few moments.* BRO *glances through the window.*)

BRO. Here's young Bobby coming across the garden.

MIDDIE (*with a glance through the window*). Nora must have sent him. (*She rises and moves toward the door.*) She'll have sent him over with the snake.

(MIDDIE *exits, leaving the door open.*)

BRO. We're exchanging the elephant with Mrs. Mortice. She's letting us have her snake.

UNCLE TED. Won't she need it herself?

BRO. It's too small for her. They sent her the wrong one.

UNCLE TED. I suppose they thought they'd better deal with you both on the same footing.

BRO. They generally do their best to be fair.

UNCLE TED. If they'd sent her the right one after having sent you the wrong one it would have led to all sorts of confusion.

BRO. No. It was Mrs. Mortice who got the wrong one delivered first. We were after her.

UNCLE TED. Oh.

BRO. Not that it would have been any less confusing that way, I suppose.

(MIDDIE *enters, carrying a pencil box. She shuts the door, and crosses to* UNCLE TED.)

MIDDIE. That was Nora's little boy. He's brought across our boa constrictor, Uncle Ted. (*She hands the box to* UNCLE TED.)

(BRO *rises to see better.*)

UNCLE TED. Do I open it? (*She slides the lid open.*)

BRO (*peering into the box*). That's never a boa constrictor. (*He sits again in the armchair.*)

MIDDIE. Don't let it get out of its loose-box. We shall have it eavesdropping.

UNCLE TED (*closing the box and handing it to* MIDDIE). You don't seem to be getting much for your elephant, do you?

MIDDIE (*crossing to the fireplace*). We may decide to have it lengthened. (*She puts the box on the mantelpiece.*)

UNCLE TED. Yes. But of course you won't get the thickness then.

(*There is a pause.* MIDDIE *resumes her seat on the sofa.*)

BRO. Was it still raining when you went to the door, Middie? 28

MIDDIE. There's a slight drizzle. It's not much.

BRO. I'll give it a few minutes longer. I don't suppose Nora will mind. I don't go out in the rain oftener than I need these days, Uncle Ted. My old hat isn't up to it.

UNCLE TED. That's what you're always saying, Bro. Isn't he, Middie?

MIDDIE. Hats aren't everything in this world. There are other things besides hats.

BRO. We know they aren't everything.

UNCLE TED. I dare say there are plenty of people who wouldn't mind having a hat like yours, Bro, all the same.

BRO. It isn't so much having the hats as knowing how to make the best use of them.

MIDDIE. We can't all be blessed with hats.

28. Was it still raining . . . Middie?: The discussion that follows about rain-hats is, for the editor, one of the most beguiling in the play. Among other things, it makes fun of some of the platitudes that are overworked in everyday conversation. Can you find some of these? And you will be impressed with the courage of Bro's niece, Myrtle, who, properly hatted, has just got through her first thunderstorm, and for whom they prophesy still greater achievements to come.

UNCLE TED. I suppose plenty of people do get by without hats, but it's rather silly to pretend they don't matter.

BRO. Look at Mrs. Blackboy's husband and the showers he's got through in his time with that green plastic bag he carries round on his head.

MIDDIE. That's not a hat.

BRO. Or Bella for that matter.

MIDDIE. Bella overdoes it. The time she spends on millinery she could spend on something else.

UNCLE TED. She gets through the rain though.

MIDDIE. A lot of those who are supposed to have such wonderful hats go around half the time in other people's.

UNCLE TED. Why don't you weatherproof an old lampshade or something for yourself, Bro?

BRO. I'm not much of a one for millinery, Uncle Ted.

MIDDIE. That sort of thing's all right if you've got millinery in your make-up.

BRO. I've always known what I could do, and I've always known what I couldn't do. That's the reason I never became an air hostess.

MIDDIE. Bro and I prefer to leave the showers to the ones who've got the hats for it.

BRO. The older you get the less hats you seem to have.

MIDDIE. I don't want any more hats than I've got. It's very often the people who bother least about hats who come out of it best whenever there's heavy rain.

UNCLE TED. I've never made any pretensions to hats myself, but I prefer people who've got a few hats to the ones who haven't.

MIDDIE. I can tell you someone who *has* got a good little hat on her head. You've never met Bro's niece, Uncle Ted, have you?

BRO. Oh. Myrtle.

UNCLE TED. Isn't it Myrtle who's just got through her first thunderstorm?

MIDDIE. She sailed right through it just as if she'd got a sou'-wester on.

BRO. I'd like to see her have a try at a hailstorm. She's got the hat for it.

MIDDIE. Don't you put ideas into her head. We don't want her trying to do too much all at once.

BRO. Or a storm at sea.

MIDDIE. She's all right as she is.

BRO. I think that girl's got a sou-'wester hidden away somewhere. You watch. She'll bring it out one of these days and surprise all of us. She looks to me as if she's got her father's sou'-wester.

MIDDIE. Stan never had a sou'-wester in his life. It was his plastic saucer that got him where he was. Anybody would think he was a thorough-going sou'-wester man the way you talk about him.

Neil Newton

"I'm sure that waste-paper basket of yours has possibilities, Middie." Uncle Ted tries on the waste-paper basket, as Middie and Bro watch, in the Trinity College Dramatic Society production.

BRO. It wasn't that he didn't have a sou'-wester so much as that he could never get round to putting it on.

MIDDIE. He never had one. (*To* UNCLE TED.) Stan was Bro's brother in the navy, Uncle Ted. (*To* BRO.) You know perfectly well he used to borrow quite shamelessly from the other men whenever there was an important storm at sea and he couldn't get by with just his plastic saucer.

UNCLE TED (*loudly*). I'm sure that waste-paper basket of yours has possibilities, Middie.

MIDDIE. Do you like it?

UNCLE TED. It would trim up very nicely for Bro.

MIDDIE. He's had it on. Haven't you, Bro? He tried it on for size. But he won't be seen out in it.

BRO. That sort of thing's all right for the summer.

MIDDIE. Bro hates anything that he thinks makes him look younger.

BRO. I happen to have a death-wish, that's all.

UNCLE TED (*looking at her watch*). We're going to miss the service.

MIDDIE. It's never that time already?

29. We're . . . miss the service: The service is the most serious part of the play. It is true that it has absurd and satirical aspects. But these should not be construed in any way as an attack on true religion. It is not the church that is satirized, but the vagueness and near-materialism of much that passes for "uplift" and religion, and the mere lip-service to religion rendered by some church-goers whose responses are hollow and completely lacking in conviction.

    On the positive side there is much to challenge thought in the service. You will notice that Herbert Whittaker, in his note that follows the play, quotes two of the final sentences of the service. And in his book *The Theatre of the Absurd,* Martin Esslin quotes the last three prayers and responses. He comments, "There could hardly be a better statement of the objectives not merely of Simpson himself but of the Theatre of the Absurd."

BRO (*rising and crossing to the radio*). We shan't miss much.

MIDDIE. Uncle Ted doesn't want to miss any of it.

(BRO *switches on the radio and tunes it in.*)

BRO. It may just have started.

MIDDIE. She's travelled all the way up to Euston for it since four o'clock this morning.

BRO. Sh! (*He crosses and sits in the armchair.*)

(*The prayers from the radio gradually become audible.* UNCLE TED *listens with determined seriousness, joining in the responses from time to time.* BRO *and* MIDDIE *listen in a manner suggesting boredom half-heartedly concealed.*)

PRAYER. . . . weep at the elastic as it stretches:

RESPONSE. And rejoice that it might have been otherwise.

MIDDIE (*whispering*). We've missed the start.

BRO. Sh!

PRAYER. Let us sing because round things roll:

RESPONSE. And rejoice that it might have been otherwise.

PRAYER. Let us give praise for woodlice and for buildings sixty-nine feet three inches high:

RESPONSE. For Adam Smith's *Wealth of Nations* published in seventeen seventy-six.

PRAYER. For the fifth key from the left on the lower manual of the organ of the Church of the Ascension in the Piazza Vittorio Emanuele the Second in the town of Castelfidardo in Italy:

RESPONSE. And for bats.

PRAYER. Let us give praise for those who compile dictionaries in large, rambling buildings, for the suitably clad men and women on our commons and in our hotels, for all those who in the fullness of time will go out to meet whatever fate awaits them; for the tall, the ham-fisted, the pompous; and for all men everywhere and at all times:

RESPONSE. Amen.

PRAYER. And now let us dwell upon drugs, for their effects enlighten us; upon judo and hypnosis, for their effects enlighten us; upon privation and upon loneliness, upon the heat of the sun and the silence of deserts; upon torture, upon interrogation, upon death – for their effects enlighten us:

RESPONSE. Give us light, that we may be enlightened.

PRAYER. Give us light upon the nature of our knowing; for the illusions of the sane man are not the illusions of the lunatic, and the illusions of the flagellant are not the illusions of the alcoholic, and the illusions of the delirious are not the illusions of the lovesick, and the illusions of the genius are not the illusions of the common man:

RESPONSE. Give us light, that we may be enlightened.

PRAYER. Give us light, that, sane, we may attain to a distortion more acceptable than the lunatic's and call it truth:

RESPONSE. That, sane, we may call it truth and know it to be false.

PRAYER. That, sane, we may know ourselves, and by knowing ourselves may know what it is we know:

RESPONSE. Amen.

(*There is a pause.*)

MIDDIE. That was rather nice.

(*The introductory bars of "Sweet Polly Oliver" in a metrical version are heard through the radio.*)

UNCLE TED (*rising*). This is where we stand.

(BRO *and* MIDDIE *rise.* UNCLE TED *joins softly in the hymn-like singing. As* MIDDIE *becomes aware of this, she surreptitiously draws* BRO*'s attention to it, and both suppress their amusement. When the singing ends, there is a momentary silence, and then all begin to be excessively normal by way of neutralizing their embarrassment.* UNCLE TED *and* MIDDIE *resume their seats on the sofa.* BRO *crosses to the radio.*)

VOICE (*from the radio*). This evening's service, from the

Church of the Hypothetical Imperative in Brinkfall, was conducted by Father Gerontius.

(BRO *switches off the radio.*)

MIDDIE. It's a pity we missed the first part.

BRO (*sitting in the armchair*). At any rate we got the last part.

MIDDIE. Naturally we got it.

BRO. Why naturally?

MIDDIE. It isn't so very easy once you've switched it on to miss the last part, is it?

BRO. Not if we switched it off too soon?

UNCLE TED. We didn't miss much of it. How did you both enjoy it? I thought it was very good.

MIDDIE. It was a lot better this week. Didn't you think so, Bro? It hasn't been at all uplifting the last few weeks.

BRO. They can't expect to keep it up week after week. They ought to give it a rest for a time.

MIDDIE. Of course, I think you got more of a real, good worship, if you know what I mean, in the old days when they weren't afraid to let themselves go with idols and things.

UNCLE TED. You're both getting jaded. If you were to come to it fresh after a few weeks without any service at all, you'd be surprised what a difference it would make. You'd be as inspired as anything by it. It's made *me* feel thoroughly uplifted, anyway.

BRO. Isn't it rather a long journey for you, though – every time you want to hear the service? Travelling up to Euston from four o'clock in the morning?

UNCLE TED. What's the alternative? It would mean having a radio down there.

BRO. I suppose it would.

UNCLE TED. Besides, I like to come up occasionally. The only trouble about that is that it's such a long journey; and if I come here it hardly leaves me time to get back. (*She looks at her watch.*)

BRO. When's your train, Uncle Ted?

UNCLE TED. It leaves Euston at nine. I shall have to be off soon.

MIDDIE. Not until you've had another read. I'm not letting you go out on a miserable two stanzas. It won't take me long to get down some more books. (*She rises and goes to the book-shelves.*)

UNCLE TED. Thank you, Middie – but I really oughtn't to stop for another read.

BRO (*rising*). You're going to stay and get some prose inside you first. Don't get those down, Middie. I've got some others outside.

MIDDIE (*moving to the sofa*). He's got a special little store out there, for when anybody comes unexpectedly. I expect he'll bring in one of the new books on the physical nature of the universe. (*She sits on the sofa.*)

(BRO *enters with three new books, and a pair of scissors.*)

BRO. You've got time for a dip in one of these before you go. (*He puts the books on the sideboard and, opening one of them, begins cutting out part of a page with the scissors.*)

UNCLE TED. Just a paragraph, then, Bro.

MIDDIE. You won't get anything like this in the Queen's Road. Will she, Bro?

UNCLE TED. That's surely not for me, Bro? I shall never finish it in time.

BRO (*indicating with the scissors a shorter passage*). How about that, then? You can't have anything shorter than that

30. When's . . . Uncle Ted?: Before Uncle Ted leaves he has his second "read". The comic idea is enriched with a new invention – with his scissors Bro cuts paragraphs for each of them from a new book. The analogy is deliberately extended to drinking. They can have their paragraph "neat" or, if it is too strong, with a definition or two to "take the edge off it". From this mad premise they proceed to the parting toast, and to the discussion of the monosyllables which give the read "that extra something".

– it's only a paragraph.

UNCLE TED. That's fine, thanks, Bro. He was going to give me nearly half a page, Middie.

BRO. You may want some of this with it. (*He fetches a large dictionary from the bookshelf and puts it on the coffee-table.*) But try it neat first of all.

MIDDIE. What's that you're offering her with it, Bro?

BRO. It's just a dictionary. She can take the edge off it, if she finds it too strong, with a definition or two.

UNCLE TED. I'll try it without first.

(BRO *hands a cutting to* UNCLE TED.)

Thank you, Bro.

BRO. Do you want one, Middie?

MIDDIE. Of course I want one.

(BRO *takes two cuttings, hands one to* MIDDIE, *keeps the other for himself, then sits in the armchair.*)

Well, let's hope it won't be so long next time before we see you, Uncle Ted.

(*All raise their cuttings.*)

UNCLE TED. Cheers.

BRO / MIDDIE (*together*). Cheers.

(*All read, looking up abstractedly from time to time.*)

UNCLE TED (*lowering her cutting*). Well – it's certainly got a kick to it. (*She puts the cutting on the coffee-table.*)

BRO (*raising his eyes momentarily*). I was hoping you'd like it.

MIDDIE (*putting her cutting on the coffee-table*). You didn't find it too strong, then?

UNCLE TED. I thought it was just right, Middie.

BRO (*putting his cutting on the floor*). Why should she find it too strong? It's supposed to have a bit of a bite to it.

UNCLE TED. Is it my imagination – or could I detect monosyllables in it?

BRO. Ah – I wondered if you'd spot the monosyllables. They do give it just that extra something, I think. Middie thinks they spoil it, but . . .

UNCLE TED. Oh, no – it needed just that flavouring of monosyllables to give it a tang. But you shouldn't have cut into a new book, Bro. (*She rises, picks up her gloves and handbag and prepares to leave.*)

MIDDIE (*rising*). It isn't often we have the opportunity, Uncle Ted. You mustn't leave it so long next time.

BRO (*rising*). You know you're very welcome to come up here for the service any time you feel you need uplifting.

UNCLE TED. I must try and get up a bit oftener. It's that awful long journey; if only there were some way of getting round that.

MIDDIE. Couldn't you make a detour?

UNCLE TED. I'd never get here, Middie. Thanks for the read, – and the service. I shall have to be off.

MIDDIE. She'll miss her train.

BRO. Yes – well, good-bye, then, Uncle Ted. Have a good journey.

UNCLE TED. Good-bye, Bro.

MIDDIE. Have you got everything?

UNCLE TED. Yes, I left my cases out in the hall.

(UNCLE TED *exits, followed by* MIDDIE, *who closes the door behind her, leaving* BRO *alone.* BRO *gets a tray of stamps, etc., from the sideboard and sits in the armchair.* MIDDIE *re-enters.*)

BRO. We forgot to ask about the motor-scooter.

MIDDIE. She's sold it. (*She sits on the sofa.*)

BRO. When did she say that?

MIDDIE. I asked her about it in the hall. She said she'd sold it to a salesman.

(*There is a pause.*)

BRO. The last time she was here she told us she'd bought it.

(*There is a pause.*)

MIDDIE. Oh – Bro. On the news this morning – I meant to tell you – they gave the figure as eight million. 31

BRO. No!

MIDDIE. That was the figure they gave. He said that a normal female cod could be the mother of eight million eggs.

BRO. Not eight million!

MIDDIE. I thought myself it seemed rather a lot.

BRO. It's irresponsibility run riot.

(*There is a pause.*)

Who on earth do they hope to get to count eight million eggs?

MIDDIE. And they're such fiddling things to count.

BRO. Not only that – it would take eight hundred thousand pairs of hands before you'd have enough fingers to count them on. You couldn't do it with less.

MIDDIE. I don't know I'm sure.

BRO. Eight hundred thousand people to count the eggs of a single cod. It's ludicrous.

MIDDIE. That was the figure they gave on the news.

(*There is a pause.*)

It's Aunt Chloe's birthday next week.

31. Oh – Bro . . . morning: After Uncle Ted goes, three nonsensical subjects are discussed – the eight million eggs of the normal female cod, a birthday present for Aunt Chloe (a deaf-aid, although she isn't deaf), and the newspaper's claim that four goes into twenty five times. Then comes the big moment – the beginning of the crisis. After two unsuccessful tries, Bro leaves to take the elephant to Nora. How skilfully the playwright fills in the interval, and how amusingly he manages Bro's return and the climax, are discussed in the introductory note. But you will observe with pleasure, as you read these final pages, Mrs. Stencil exercising her butterflies in the evening, the delightful reprise of the bungalow-semi theme, Mrs. Stencil's concern for the eagles that get cramps and might need parachutes, and Bro's voice, in the radio play, telling how he tried to get the "blasted dinosaur" through the garden gate.

BRO (*abstractedly*). We shall have to try and think of something for her.

(*There is a pause.*)

MIDDIE. There's a brand-new deaf-aid upstairs. We've never used it.

BRO. Aunt Chloe hasn't been deaf for years.

(*There is a pause.*)

It's the same whatever you think of, for that matter. Either she's got it or she doesn't need it. And she certainly doesn't need a deaf-aid.

(*There is a pause.*)

MIDDIE. Unless we were to burst a paper bag in her ear?

(*There is a pause.*)

BRO. You wouldn't do any good with a paper bag.

(*There is a pause.*)

We should have to get a blank cartridge and fire that.

MIDDIE. I don't think she'd really expect anything as elaborate as that.

BRO. I wasn't suggesting we should do it.

MIDDIE. It would look a bit ostentatious.

BRO. I was only saying that that would be how we should have to do it if we were going to do it at all.

MIDDIE. After all, it isn't as if it's her twenty-first.

(*There is a pause.*)

You won't forget you've got an elephant to deliver, Bro?

BRO. No. I was just reading in the paper here – apparently what they said at the elementary school is true about four going into twenty five times.

MIDDIE. I should want to see it first.

BRO. It's no good just dismissing it as textbook talk, Middie. It wouldn't be in the paper unless there was something in it.

MIDDIE. No, I suppose not.

(*There is a pause.*)

BRO. I suppose I'd better get round to Nora's with the elephant. (*He rises, puts the tray on the sideboard and goes to the door.*) Where are my gumboots?

MIDDIE. What do you want gumboots for to go down the road a few doors with an elephant? Where are your other shoes?

BRO. I'm not going without my gumboots.

MIDDIE. For goodness' sake get them on, then, and go.

(BRO *goes into the hall, picks up a pair of gumboots and comes into the room.*)

BRO. If you switch on the radio while I'm out you can listen to the play. (*He sits on the upstage arm of the armchair, takes off his shoes and puts on the gumboots.*)

MIDDIE. How long are you going to be?

BRO. You'll get the last half-hour or so of it. I don't know how long I shall be – it depends whether I meet Mrs. Stencil on the way.

MIDDIE. For goodness' sake go the other way then. We don't want Mrs. Stencil asking a lot of questions.

BRO. She won't be out at this time.

MIDDIE. This is just when she will be out. She always goes out in the evening exercising her butterflies.

BRO. I thought they were in quarantine. (*He rises.*)

MIDDIE. They came out of quarantine weeks ago. She's had the vet to them since then.

BRO (*moving to the door*). Well – if I meet her, I meet her.

MIDDIE. Try not to let her see the elephant.

BRO. I certainly shan't draw attention to it. (*He stands in the open doorway.*) You'd better get up to bed if I'm late.

MIDDIE. *Up* to bed? I thought we were living in a bungalow?

(BRO *looks bewilderedly around, then exits to the hall closing the door behind him.* MIDDIE *leans over to the radio, switches it on then works on her rug-making.* BRO*'s and* MIDDIE*'s voices are heard through the radio.*)

BRO'*s* VOICE. It was your idea it would make a pleasant change to give the name to a sea-lion instead of a dinosaur.

MIDDIE'*s* VOICE. We've done nothing except bicker since they came with it.

(*The telephone rings.*)

BRO'*s* VOICE. We weren't in when they came with it.

(MIDDIE *rises.*)

MIDDIE'*s* VOICE. That's the whole point.

(MIDDIE *switches off the radio, crosses to the telephone and lifts the receiver.*)

MIDDIE (*into the telephone*). Mrs. Paradock. . . . Oh, Mrs. Stencil. . . . Yes. . . . No, Bro's just this moment gone out. . . . Yes. . . . Yes. . . . Yes, I can imagine. . . . Of course it is. . . . Of course. . . . Yes. . . . Yes. . . . Oh, but I think they get used to it, Mrs. Stencil, don't they? . . . They get a sort of head for heights. . . . I really don't think heights worry them, Mrs. Stencil. . . . Some birds, perhaps – but not eagles. . . . Oh, yes. Eagles do. . . . Yes. . . . But it must be very rare, however high they fly. . . . It must be very rare for an eagle to come over dizzy. . . . Yes. . . . Yes. . . . But wouldn't that give them the feeling of being rather hampered? . . . Yes. . . . But I do think an eagle likes to swoop down sometimes. . . . But not if it's wearing a parachute. . . . Oh, I can understand how you feel, Mrs. Stencil. . . . Yes. . . . Yes. . . . (*Hesitantly.*) I'm afraid it would have to be more or less a token subscription this time – this is always our expensive quarter. . . . No, naturally. . . . No. . . . Anyway, I'll tell Bro when he comes in, and. . . . Yes. . . . Yes. . . . I suppose they must. . . . It's the peering down, I expect. . . . Yes. . . .They must be peering down most of the time. . . . And of course with some of them they're supposed to stare into the sun as well, aren't they? . . . Don't eagles stare at the sun? . . . Yes. . . . Still, I should think if they found that. . . . Yes. . . . But if they found it was becoming a strain on their eyes they'd surely stop doing it. . . . Yes. . . . But I doubt whether they'd take the trouble to wear them once the novelty had worn off. . . . Oh, they are – they're very expensive. Even the steel-rimmed ones. . . . Yes. . . . Yes. . . . A kind of Welfare State for animals, in fact. . . . Yes – well, I'll tell Bro, Mrs. Stencil, when he comes in and . . . Yes. . . . Yes, I will, Mrs. Stencil. . . . Good-bye. (*She replaces the receiver, switches on the radio, then sits on the sofa.*)

(BRO'*s and* MIDDIE'*s* VOICES *are heard through the radio.*)

MIDDIE'*s* VOICE. What do you want gumboots for to go down the road a few doors with a dinosaur? Where are your other shoes?

BRO'*s* VOICE. I'm not going without my gumboots.

MIDDIE'*s* VOICE. For goodness' sake get them on, then, and go.

(BRO *enters, wearing his gumboots. The voices on the radio give way to interval music.* BRO *closes the door, sits in the armchair and takes off his gumboots.*)

MIDDIE. You didn't stay at Nora's long. (*She switches off the radio.*)

BRO. I didn't stay at Nora's at all. Where are my slippers?

MIDDIE. Mrs. Stencil rang up.

BRO (*putting on his shoes*). Oh? What is it this time? Emergency breathing apparatus for deep-sea fish again?

MIDDIE. Apparently she's still on the Appeals Committee for the Birds of Prey Protection League.

BRO. I'm not putting my hand in my pocket every few weeks for that. And you can tell her I said so. Birds of prey! They're just as capable of looking after themselves as we are.

MIDDIE. That's what I said to Mrs. Stencil. Besides, what do eagles want with parachutes?

BRO. Is that what she's collecting for?

MIDDIE. Or any other bird for that matter. She's got it into her head they need to have some kind of safety equipment.

BRO. They've got their two wings, haven't they?

MIDDIE. Mrs. Stencil's worried what would happen if they were to get cramp or anything while they were up there.

BRO. She fusses.

MIDDIE. I think she's hoping that if the League can provide a few parachutes out of their own funds, she might be able . . .

BRO. Out of *our* funds.

MIDDIE. She's hoping she might get the authorities interested in supplying spectacles for them.

BRO. For whom?

MIDDIE. For the eagles and things. I told her I didn't think many of them would bother wearing glasses once the novelty had worn off.

(*There is a pause.* BRO *picks up his newspaper and reads.*)

It's the height they have to peer down from before they swoop. She thinks it puts too much strain on their eyes.

BRO. They don't have to peer down. They're free agents.

MIDDIE. That's what I said to her.

BRO. Parachutes. Glasses. They get too much done for them.

(*There is a pause.*)

Was that the play you were listening to when I came in?

MIDDIE. You didn't want it, did you? I switched it off.

BRO. We may as well see how it ends.

(MIDDIE *switches on the radio and takes up her rug.* BRO *continues to be occupied with the newspaper.* MIDDIE*'s and* BRO*'s* VOICES *are heard through the radio.*)

MIDDIE*'s* VOICE. And what did Edna say?

BRO*'s* VOICE. I didn't get as far as Edna's.

MIDDIE*'s* VOICE. Where have you been, then?

BRO*'s* VOICE. I've been in the garden.

MIDDIE*'s* VOICE. Not all the time? (*She pauses.*) In the garden doing what?

BRO*'s* VOICE (*exasperated*). In the garden trying to get that blasted dinosaur through the gate!

MIDDIE*'s* VOICE. *Really!* (*She pauses.*) I'm going out to make a drink for myself. (*She pauses.*) What are *you* having –

coffee? Or cocoa?

BRO'*s* VOICE. Hot milk.

(*The interval music is heard again.* MIDDIE *switches off the radio.*)

BRO (*gloomily*). What was the rest of it like?

MIDDIE. You didn't miss much.

(MIDDIE *takes up her rug.* BRO *reads. A long silence intervenes.*)

And what did Nora say?

BRO. I didn't get as far as Nora's.

MIDDIE. You've been out there for hours. What have you been doing?

BRO. I've been in the garden.

MIDDIE. Not all the time.

BRO. I was out there for less than twenty minutes and I shouldn't have met with any more success if I'd been out there all night.

MIDDIE. I don't know what you're talking about.

BRO. I'm talking about that bloody elephant!

MIDDIE. Bro!

BRO. How do you expect me or anybody else to get a whacking great oaf of an elephant through a gate wide enough to take a pram?

(MIDDIE *puts down her rug and is about to go, tight-lipped, to the door.*)

MIDDIE (*rising; conclusively*). It was got in. (*She moves to the door.*) What are you having to drink? Cocoa? Or coffee?

(MIDDIE *pauses at the door, and turns in the act of going out as she waits in tightly-reined impatience for* BRO'*s answer.* BRO *is still under the influence of his own irritation, so that some seconds pass before he registers* MIDDIE'*s question. When he does so, he reflects for a moment before answering.*)

BRO. Hot milk.

CURTAIN

NOTES ON THE PLAY AND THE THEATRE OF THE ABSURD

by Herbert Whittaker
Drama critic, *The Globe and Mail*

The play you have just read is an abbreviated version of Norman Frederick Simpson's original prize-winning play. Now playwrights, like other creative writers, generally wince at the thought of cutting their completed work. Simpson, an adult-education lecturer, seems to have suffered no special qualms. Perhaps this is partially explained by a comment he made on the original play. "From time to time parts of the play may seem to become detached from the main body. No attempt, well-intentioned or not, should be made from the audience to nudge these back into position while the play is in motion. They will eventually drop off and are quite harmless."

Simpson's unconcern about detachable sequences is significant, especially when you know the delicious morsels he eliminated from the full-length play – the introduction of the comedians who discuss Bergson's theory of laughter, the skittish neighbour, the scientist with the reaction-index, and the brains-trust session held about this very play.

Listen to Simpson again, speaking as the author in the full-length version: "There is no desire, no intention on my part, or on the part of any of us on this side of the footlights, to impose upon you any ready-made idea of our own as to what this play ought to turn out to be. No. It is together that we must share the experience which is the play we shall all of us have shared."

This sharing of experience between the people on Simpson's side of the footlights and on ours is, of course, the aim of every production of every play. But Simpson, like Eugene Ionesco and that whole body of abstract writers (whose plays Martin Esslin has labelled Theatre of the Absurd), declines to guide and influence you through that experience. He merely offers, he says, the raw materials for such an experience – some arbitrarily allotted sets of speeches, some casually selected situations, or themes, some carelessly chosen locales. As you would with any abstract painting, he seems to say, make what you like out of it. Don't come whining to me to find out what it's all about.

But Simpson, any more than Ionesco, can't speak for everybody on his side of the footlights, only for the playwright. He is not responsible for what evolves when a director, a designer and a group of players apply their imaginations to his sets of speeches, situations, themes and locales. They must impose shape, point and colour in terms of their own experiences. They can't wait for the audience to tell them what the play means to it.

So it was when the Trinity College Dramatic Society invited me to stage a production of *A Resounding Tinkle* at the University of Toronto's Hart House Theatre on January 11, 1961. Our setting reflected some of the *non-sequiturs* of Simpson's style. A collection of family photographs climbed one wall beyond the ceiling, the grape clusters on the wallpaper extended into the foliage outside, and the chimneys looked suspiciously like bottles. This was perhaps because, in the full-length version, the Paradocks seemed to do a great deal of drinking.

But the various situations were not treated in any bizarre fashion. The Paradocks must be recognizable if we are to enjoy them. Their problems – of a too-large elephant, a relative who changes sex overnight – must be matter-of-fact in terms of English suburban life, which doesn't differ too enormously from suburban life elsewhere, if we are to see what Simpson is getting at.

These problems of the Paradocks do not add up to a well-made plot, any more than any other abstractions add up to realistic representations of life. But if we allow our imaginations and perceptions free rein, we may find, as did my Trinity actors, a great deal of fun, in the nonsense tradition of Lewis Carroll and Edward Lear, some rather affectionate social satire, and even a hint of what Simpson is saying in his prayer: "Give us light upon the nature of our knowing; for the illusions of the sane man are not the illusions of the lunatic . . . . That, sane, we may know ourselves, and by knowing ourselves we may know what it is we know." The different views we have of the world around us, according to what we bring to it, are Simpson's concern. They must be ours when we come into the world he and many of his contemporaries set forth in their plays.

At Trinity, we entered into the silliness of *A Resounding Tinkle* with a great many giggles, but as we came to rehearse it over and over, we discovered that much of it was silliness with a purpose, as silliness often is. We enjoyed it all the more.

THINKING ABOUT THE PLAY

1. Look up I Corinthians 13:1 and suggest why Simpson might have chosen his title.
2. Martin Esslin in *The Theatre of the Absurd* suggests that in the central situation, N. F. Simpson is satirizing the "pointless buying and exchanging" of merchandise. Discuss this idea.
3. Compare *A Resounding Tinkle* with *Alice in Wonderland* as examples of extravagant fantasy.
4. Most authorities agree that N. F. Simpson is indebted to Eugene Ionesco. Read any Ionesco play, such as *The Bald Soprano,* and compare the work of the two authors, pointing out the differences and similarities in style and idea.
5. Simpson's plays have been criticized because their characters are not differentiated one from the other. Is this true in the case of our version of *A Resounding Tinkle*? Give reasons for your answer.

A THEATRE LIBRARY

ANTHOLOGIES OF PLAYS

Block, Haskell M., and Robert G. Shedd, *Masters of Modern Drama*. Random House of Canada Ltd., 1962.

Clayes, Stanley A., and David G. Spencer, *Contemporary Drama – Thirteen Plays*. Saunders of Toronto Limited, 1962.

Gassner, John, *A Treasury of the Theatre*, 3 vols. Musson Book Company, 1963.

Gassner, John, *20 Best European Plays on the American Stage*. Random House of Canada Ltd., 1960.

Griffin, Alice V., *Living Theatre*. Burns & MacEachern Limited, 1958.

HISTORY OF THE THEATRE

Cheney, Sheldon, *The Theatre: Three Thousand Years of Drama, Acting and Stagecraft*. Longmans Canada Ltd., 1958.

Freedley, George, and John A. Reeves, *A History of the Theatre*. Ambassador Books Ltd., 1955.

MacGowan, Kenneth, and William Melnitz, *The Living Stage*. Prentice-Hall of Canada Ltd., 1961.

Nicoll, Allardyce, *The Development of the Theatre*. Clarke, Irwin & Company Ltd., 1961.

DRAMATIC THEORY

Bentley, Eric, *The Life of the Drama*. McClelland & Stewart Ltd., 1964.

Esslin, Martin, *The Theatre of the Absurd*. The Ryerson Press, 1962.

Gassner, John, *Masters of the Drama*. General Publishing Co. Ltd., 1954.

Gorelik, Mordecai, *New Theatres for Old*. Samuel French (Canada) Ltd., 1955.

PLAYWRITING

Cole, Toby, *Playwrights on Playwriting*. The Copp Clark Publishing Co. Ltd., 1960.

Herman, Lewis, *A Practical Manual of Screen Playwriting for Theatre and Television Films*. The World Publishing Company, 1963.

Kerr, Walter, *How Not to Write a Play*. Musson Book Company, 1955.

Langner, Lawrence, *The Play's the Thing*. Longmans Canada Ltd., 1960.

PLAY PRODUCTION

Bamford, T. W., *Practical Make-up for the Stage*. Sir Isaac Pitman (Canada) Limited, 1959.

Boleslavsky, Richard, *Acting, The First Six Lessons*. Burns & MacEachern Limited, 1949.

Burris-Meyer, Harold, and Edward C. Cole, *Scenery for the Theatre*. Oxford University Press, 1938.

Cole, Toby, and Helen K. Chinoy, *Directors on Directing*. Thomas Allen & Son Ltd., 1963.

Crampton, Esmé, *A Handbook of the Theatre*. W. J. Gage Limited, 1964.

Dean, Alexander, *Fundamentals of Play Directing*. Oxford University Press, 1941.

Dolman, John, *The Art of Play Production*. Longmans Canada Ltd., 1946.

Dow, Marguerite R., *The Magic Mask*. The Macmillan Company of Canada Ltd., 1966.

Duerr, Edwin, *The Length and Depth of Acting*. Holt, Rinehart and Winston of Canada Ltd., 1962.

Hewitt, Barnard, J. F. Foster, and Muriel Sibell Wolle, *Play Production Theory and Practice*. McClelland & Stewart Ltd., 1959.

McCandless, S. R., *A Method of Lighting the Stage*. Ambassador Books Ltd., 1954.

Melville, Harald, *Historic Costume for the Amateur Theatre, and How to Make It*. Smithers & Bonellie Ltd., 1961.

Philippi, Herbert, *Stagecraft and Stage Design*. Thomas Allen & Son Ltd., 1953.

Selden, Samuel, and Hunton D. Sellman, *Stage Scenery and Lighting*. General Publishing Co. Ltd., 1959.

Stanislavski, Constantin, *An Actor Prepares*. Ambassador Books Ltd., 1948.

66 76 86 96 07 17 27 37 47 THB 9 8 7 6 5 4 3 2 1